Roo
ST
ROOSEVELTS CHRIS   11 08

Date Due

68		
DE 17 69		
JAN 30 7		
11-3-94		

ELEANOR ROOSEVELT'S
CHRISTMAS BOOK

Eleanor Roosevelt's
CHRISTMAS
BOOK

❧❧

Including her own descriptions of Christmas at Hyde

Park and the White House, together with her original

story *Christmas* and her favorite selections of prose and

verse devoted to the Christmas season

❧❧

DODD, MEAD & COMPANY
NEW YORK

Printed in the United States of America
by The Cornwall Press, Inc., Cornwall, N.Y.

Grateful acknowledgment is made to the following for permission to use the material indicated:

The Bobbs-Merrill Company: for "Why the Chimes Rang" by Raymond MacDonald Alden. Reprinted by special permission of The Bobbs-Merrill Company.

Heywood Hale Broun and Constance M. Broun: for "A Shepherd" by Heywood Broun. Copyright © 1929, 1941 by Heywood Hale Broun. Reprinted by permission.

The Literary Trustees of Walter de la Mare and the Society of Authors as their representative: for "Nowel" by Walter de la Mare. Reprinted by permission.

Dodd, Mead & Company: for "The House of Christmas" from *The Collected Poems of G. K. Chesterton*. Copyright, 1932, by Dodd, Mead & Company.

"Our Lady's Juggler" from *Mother of Pearl* by Anatole France.

"Childhood Christmas" from *Fullness of Days* by Lord Halifax. Copyright © 1956, 1957 by Edward Frederick Lindley Wood, 1st Earl of Halifax.

"The Errors of Santa Claus" from *Wet Wisdom and Dry Humor* by Stephen Leacock. Copyright, 1931, by Dodd, Mead & Company.

"God Rest You Merry" from *Soap Behind the Ears* by Cornelia Otis Skinner. Copyright, 1940, 1941 by Cornelia Otis Skinner.

Doubleday & Company, Inc.: for "The Gift of the Magi" from *The Four Million* by O. Henry. Reprinted by permission of Doubleday & Company, Inc.

"White Christmas" by Fannie Hurst. Copyright 1942 by Fannie Hurst. Reprinted by permission of Doubleday & Company, Inc.

"Legend of the Christmas Rose" from *The Girl from the Marsh Croft* by Selma Lagerlöf. Copyright 1910 by Doubleday & Company, Inc. Reprinted by permission of the publisher.

"Valley Forge: 24 December 1777" by F. Van Wyck Mason. Copyright 1946 by F. Van Wyck Mason. Reprinted by permission of Doubleday & Company, Inc.

Harper & Row: for "Mr. Edwards Meets Santa Claus" from *Little House on the Prairie* by Laura Ingalls Wilder. Copyright, 1935 by Laura Ingalls Wilder.

Rupert Hart-Davis: for "Mr. Huffam" by Hugh Walpole. Published by Rupert Hart-Davis Limited. Reprinted by permission.

Holt, Rinehart and Winston, Inc.: for "Christmas Trees" from *Complete Poems of Robert Frost*. Copyright 1916, 1921 by Holt, Rinehart and Winston, Inc. Copyright renewed 1944 by Robert Frost. Reprinted by permission of Holt, Rinehart and Winston, Inc.

Houghton Mifflin Company: for "The Peterkins' Christmas-Tree" from *The Peterkin Papers* by Lucretia Hale.

"A Christmas Letter to His Grandson (on His First Christmas)" by Walter H. Page.

Mrs. Joseph Henry Jackson: for "The Christmas Flower" by Joseph Henry Jackson. Copyright 1951 by Joseph Henry Jackson. Published by Harcourt, Brace & World, Inc. Used by permission of Mrs. Joseph Henry Jackson.

Robert Keith Leavitt: for "The Christmas Miracle" by Robert Keith Leavitt.

Anne M. Lindbergh and Morgan Guaranty Trust Company: for "A Pint of Judgment" by Elizabeth C. Morrow. Copyright © 1939, Anne M. Lindbergh and Morgan Guaranty Trust Company, Trustees of the Estate of Elizabeth C. Morrow.

J. B. Lippincott Company: for "The Shepherd and the King" from *Poems for Children* by Eleanor Farjeon. Copyright 1927–1955 by Eleanor Farjeon. Published by J. B. Lippincott Company.

"The Tree That Didn't Get Trimmed" from *Essays* by Christopher Morley. Copyright 1919, 1947 by Christopher Morley. Published by J. B. Lippincott Company.

Little, Brown and Company: for "A Carol for Children" from *Verses from 1929 on* by Ogden Nash. Copyright 1934 by Ogden Nash; originally appeared in the *New Yorker*. By permission of Little, Brown and Co.

The Macmillan Company: for "Christmas in London." Reprinted with permission of the publisher from *Little Dog Toby* by Rachel Field. Copyright 1928 by The Macmillan Company, Renewed 1956 by Arthur S. Pederson.

"Christmas Eve at Sea." Reprinted with permission of The Macmillan Company from *Salt Water Poems and Ballads* by John Masefield. Copyright 1916, 1944 by John Masefield.

New Directions: for "Conversation about Christmas" by Dylan Thomas. Copyright 1954 by New Directions. Used by permission.

Oxford University Press: for "Carol" ("High O'er the lonely hills") by Jan Struther, 1901–1953. From *Enlarged Songs of Praise*. Reprinted by permission of Oxford University Press, London.

Mrs. Eric Posselt: for "A Christmas Tale" by Marie, Queen of Romania from *The World's Greatest Christmas Stories*, edited by Eric Posselt. Copyright 1949 by Eric Posselt.

Mrs. Jacob A. Riis: for "Is There a Santa Claus?" Reprinted by permission of the Estate of Jacob A. Riis from *Christmas Stories* by Jacob A. Riis. Copyright 1923 by Jacob A. Riis.

G. Schirmer, Inc.: for English text of the "Carol of the Bagpipers" from *Songs of Italy*, English translation by Dr. Theodore Baker, copyright 1904 by G. Schirmer, Inc. Used by permission of the copyright owner, G. Schirmer, Inc.

"Amahl and the Night Visitors" by Gian-Carlo Menotti. Copyright, 1951, 1952 by G. Schirmer, Inc. Used by permission.

Charles Scribner's Sons: for "Carol," reprinted with the permission of Charles Scribner's Sons from *The Wind in the Willows* by Kenneth Grahame.

"The Christmas Angel" (from *The Spirit of Christmas*, 1905) by Henry Van Dyke. Reprinted with permission of Charles Scribner's Sons.

Unitarian Universalist *Register-Leader*: for "A Christmas Fable" by Harold S. Stewart. Originally published by the *Register-Leader*.

The Viking Press, Inc.: for "The Ballad of Befana: An Epiphany Legend" from *Merry Christmas, Happy New Year* by Phyllis McGinley. Copyright © 1957 by Phyllis McGinley. Reprinted by permission of The Viking Press, Inc.

PUBLISHER'S NOTE

It is characteristic that Eleanor Roosevelt, who was fondly acclaimed as the first lady of the world, should have had a particular affection for the season of peace and good will toward all men. She loved the writings about Christmas, to which she made her own contributions, and at the time of her death, was collecting her favorites among them to share with others in a published volume. Most of the selections had been made under her auspices so that it was possible for those who knew her taste to complete the book, guided by the spirit with which she had endowed it. Thus, with her *Christmas Book*, she has left an enduring gift to enrich the season for young and old.

Contents

I BY ELEANOR ROOSEVELT

3   Christmas at Hyde Park
6   Christmas in the White House
10   Christmas—A Story

II PROSE

23   Why the Chimes Rang—*Raymond MacDonald Alden*
28   The Fir Tree—*Hans Christian Andersen*
36   A Shepherd—*Heywood Broun*
39   Christmas in Maine—*Robert P. Tristram Coffin*
46   A Christmas Carol—*Charles Dickens*
76   Christmas in London—*Rachel Field*
86   Our Lady's Juggler—*Anatole France*
92   The Peterkins' Christmas-Tree—*Lucretia P. Hale*
97   Childhood Christmas from *Fullness of Days*—Lord *Halifax*
105   The Gift of the Magi—*O. Henry*
111   Recollections of a Boyhood Christmas Visit to a
      Neighboring Farm—*A. M. Hopkins*
116   Christmas Every Day—*W. D. Howells*
124   White Christmas—*Fannie Hurst*
138   The Christmas Dinner—*Washington Irving*
151   The Christmas Flower—*Joseph Henry Jackson*
161   The Legend of the Christmas Rose—*Selma Lagerlöf*
170   The Errors of Santa Claus—*Stephen Leacock*

174   The Christmas Miracle—*Robert Keith Leavitt*

176   A Christmas Tale—*Queen Marie of Romania*

187   Valley Forge: 24 December 1777—*F. Van Wyck Mason*

203   Amahl and the Night Visitors—*Gian-Carlo Menotti*

211   The Tree That Didn't Get Trimmed—*Christopher Morley*

216   A Pint of Judgment—*Elizabeth Morrow*

228   Christmas Letter to His Grandson—*Walter H. Page*

232   Is There a Santa Claus?—*Jacob A. Riis*

237   God Rest You Merry—*Cornelia Otis Skinner*

244   A Christmas Sermon—*Robert Louis Stevenson*

252   A Christmas Fable—*Harold S. Stewart*

255   Conversation about Christmas—*Dylan Thomas*

261   The Christmas Angel—*Henry Van Dyke*

270   Mr. Huffam—*Hugh Walpole*

287   Mr. Edwards Meets Santa Claus—*Laura Ingalls Wilder*

294   Is There a Santa Claus?—*New York Sun*

III   POEMS AND CAROLS

299   Christmas Greeting from a Fairy to a Child—*Lewis Carroll*

300   The House of Christmas—*Gilbert Keith Chesterton*

302   The Shepherd and the King—*Eleanor Farjeon*

304   Christmas Trees—*Robert Frost*

307   Carol—*Kenneth Grahame*

308   The Oxen—*Thomas Hardy*

309   To a Child—*Robert Herrick*

310   Christmas Bells—*Henry Wadsworth Longfellow*

312   Nowel—*Walter de la Mare*

313   Christmas Eve at Sea—*John Masefield*

315   The Ballad of Befana—*Phyllis McGinley*

317   A Visit from St. Nicholas—*Clement Clarke Moore*

319   A Carol for Children—*Ogden Nash*

321   The Three Ships—*Alfred Noyes*

323   Christmas in the Olden Time—*Sir Walter Scott*

325 "Some Say . . ."—*William Shakespeare*

326 Carol—*Jan Struther*

328 Christmas and New Year Bells—*Alfred Tennyson*

From the Repertoire of the United Nations Singers

330 Weihnachtslied—*Austrian*

331 What Child Is This?—*English*

332 Il est né, le Divin Enfant—*French*

334 Canzone d'i Zampognari—*Italian*

335 Gdy Sie Chrystus Rodzi—*Polish*

336 A la Nanita Nana—*Spanish*

338 Nu är det Jul igen—*Swedish*

I

—◆—

BY ELEANOR ROOSEVELT

ELEANOR ROOSEVELT

<del>~§ §~</del>

Christmas at Hyde Park

WHEN our children were young, we spent nearly every Christmas holiday at Hyde Park. We always had a party the afternoon of Christmas Eve for all the families who lived on the place. The presents were piled under the tree, and after everyone had been greeted, my husband would choose the children old enough to distribute gifts and send them around to the guests. My mother-in-law herself always gave out her envelopes with money, and I would give out ours. The cornucopias filled with old-fashioned sugar candies and the peppermint canes hanging on the tree were distributed, too, and then our guests would leave us and enjoy their ice cream, cake, and coffee or milk in another room. Later in the day, when the guests had departed, my husband would begin the reading of A *Christmas Carol*. He never read it through; but he would select parts he thought suitable for the youngest members of the family. Then, after supper, he would read other parts for the older ones.

On Christmas morning, I would get up and close the windows in our room, where all the stockings had been hung on the mantel. The little children would be put into our bed and given their stockings to open. The others would sit around the fire. I tried to see that they all had a glass of orange juice before the opening of stockings really began, but the excitement was so great I was not always successful.

Breakfast was late Christmas morning, and my husband resented having to go to church on Christmas Day and sometimes flatly refused to attend. But I would go with my mother-in-law and such children as she could persuade to accompany us. For the most part, however, the children stayed home. In later years, I went to midnight service on Christmas Eve, and we gave up going to church in the morning.

I remember the excitement as each child grew old enough to have his own sled and would start out after breakfast to try it on the hill behind the stable. Franklin would go coasting with them, and until the children were nearly grown, he was the only one who ever piloted the bobsled down the hill. Everyone came in for a late lunch, and at dusk we would light the candles on the tree again. Only outdoor presents like sleds and skates were distributed in the morning. The rest were kept for the late-afternoon Christmas tree. Again they were piled under the tree, and my husband and the children scrambled around under it, and he called the names.

At first, my mother-in-law did a great deal of shopping and wrapping, and the Hyde Park Christmas always included her gifts. Later, she found shopping too difficult. Then she would give each person a check, though she managed very often to give her son the two things she knew he would not buy for himself—silk shirts and silk pajamas. These she bought in London, as a rule, and saved for his Christmas, which to her was always very special.

In the early years of our marriage, I did a great deal more sewing and embroidering than I've done since, so many of my gifts were things I had made. The family still has a few pieces of Italian cut-work embroidery and other kinds of my perfectly useless handwork. I look back, however, with some pleasure on the early Hyde Park days, when I would have a table filled with pieces of silk and make sachets of different scents. I would dry pine needles at Campobello Island and make them into sweet-smelling bags for Christmas. Now I rarely give a present I have made, and perhaps it is just as well, for what one buys is likely to be better made!

Each of the children had a special preference in gifts. When Anna was a small child, her favorite present was a rocking horse, on which she spent many hours. Later, she was to spend even more hours training her own horse, which her great-uncle Mr. Warren Delano gave her. One of the nicest gifts we could possibly give her as she grew older was something for her horse, Natomah. Jimmy loved boats from the very beginning, whether he floated them in the bathtub or later competed with his father in the regattas of toy boats on the Hudson River. Elliott was always trying to catch up with his older brother and sister; but because he was delicate as a child, I think he read more than the others. I remember that books and games were very acceptable gifts for him. Franklin, Jr., and John were a pair and had to have pretty much the same things, or they would quarrel over them. They had learned together to ride and to swim, so gifts for outdoor sports were always favorites of theirs.

My children teased me because their stockings inevitably contained toothbrushes, toothpaste, nail cleaners, soap, washcloths, etc. They said Mother never ceased to remind them that cleanliness was next to godliness—even on Christmas morning. In the toe of each stocking, I always put a purse, with a dollar bill for the young ones and a five-dollar bill for the older ones. These bills were hoarded to supplement the rather meager allowances they had. When I was able to buy *sucre d'orge* (barley sugar), I put that in their stockings, together with some old-fashioned peppermint sticks; but as they grew older, this confection seemed to vanish from the market, and I had to give it up and substitute chocolates. The stockings also contained families of little china pigs or rabbits or horses, which the children placed on their bookshelves.

The children themselves could probably tell much better than I can the things they remember most about these years. But I know that all of them have carried on many of the Hyde Park Christmas traditions with their children. Today, some of my grandchildren are establishing the same customs, and my great-grandchildren will one day remember the same kind of Christmas we started so many years ago.

ELEANOR ROOSEVELT

ᴥ§§ᴥ

Christmas in the White House

I AM SURE *everyone would love to know just what the Christmases were like while you lived in the White House.*

When Christmas is spent outside one's own home, particularly in government surroundings such as the White House, you divide your Christmas in two parts. One covers your official obligations; the other, as far as possible, is the preservation of the home atmosphere and the home routine.

In Washington, ceremonies began on Christmas Eve. Franklin and I would greet our office people as they left, shaking hands with each one and wishing him a Merry Christmas. Franklin would give each one some small remembrance. This little ceremony might take place on Christmas Eve—or a day earlier if the holiday fell on a weekend—and usually was held between twelve and one o'clock in the afternoon.

If it was Christmas Eve, my day had begun much earlier, with an appearance between nine and ten at one of the Washington theaters, where I gave out Christmas stockings to children gathered together by some civic groups. My next stop would be at the Volunteers of America, where baskets were being distributed to the needy, and I would give out a few of these and listen to some speeches and singing.

If the office party was at twelve o'clock, I had to hurry to get back to the White House and stand by the President during the reception. Then, immediately after lunch, there would be a Salvation Army party. After that, all of us, including the President, would get into White House cars and go to the municipal tree-

6

lighting ceremony, which was impressive, with lovely music. Then back to the White House, and at five o'clock, the President and I, his mother when she was alive, and any of the children who happened to be with us would receive the whole White House staff, with their families, in the East Room. Here, a handsome tree was set up in the east window, between the portraits of George and Martha Washington. It was always decorated completely in white and silver, and when the lights were lit, the toys for the children scattered under the tree, and the tables fanning out on either side laden with the older people's gifts, the scene was festive and beautiful.

Any distinguished guests who were visiting with us joined in the receiving line, and that, I think, added interest for the staff, because they so often worked without getting much chance to see the famous guests whom they served.

After the party for the staff in the East Room, the little children had their supper while the big children decorated the family tree on the second floor. My husband would often start to read A *Christmas Carol* and would finish after dinner. Later in the evening, I always filled the Christmas stockings, which were hung in my husband's bedroom, and then attended church services, beginning at eleven-thirty. Getting to bed was a late affair, for every stocking had to be replaced exactly where each child or grandchild had hung it up.

In the morning, I got up early, closed the windows to warm the rooms, and dressed sufficiently to be presentable when the first grandchild would demand to go into "Papa's" room, as they called their grandfather. Then the littlest ones, sitting on his bed, would always empty their stockings. His own stocking would lie beside him—unopened, as a rule. My mother-in-law, if she was with us, had a stocking, and some of the children would get together with Franklin and fill one for me. I am afraid my interest was never as great in what I would find in my stocking as it was in what the various children sitting around on the floor would discover. My own children, most of them grown by this time, used to tease me about their stockings and say I took this opportunity to see that they were all equipped for cleanliness. Toothbrushes, soap, nail files were always somewhere in their stockings, and they took this laughingly. But I did try to find a few other things that might be more acceptable and interesting!

During the stocking opening, orange juice was brought in for everybody, and when the last gifts had been found in the toes of the stockings, we would all have breakfast in the West Hall of the White House, leaving Franklin to a little peace and his breakfast on a tray, with the usual array of newspapers.

Our own Christmas tree in the second corridor was not lighted until late in the afternoon of Christmas Day, because we went to church in the morning, and then there was lunch, and, for the President, work.

Christmas afternoon, I always made the rounds of Christmas trees in the Alleys. The Alleys were some of the slums of Washington, and a group would set up sad little trees, around which children would gather for presents. It would be arranged that I would drop in on each little group as they collected. From these gatherings, I always went back to the White House with an added awareness of the inequality of our earthly blessings.

It was after five before our own Christmas-tree party began. We nearly always had as guests some friends as well as such family as could be mustered, and I would arrange piles of presents on chairs or even on the floor, always leaving some toys under the tree and handing these to Franklin to give to the children.

Franklin would get so interested in everyone else's presents that it might be four or five days after Christmas before we finally enticed him to open all his own gifts. Being an orderly person, I would always get mine opened before I went to bed, so I could prepare the list for thanking as soon as possible and get everything put away. But my husband was never troubled by any considerations of this kind and would often read a book he received all the way through before he opened the next present! Nice men, I think, often have the traits of little boys all their lives, and this trait of enjoying presents I always noticed in my husband. You could not hurry him when he had a gift to enjoy.

Christmas dinner always meant gathering together any of our family who lived in Washington. We had a number of relatives there, and we also invited certain friends.

After dinner, we usually had a movie, and then everyone went home, with the feeling that Christmas had been well celebrated. If it was possible, we would slip off the next day to Hyde Park for a few days.

I remember especially the Christmas that Mr. Churchill was with us after we were involved in World War II. After that year, the Christmases weren't so cheerful. My mother-in-law died in the autumn before that first war Christmas. The boys all went off to different war theaters. Their absence meant that we did what we could to cheer their families if they were with us, or we tried to get in touch with them by telephone if they were far away. We did more in those years for foreign people cut off from their homelands by war, but it was no longer the old-time Christmas and never was to be again.

ELEANOR ROOSEVELT

⊷ঌৡ⊷

Christmas—A Story

T HE TIMES *are so serious that even children should be made to understand that there are vital differences in people's beliefs which lead to differences in behavior.*

This little story, I hope, will appeal enough to children so they will read it and as they grow older, they may understand that the love, and peace and gentleness typified by the Christ Child, leads us to a way of life for which we must all strive.

ELEANOR ROOSEVELT
1940

St. Nicholas's eve, 1940, was cold and the snow was falling. On the hearth in Marta's home there was a fire burning, and she had been hugging that fire all day, asking her mother to tell her stories, telling them afterwards to her doll.

This was not like St. Nicholas's Eve of last year. Then her father had come home. Seven-year-old Marta asked her mother to tell her the story over and over again, so her mother, whose fingers were never idle now that she was alone and had to feed and clothe herself and Marta, sat and knit long woolen stockings and talked of the past which would never come again, and of St. Nicholas's Eve 1939.

The war was going on in Europe in 1939, but Jon was only mobilized. He was just guarding the border, and was allowed to come home for the holiday. Marta's mother said:

"On Monday I got the letter and on Tuesday, St. Nicholas's Eve, he came. I got up early in the morning and started cleaning the house. I wanted everything to shine while your father was home. Soon I called you, and when you were dressed and had had your

10

breakfast, you took your place in the window watching for him to come. Every time you saw a speck way down the road, you would call out to me, but I had time to get much of the holiday cooking prepared and the house in good order before you finally cried: 'Here he is,' and a cart stopped by our gate. You threw open the door and ran down the path. I saw him pick you up in his arms, but he was in such a hurry that he carried you right on in with him and met me as I was running half-way down the path."

Her mother always sighed and Marta wondered why her eyes looked so bright, then she would go on and tell of Jon's coming into the house and insisting on saying: "*Vroolijk Kerstfeest,*" meaning "Merry Christmas," all over again to her and to Marta, just as though he had not greeted them both outside.

Marta's mother had been busy making cakes, "*bankletters*" and "*speculaas,*" just a few since that year none of the family or friends could come to spend St. Nicholas's Eve with them, for no one could spend money to travel in such anxious times. She and Marta had saved and saved to get the food for the feast, and now that was in the larder waiting to be cooked.

They both felt sorry that the two grandmothers and the two grandfathers could not come that year, for Jon and big Marta had lived near enough to their parents so that they could often spend the holidays together. Little Marta loved to think about her grandfathers. One grandfather could tell her so much about the animals and the birds and make them seem just like people, and her mother's father could tell her stories, long, long stories, about things that happened in cities, about processions and having seen the Queen, and so many wonderful things that she could dream about after the visit was over.

Besides, it meant that both her grandmothers helped her mother, and that gave her mother more time to go out with her, so it really was a disappointment when the grandparents could not be with them for this St. Nicholas's Eve. Little Marta did not know it, but to her father's parents it was more than a disappointment. They had wanted so much to see their son again. Like all mothers, his mother feared the worst where her own boy was concerned. Perhaps she had had a premonition of what the future held, but, as with all peasants, the hard facts of life are there to be counted, and the money saved for the trip would keep food in the larder if the winter was going to be as hard as everything indicated, so they did not travel.

Marta's mother had told her that perhaps St. Nicholas, on his white horse with his black servant, Peter, would not bring any presents that year to fill her wooden shoes, but Marta would not believe it. Her first question to her father was: "Will St. Nicholas forget us?"

"No, little Marta," said her father. "The good Saint, who loves little children, will come tonight if you go to bed like a good girl and go quickly to sleep."

Marta put her little shoes down by the big fireplace, and her mother took her into the bedroom and tucked her away behind the curtains which shielded her bunk along the wall on the cold winter night.

Then there had been a long quiet time when Jon and Marta's mother sat together and talked a little, Jon telling what life was like for the army on the frontier and then lapsing into that complete silence which can only come to two people who are very fond of each other. After a while Jon opened up his knapsack and took out the things he had managed to bring to fill those little wooden shoes, and the package which held the last present from her husband that Marta's mother was ever to receive. With it was the usual rhyme:

> *To a busy little housewife*
> *From one who thinks of her through strife,*
> *To keep her safe from all alarm*
> *And never let her come to harm,*
> *Is all he dreams of night and day*
> *And now forever "Peace" would say.*

Needless to say, she guessed the giver before they went to bed.

On Christmas morning Marta woke and ran to look for her wooden shoes. "St. Nicholas has been here," she cried, "and he's given me many sweets, a doll, and bright red mittens just like the stockings mother made me as a Christmas gift." Then the whole family went skating on the river and there were many other little girls with their fathers and mothers. Everyone glided about and the babies were pushed or dragged in their little sleds. The boys and girls chased one another, sometimes long lines took hands and, after skating away, gathered in a circle, going faster and faster until they broke up because they could not hold on any longer.

Then at last they went home to dinner. On the table a fat chicken and a good soup.

At first they ate silently and then as the edge of their hunger wore off, they began to talk.

"Marta," said her father, "have you learned to read in school yet? Can you count how many days there are in a month?"

"Oh, yes," replied Marta, "and Mother makes me mark off every day that you are gone, and when we are together we always say: 'I wonder if Father remembers what we are doing now,' and we try to do just the things we do when you are home so you can really know just where we are and can almost see us all the time."

Her father smiled rather sadly and then her mother said:

"Jon, perhaps it is good for us all that we have to be apart for a while, because we appreciate so much more this chance of being together. There is no time for cross words when you know how few minutes there are left. It should make us all realize what it would be like if we lived with the thought of how quickly life runs away before us. But you are so busy, Jon, you do not have time to think about us much in the army, do you?"

A curious look came into his eyes and Jon thought for a moment with anguish of what he might have to do some day to other homes and other children, or what might happen to his, and then he pulled himself together and you could almost hear him say: "This at least is going to be a happy memory," and turning to Marta, he began to tease her about her fair hair, which stuck out in two little pigtails from the cap which she wore on her head. Seizing one of them he said:

"I can drive you just like an old horse. I will pull this pigtail and you will turn this way. I will pull the other one and you go that way."

Peals of laughter came from Marta, and before they knew it, the meal was over and the dishes washed and she had demanded that they play a make-believe game with her new doll, where she was a grown-up mother and they had come to see her child.

Such a jolly, happy time, and then as the dusk fell, Marta's father put on his uniform again, kissed her mother, took Marta in his arms, and hugged her tightly, saying: "Take good care of Moeder until I come back."

Then he was gone and they were alone again. The year seemed to travel heavily. First letters came from Jon, and then one day a telegram, and her mother cried and told Marta that her father would never come back, but her mother never stopped working, for now there was no one to look after them except God and He was far away in His heaven. Marta talked to Him sometimes because mother said He was everyone's Father, but it never seemed quite true. Marta could believe, however, that the Christ Child in the Virgin's arms in the painting in the church was a real child and she often talked to Him.

Strange things Marta told the Christ Child. She confided in Him that she never had liked that uniform which her father went away in. It must have had something to do with his staying away. He had never gone away in the clothes he wore every day and not come back. She liked him best in his everyday clothes, not his Sunday ones, which made him look rather stiff, but his nice comfortable, baggy trousers and blouse. She was never afraid of him then, and he had a nice homey smell; something of the cows and horses came into the house with him, and like a good little country girl Marta liked that smell. She told the Christ Child that her mother had no time to play with her any more. She had to work all the time, she looked different, and sometimes tears fell on her work and she could not answer Marta's questions.

There was no school any more for her to go to and on the road she met children who talked a strange language and they made fun of her and said now this country was theirs. It was all very hard to understand and she wondered if the Christ Child really did know what was happening to little children down here on earth. Sometimes there was nothing to eat in the house, and then both she and her mother went hungry to bed and she woke in the morning to find her mother gone and it would be considerably later before her mother returned with something for breakfast.

Thinking of all these things as her mother told the story again, on this St. Nicholas's Eve, 1940, Marta took off her wooden shoes and put them down beside the open fire. Sadly her mother said: "St. Nicholas will not come tonight," and he did not. Marta had an idea of her own, however, which she thought about until Christmas Eve came. Then she said to her mother: "There is one candle in the cupboard left from last year's feast. May I light it in the house so the light will shine out for the Christ Child to see His way? Perhaps He will come to us since St. Nicholas forgot us."

Marta's mother shook her head, but smiled, and Marta took out the candle and carefully placed it in a copper candlestick which had always held a lighted candle on Christmas Eve.

Marta wanted to see how far the light would shine out into the night, so she slipped into her wooden shoes again, put her shawl over her head, opened the door, and slipped out into the night. The wind was blowing around her and she could hardly stand up. She took two or three steps and looked back at the window. She could see the twinkling flame of the candle, and while she stood watching it, she was conscious of a tall figure in a dark cloak standing beside her.

Just at first she hoped the tall figure might be her father, but he would not have stood there watching her without coming out into the candlelight and picking her up and running into the house to greet her mother. She was not exactly afraid of this stranger, for she was a brave little girl, but she felt a sense of chill creeping through her, for there was something awe-inspiring and rather repellent about this personage who simply stood in the gloom watching her.

Finally he spoke:

"What are you doing here, little girl?"

Very much in awe, Marta responded: "I came out to make sure that the Christ Child's candle would shine out to guide His footsteps to our house."

"You must not believe in any such legend," remonstrated the tall, dark man. "There is no Christ Child. That is a story which is told for the weak. It is ridiculous to believe that a little child could lead the people of the world, a foolish idea claiming strength through love and sacrifice. You must grow up and acknowledge only one superior, he who dominates the rest of the world through fear and strength."

This was not very convincing to Marta. No one could tell her that what she had believed in since babyhood was not true. Why, she talked to the Christ Child herself. But she had been taught to be respectful and to listen to her elders and so silence reigned while she wondered who this man was who said such strange and curious things. Was he a bad man? Did he have something to do with her father's going away and not coming back? Or with her mother's worrying so much and working so hard? What was he doing near her house anyway? What was a bad man like? She had never known one.

He had done her no harm—at least, no bodily harm—and yet down inside her something was hurt. Things could be taken away from people. They had had to give up many of their chickens and cows because the government wanted them. That had been hard because they loved their animals and they had cared for them and it meant also that they would have little to eat and much less money when they lost them, but that was different from the way this man made her feel. He was taking away a hope, a hope that someone could do more even than her mother could do, could perhaps make true the dream, that story she told herself every night, both awake and asleep, of the day when her father would come home, the day when hand in hand they would walk down the road again together. When he would put her on his shoulder and they would go skating on the canal. Somehow this man hurt that dream and it was worse than not having St. Nicholas come. It seemed to pull down a curtain over the world.

Marta was beginning to feel very cold and very much afraid, but all her life she had been told to be polite to her elders and ask for permission to do anything she wished to do. She said: "I am hoping the Christ Child will come. May I go in now and will you not come into my house?"

The man seemed to hesitate a minute, but perhaps he decided it would be interesting to see the inside of such a humble home where there was so much simple faith. In any case, he wanted to impress upon this child and upon her mother that foolish legends were not the right preparation for living in a world where he, the power, dominated, so he followed Marta into the house without knocking. Marta's mother, who had been sitting by the fire knitting when Marta went out, was still there, yes, but in her arms was a baby and around the baby a curious light shone and Marta knew that the Christ Child had come. The man in the door did not know, he thought it was an ordinary room with an ordinary baby in a woman's arms.

Striding in, he said: "Madam, you have taught this child a foolish legend. Why is this child burning a candle in the hope that the Christ Child will come?"

The woman answered in a very low voice: "To those of us who suffer, that is a hope we may cherish. Under your power, there is fear, and you have created a strength before which people tremble. But on Christmas Eve strange things happen and new powers are sometimes born."

Marta was not interested any more in the tall figure in the cloak. The Christ Child was there in her mother's lap. She could tell Him all her troubles and He would understand why she prayed above everything else for the return of her father. St. Nicholas would never again leave them without the Christmas dinner and she could have the new doll, and the sweets which she longed to taste again. Perhaps if only she went to sleep like a good little girl, there would be a miracle and her father would be there. Off she trotted to the second room, slipped off her shoes, and climbed behind the curtain.

Marta could not go to sleep at once, because though there was no sound from the other room, she still could not free herself from the thought of that menacing figure. She wondered if he was responsible for the tears of the little girl up the road whose father had not come home last year and who had not been visited either by St. Nicholas.

Then before her eyes she suddenly saw a vision of the Christ Child. He was smiling and seemed to say that the little girl up the road had her father this year and that all was well with her. Marta was happy, fathers are so very nice. Perhaps if she prayed again to the Christ Child, when she woke up He would have her father there too, and so she said first the prayer she had always been taught to say and then just for herself she added: "Dear Christ Child, I know you will understand that though God is the father of all of us, He is very, very far away and the fathers we have down here are so much closer. Please bring mine back so that we can have the cows, the pigs and the chickens again and all we want to eat and the tears will not be in my mother's eyes." The murmur of her prayer died away as she fell asleep.

A long time the power stood and watched Marta's mother, and finally there came over him a wave of strange feeling. Would anyone ever turn eyes on him as lovingly as this woman's eyes turned on that baby? Bowing low before her, he said: "Madam, I offer you ease and comfort, fine raiment, delicious food. Will you come with me where these things are supplied, but where you cannot keep to your beliefs?"

Marta's mother shook her head and looked down at the baby lying in her lap. She said: "Where you are, there is power and hate and fear among people, one of another. Here there are none of the things which you offer, but there is the Christ Child. The Christ Child taught love. He drove the money-changers out of the temple, to be sure, but that was because He hated the system which they represented. He loved His family, the poor, the sinners, and He tried to bring out in each one the love for Him and for each other which would mean a Christlike spirit in the world. I will stay here with my child, who could trust the legend and therefore brought with her into this house the Christ Child spirit which makes us live forever. You will go out into the night again, the cold night, to die as all must die who are not born again through Him at Christmas time."

The man turned and went out, and as he opened the door, he seemed to be engulfed in the dark and troubled world without. The snow was falling and the wind was howling, the sky was gloomy overhead. All that he looked upon was fierce and evil. These evil forces of nature were ruling also in men's hearts and they brought sorrow and misery to many human beings. Greed, personal ambition, and fear all were strong in the world fed by constant hate. In the howling of the wind he heard these evil spirits about him, and they seemed to run wild, unleashed with no control.

This has happened, of course, many times in the world before, but must it go on happening forever? Suddenly he turned to look back at the house from which he had come. Still from the window shone the little child's candle and within he could see framed the figure of the mother and the Baby. Perhaps that was a symbol of the one salvation there was in the world, the heart of faith, the one hope of peace. The hope he had taken away from Marta for the moment shone out increasingly into the terrible world even though it was only the little Christ Child's candle.

With a shrug of his shoulders, he turned away to return to the luxury of power. He was able to make people suffer. He was able to make people do his will, but his strength was shaken and it always will be. The light in the window must be the dream which holds us all until we ultimately win back to the things for which Jon died and for which Marta and her mother were living.

II

PROSE

RAYMOND MACDONALD ALDEN

Why the Chimes Rang

THERE was once, in a far-away country where few people have ever traveled, a wonderful church. It stood on a high hill in the midst of a great city; and every Sunday, as well as on sacred days like Christmas, thousands of people climbed the hill to its great archways, looking like lines of ants all moving in the same direction.

When you came to the building itself, you found stone columns and dark passages, and a grand entrance leading to the main room of the church. This room was so long that one standing at the doorway could scarcely see to the other end, where the choir stood by the marble altar. In the farthest corner was the organ; and this organ was so loud, that sometimes when it played, the people for miles around would close their shutters and prepare for a great thunderstorm. Altogether, no such church as this was ever seen before, especially when it was lighted up for some festival, and crowded with people, young and old. But the strangest thing about the whole building was the wonderful chime of bells.

At one corner of the church was a great gray tower, with ivy growing over it as far up as one could see. I say as far as one could see, because the tower was quite great enough to fit the great church, and it rose so far into the sky that it was only in very fair weather that any one claimed to be able to see the top. Even then one could not be certain that it was in sight. Up, and up, and up climbed the stones and the ivy; and, as the men who built the church had been dead for hundreds of years, every one had forgotten how high the tower was supposed to be.

Now all the people knew that at the top of the tower was a chime of Christmas bells. They had hung there ever since the

23

church had been built, and were the most beautiful bells in the world. Some thought it was because a great musician had cast them and arranged them in their place; others said it was because of the great height, which reached up where the air was clearest and purest: however that might be, no one who had ever heard the chimes denied that they were the sweetest in the world. Some described them as sounding like angels far up in the sky; others, as sounding like strange winds singing through the trees.

But the fact was that no one had heard them for years and years. There was an old man living not far from the church, who said that his mother had spoken of hearing them when she was a little girl, and he was the only one who was sure of as much as that. They were Christmas chimes, you see, and were not meant to be played by men or on common days. It was the custom on Christmas Eve for all the people to bring to the church their offerings to the Christ-child; and when the greatest and best offering was laid on the altar, there used to come sounding through the music of the choir the Christmas chimes far up in the tower. Some said that the wind rang them, and others that they were so high that the angels could set them swinging. But for many long years they had never been heard. It was said that people had been growing less careful of their gifts for the Christ-child, and that no offering was brought, great enough to deserve the music of the chimes.

Every Christmas Eve the rich people still crowded to the altar, each one trying to bring some better gift than any other, without giving anything that he wanted for himself, and the church was crowded with those who thought that perhaps the wonderful bells might be heard again. But although the service was splendid, and the offerings plenty, only the roar of the wind could be heard, far up in the stone tower.

Now, a number of miles from the city, in a little country village, where nothing could be seen of the great church but glimpses of the tower when the weather was fine, lived a boy named Pedro, and his little brother. They knew very little about the Christmas chimes, but they had heard of the service in the church on Christmas Eve, and had a secret plan, which they had often talked over when by themselves, to go to see the beautiful celebration.

"Nobody can guess, Little Brother," Pedro would say, "all the fine things there are to see and hear; and I have even heard it said that the Christ-child sometimes comes down to bless the service. What if we could see Him?"

The day before Christmas was bitterly cold, with a few lonely snowflakes flying in the air, and a hard white crust on the ground. Sure enough, Pedro and Little Brother were able to slip quietly away early in the afternoon; and although the walking was hard in the frosty air, before nightfall they had trudged so far, hand in hand, that they saw the lights of the big city just ahead of them. Indeed, they were about to enter one of the great gates in the wall that surrounded it, when they saw something dark on the snow near their path, and stepped aside to look at it.

It was a poor woman, who had fallen just outside the city, too sick and tired to get in where she might have found shelter. The soft snow made of a drift a sort of pillow for her, and she would soon be so sound asleep, in the wintry air, that no one could ever waken her again. All this Pedro saw in a moment, and he knelt down beside her and tried to rouse her, even tugging at her arm a little, as though he would have tried to carry her away. He turned her face toward him, so that he could rub some of the snow on it, and when he had looked at her silently a moment he stood up again, and said:

"It's no use, Little Brother. You will have to go on alone."

"Alone?" cried Little Brother. "And you not see the Christmas festival?"

"No," said Pedro, and he could not keep back a bit of a choking sound in his throat. "See this poor woman. Her face looks like the Madonna in the chapel window, and she will freeze to death if nobody cares for her. Every one has gone to the church now, but when you come back you can bring some one to help her. I will rub her to keep her from freezing, and perhaps get her to eat the bun that is left in my pocket."

"But I can not bear to leave you, and go on alone," said Little Brother.

"Both of us need not miss the service," said Pedro, "and it had better be I than you. You can easily find your way to the church; and you must see and hear everything twice, Little Brother—once for you and once for me. I am sure the Christ-child must know how I should love to come with you and worship Him; and oh! if you get

a chance, Little Brother, to slip up to the altar without getting in
any one's way, take this little silver piece of mine, and lay it down
for my offering, when no one is looking. Do not forget where you
have left me, and forgive me for not going with you."

In this way he hurried Little Brother off to the city, and winked
hard to keep back the tears, as he heard the crunching footsteps
sounding farther and farther away in the twilight. It was pretty hard
to lose the music and splendor of the Christmas celebration that he
had been planning for so long, and spend the time instead in that
lonely place in the snow.

The great church was a wonderful place that night. Every one
said that it had never looked so bright and beautiful before. When
the organ played and the thousands of people sang, the walls shook
with the sound, and little Pedro, away outside the city wall, felt the
earth tremble around him.

At the close of the service came the procession with the offerings
to be laid on the altar. Rich men and great men marched proudly
up to lay down their gifts to the Christ-child. Some brought wonderful jewels, some baskets of gold so heavy that they could scarcely
carry them down the aisle. A great writer laid down a book that he
had been making for years and years. And last of all walked the king
of the country, hoping with all the rest to win for himself the chime
of the Christmas bells. There went a great murmur through the
church, as the people saw the king take from his head the royal
crown, all set with precious stones, and lay it gleaming on the altar,
as his offering to the Holy Child. "Surely," every one said, "we shall
hear the bells now, for nothing like this has ever happened before."

But still only the cold old wind was heard in the tower, and the
people shook their heads; and some of them said, as they had before, that they never really believed the story of the chimes, and
doubted if they ever rang at all.

The procession was over, and the choir began the closing hymn.
Suddenly the organist stopped playing as though he had been shot,
and every one looked at the old minister, who was standing by the
altar, holding up his hand for silence. Not a sound could be heard
from any one in the church, but as all the people strained their ears
to listen, there came softly, but distinctly, swinging through the air,
the sound of the chimes in the tower. So far away, and yet so clear

the music seemed—so much sweeter were the notes than anything that had been heard before, rising and falling away up there in the sky, that the people in the church sat for a moment as still as though something held each of them by the shoulders. Then they all stood up together and stared straight at the altar, to see what great gift had awakened the long-silent bells.

But all that the nearest of them saw was the childish figure of Little Brother, who had crept softly down the aisle when no one was looking, and had laid Pedro's little piece of silver on the altar.

HANS CHRISTIAN ANDERSEN

‹§ §›

The Fir Tree

Out in the forest stood a pretty little Fir Tree. It had a good place; it could have sunlight, air there was in plenty, and all around grew many larger comrades—pines as well as firs. But the little Fir Tree wished ardently to become greater. It did not care for the warm sun and the fresh air; it took no notice of the peasant children, who went about talking together, when they had come out to look for strawberries and raspberries. Often they came with a whole potful, or had strung berries on a straw; then they would sit down by the little Fir Tree and say, "How pretty and small that one is!" and the Fir Tree did not like to hear that at all.

Next year he had grown a great joint, and the following year he was longer still, for in fir trees one can always tell by the number of rings they have how many years they have been growing.

"Oh, if I were only as great a tree as the others!" sighed the little Fir, "then I would spread my branches far around and look out from my crown into the wide world. The birds would then build nests in my boughs, and when the wind blew I could nod just as grandly as the others yonder."

He took no pleasure in the sunshine, in the birds, and in the red clouds that went sailing over him morning and evening.

When it was winter, the snow lay all around, white and sparkling, a hare would often come jumping along, and spring right over the little Fir Tree. Oh! this made him so angry. But two winters went by, and when the third came the little Tree had grown so tall that the hare was obliged to run around it.

"Oh! to grow, to grow, and become old; that's the only fine thing in the world," thought the Tree.

28

In the autumn woodcutters always came and felled a few of the largest trees; that was done this year too, and the little Fir Tree, that was now quite well grown, shuddered with fear, for the great stately trees fell to the ground with a crash, and their branches were cut off, so that the trees looked quite naked, long, and slender—they could hardly be recognized. But then they were laid upon wagons, and horses dragged them away out of the wood. Where were they going? What destiny awaited them?

In the spring when the Swallows and the Stork came, the Tree asked them, "Do you know where they were taken? Did you not meet them?"

The Swallows knew nothing about it, but the Stork looked thoughtful, nodded his head, and said:

"Yes, I think so. I met many new ships when I flew out of Egypt; on the ships were stately masts; I fancy these were the trees. They smelled like fir. I can assure you they're stately—very stately."

"Oh that I were only big enough to go over the sea! What kind of thing is this sea, and how does it look?"

"It would take too long to explain all that," said the Stork, and he went away.

"Rejoice in thy youth," said the Sunbeams; "rejoice in thy fresh growth, and in the young life that is within thee."

And the wind kissed the Tree, and the dew wept tears upon it; but the Fir Tree did not understand about that.

When Christmas time approached, quite young trees were felled, sometimes trees which were neither so old nor so large as this Fir Tree, that never rested, but always wanted to go away. These young trees, which were always the most beautiful, kept all their branches; they were put upon wagons, and the horses dragged them away out of the wood.

"Where are they all going?" asked the Fir Tree. "They are not greater than I—indeed, one of them was much smaller. Why do they keep all their branches? Whither are they taken?"

"We know that! We know that!" chirped the Sparrows. "Yonder in the town we looked in at the windows. We know where they go. Oh! they are dressed up in the greatest pomp and splendor that can be imagined. We have looked in at the windows, and have perceived that they are planted in the middle of a warm room, and adorned with the most beautiful things—gilt apples, honey cakes, playthings, and many hundreds of candles."

"And then?" asked the Fir Tree, and trembled through all its branches. "And then? What happens then?"

"Why, we have not seen anything more. But it is incomparable."

"Perhaps I may be destined to tread this glorious path one day!" cried the Fir Tree, rejoicingly. "That is even better than traveling across the sea. How painfully I long for it! If it were only Christmas now! Now I am great and grown up, like the rest who were led away last year. Oh, if I were only on the carriage! If I were only in the warm room, among all the pomp and splendor! And then? Yes, then something even better will come, something far more charming, or else why should they adorn me so? There must be something grander, something greater still to come; but what? Oh! I'm suffering. I'm longing! I don't know myself what is the matter with me!"

"Rejoice in us," said the Air and Sunshine. "Rejoice in thy fresh youth here in the woodland."

But the Fir Tree did not rejoice at all, but it grew and grew; winter and summer it stood there, green, dark green. The people who saw it said, "That's a handsome tree!" and at Christmas time it was felled before any of the others. The ax cut deep into its marrow, and the tree fell to the ground with a sigh; it felt a pain, a sensation of faintness, and could not think at all of happiness, for it was sad at parting from its home, from the place where it had grown up; it knew that it should never again see the dear old companions, the little bushes and flowers all around—perhaps not even the birds. The parting was not at all agreeable.

The Tree only came to itself when it was unloaded in a yard, with other trees, and heard a man say:

"This one is famous; we want only this one!"

Now two servants came in gay liveries, and carried the Fir Tree into a large, beautiful salon. All around the walls hung pictures, and by the great stove stood large Chinese vases with lions on the covers; there were rocking-chairs, silken sofas, great tables covered with picture-books, and toys worth a hundred times a hundred dollars, at least the children said so. And the Fir Tree was put into a great tub filled with sand; but no one could see that it was a tub, for it was hung round with green cloth, and stood on a large, many-colored carpet. Oh, how the Tree trembled! What was to happen now? The servants, and the young ladies also, decked it out. On one branch they hung little nets, cut out of colored paper; every net was filled with sweetmeats; golden apples and walnuts hung down, as if they grew there, and more than a hundred little candles, red, white, and blue, were fastened to the different boughs. Dolls that looked exactly like real people—the tree had never seen such before—swung among the foliage, and high on the summit of the Tree was fixed a tinsel star. It was splendid, particularly splendid.

"This evening," said all, "this evening it will shine."

"Oh," thought the Tree, "that it were evening already! Oh, that the lights may soon be lit up! When may that be done? Will the sparrows fly against the panes? Shall I grow fast here, and stand adorned in summer and winter?"

Yes, he did not guess badly. But he had a complete backache from mere longing, and backache is just as bad for a tree as a headache for a person.

At last the candles were lighted. What a brilliance, what a splendor! The Tree trembled so in all its branches that one of the candles set fire to a green twig, and it was scorched.

"Heaven preserve us!" cried the young ladies; and they hastily put the fire out.

Now the Tree might not even tremble. Oh, that was terrible! It was so afraid of setting fire to some of its ornaments, and it was quite bewildered with all the brilliance. And now the folding doors were thrown wide open, and a number of children rushed in as if they would have overturned the whole Tree; the older people followed more deliberately. The little ones stood quite silent, but only for a minute; then they shouted till the room rang; they danced gleefully round the Tree, and one present after another was plucked from it.

"What are they about?" thought the Tree. "What's going to be done?"

And the candles burned down to the twigs, and as they burned down they were extinguished, and then the children received permission to plunder the Tree. Oh! they rushed in upon it, so that every branch cracked again: if it had not been fastened by the top and by the golden star to the ceiling, it would have fallen down.

The children danced about with their pretty toys. No one looked at the Tree except one old man, who came up and peeped among the branches, but only to see if a fig or an apple had not been forgotten.

"A story! A story!" shouted the children; and they drew a little fat man toward the tree; and he sat down just beneath it—"for then we shall be in the green wood," said he, "and the tree may have the advantage of listening to my tale. But I can only tell one. Will you hear the story of Ivede-Avede, or of Klumpey-Dumpey, who fell downstairs, and still was raised up to honor and married the Princess?"

"Ivede-Avede!" cried some, "Klumpey-Dumpey!" cried others, and there was a great crying and shouting. Only the Fir Tree was quite silent, and thought, "Shall I not be in it? Shall I have nothing to do in it?" But he had been in the evening's amusement, and had done what was required of him.

And the fat man told about Klumpey-Dumpey who fell downstairs and yet was raised to honor and married a Princess. And the children clapped their hands and cried, "Tell another! tell another!" and they wanted to hear about Ivede-Avede; but they only got the story of Klumpey-Dumpey. The Fir Tree stood quite silent and thoughtful; never had the birds in the wood told such a story as that. Klumpey-Dumpey fell downstairs, and yet came to honor and married a Princess!

"Yes, so it happens in the world!" thought the Fir Tree, and believed it must be true, because that was such a nice man who told it.

"Well, who can know? Perhaps I shall fall downstairs, too, and marry a Princess!" And it looked forward with pleasure to being adorned again, the next evening, with candles and toys, gold and fruit. "Tomorrow I shall not tremble," it thought.

"I shall rejoice in all my splendor. Tomorrow I shall hear the story of Klumpey-Dumpey again, and perhaps that of Ivede-Avede, too."

And the Tree stood all night quiet and thoughtful.

In the morning the servants and the chambermaid came in.

"Now my splendor will begin afresh," thought the Tree. But they dragged him out of the room, and upstairs to the garret, and here they put him in a dark corner where no daylight shone.

"What's the meaning of this?" thought the Tree. "What am I to do here? What is to happen?"

And he leaned against the wall, and thought, and thought. And he had time enough, for days and nights went by, and nobody came up; and when at length some one came, it was only to put some great boxes in a corner. Now the Tree stood quite hidden away, and the supposition is that it was quite forgotten.

"Now it's winter outside," thought the Tree. "The earth is hard and covered with snow, and people cannot plant me; therefore I suppose I'm to be sheltered here until Spring comes. How considerate that is! How good people are! If it were only not so dark here, and so terribly solitary!—not even a little hare? That was pretty out there in the wood, when the snow lay thick and the hare sprang past; yes, even when he jumped over me; but then I did not like it. It is terribly lonely up here!"

"Piep! piep!" said a little Mouse, and crept forward, and then came another little one. They smelled at the Fir Tree, and then slipped among the branches.

"It's horribly cold," said the two little Mice, "or else it would be comfortable here. Don't you think so, old Fir Tree?"

"I'm not old at all," said the Fir Tree. "There are many much older than I."

"Where do you come from?" asked the Mice. "And what do you know?" They were dreadfully inquisitive. "Tell us about the most beautiful spot on earth. Have you been there? Have you been in the storeroom, where cheeses lie on the shelves, and hams hang from the ceiling, where one dances on tallow candles, and goes in thin and comes out fat?"

"I don't know that," replied the Tree; "but I know the wood, where the sun shines and the birds sing."

And then it told all about its youth.

And the little Mice had never heard anything of the kind; and they listened and said:

"What a number of things you have seen! How happy you must have been!"

"I?" replied the Fir Tree; and it thought about what it had told. "Yes, those were really quite happy times." But then he told of the Christmas Eve, when he had been hung with sweetmeats and candles.

"Oh!" said the little Mice, "how happy you have been, you old Fir Tree!"

"I'm not old at all," said the Tree. "I only came out of the wood this winter. I'm only rather backward in my growth."

"What splendid stories you can tell!" said the little Mice.

And the next night they came with four other little Mice, to hear what the Tree had to relate; and the more it said, the more clearly did it remember everything, and thought. "Those were quite merry days! But they may come again. Klumpey-Dumpey fell downstairs, and yet he married a Princess. Perhaps I shall marry a Princess, too!" And the Fir Tree thought of a pretty little Birch Tree that grew out in the forest; for the Fir Tree, that Birch was a real Princess.

"Who's Klumpey-Dumpey?" asked the little Mice.

And then the Fir Tree told the whole story. It could remember every single word; and the little Mice were ready to leap to the very top of the Tree with pleasure. Next night a great many more Mice came, and on Sunday two Rats even appeared; but these thought the story was not pretty, and the little Mice were sorry for that, for now they also did not like it so much as before.

"Do you know only one story?" asked the Rats.

"Only that one," replied the Tree. "I heard that on the happiest evening of my life; I did not think then how happy I was."

"That's a very miserable story. Don't you know any about bacon and tallow candles—a storeroom story?"

"No," said the Tree.

"Then we'd rather not hear you," said the Rats.

And they went back to their own people. The little Mice at last stayed away also; and then the Tree sighed and said:

"It was very nice when they sat round me, the merry little Mice, and listened when I spoke to them. Now that's past too. But I shall remember to be pleased when they take me out."

But when did that happen? Why, it was one morning that people came and rummaged in the garret; the boxes were put away, and the Tree brought out; they certainly threw him rather roughly on the floor, but a servant dragged him away at once to the stairs, where the daylight shone.

"Now life is beginning again!" thought the Tree.

It felt the fresh air and the first sunbeam, and now it was out in the courtyard. Everything passed so quickly that the Tree quite forgot to look at itself, there was so much to look at all round. The courtyard was close to a garden, and here everything was blooming; the roses hung fresh over the paling, the linden trees were in blossom, and the swallows cried, "Quinze-wit! quinze-wit! my husband's come!" But it was not the Fir Tree they meant.

"Now I shall live!" said the Tree, rejoicingly, and spread its branches far out; but, alas! they were all withered and yellow; and it lay in the corner among nettles and weeds. The tinsel star was still upon it, and shone in the bright sunshine.

In the courtyard a couple of the merry children were playing who had danced round the tree at Christmas time, and had rejoiced over it. One of the youngest ran up and tore off the golden star.

"Look what is sticking to the ugly old fir tree!" said the child, and he trod upon the branches till they cracked again under his boots.

And the Tree looked at all the blooming flowers and the splendor of the garden, and then looked at itself, and wished it had remained in the dark corner of the garret; it thought of its fresh youth in the wood, of the merry Christmas Eve, and of the little Mice which had listened so pleasantly to the story of Klumpey-Dumpey.

"Past! past!" said the old Tree. "Had I but rejoiced when I could have done so! Past! past!"

And the servant came and chopped the Tree into little pieces; a whole bundle lay there; it blazed brightly under the great brewing copper, and it sighed deeply, and each sigh was like a little shot; and the children who were at play there ran up and seated themselves at the fire, looked into it, and cried "Puff! puff!" But at each explosion, which was a deep sigh, the Tree thought of a summer day in the woods, or of a winter night there, when the stars beamed; he thought of Christmas Eve and of Klumpey-Dumpey, the only story he had ever heard or knew how to tell; and then the Tree was burned.

The boys played in the garden, and the youngest had on his breast a golden star, which the Tree had worn on its happiest evening. Now that was past, and the Tree's life was past, and the story is past too: past! past!—and that's the way with all stories.

HEYWOOD BROUN

≈§❧≈

A Shepherd

THE HOST of heaven and the angel of the Lord had filled the sky
with radiance. Now the glory of God was gone and the shepherds
and the sheep stood under dim starlight. The men were shaken by
the wonders they had seen and heard and, like the animals, they
huddled close.

"Let us now," said the eldest of the shepherds, "go even unto
Bethlehem, and see this thing which has come to pass, which the
Lord hath made known unto us."

The City of David lay beyond a far, high hill, upon the crest of
which there danced a star. The men made haste to be away, but as
they broke out of the circle there was one called Amos who remained.
He dug his crook into the turf and clung to it.

"Come," cried the eldest of the shepherds, but Amos shook his
head. They marveled, and one called out, "It is true. It was an angel.
You heard the tidings. A Savior is born!"

"I heard," said Amos. "I will abide."

The eldest walked back from the road to the little knoll on which
Amos stood.

"You do not understand," the old man told him. "We have a sign
from God. An angel commanded us. We go to worship the Savior,
who is even now born in Bethlehem. God has made His will manifest."

"It is not in my heart," replied Amos.

And now the eldest of the shepherds was angry.

"With your own eyes," he cried out, "you have seen the host of
heaven in these dark hills. And you heard, for it was like the thunder
when 'Glory to God in the highest' came ringing to us out of the
night."

36

And again Amos said, "It is not in my heart."

Another shepherd then broke in. "Because the hills still stand and the sky has not fallen, it is not enough for Amos. He must have something louder than the voice of God."

Amos held more tightly to his crook and answered, "I have need of a whisper."

They laughed at him and said, "What should this voice say in your ear?"

He was silent and they pressed about him and shouted mockingly, "Tell us now. What says the God of Amos, the little shepherd of a hundred sheep?"

Meekness fell away from him. He took his hands from off the crook and raised them high.

"I too am a god," said Amos in a loud, strange voice, "and to my hundred sheep I am a savior."

And when the din of the angry shepherds about him slackened, Amos pointed to his hundred.

"See my flock," he said. "See the fright of them. The fear of the bright angel and of the voices is still upon them. God is busy in Bethlehem. He has no time for a hundred sheep. They are my sheep. I will abide."

This the others did not take so much amiss, for they saw that there was a terror in all the flocks and they too knew the ways of sheep. And before the shepherds departed on the road to Bethlehem toward the bright star, each talked to Amos and told him what he should do for the care of the several flocks. And yet one or two turned back a moment to taunt Amos, before they reached the dip in the road which led to the City of David. It was said, "We shall see new glories at the throne of God, and you, Amos, you will see sheep."

Amos paid no heed, for he thought to himself, "One shepherd the less will not matter at the throne of God." Nor did he have time to be troubled that he was not to see the Child who was come to save the world. There was much to be done among the flocks and Amos walked between the sheep and made under his tongue a clucking noise, which was a way he had, and to his hundred and to the others it was a sound more fine and friendly than the voice of the bright angel. Presently the animals ceased to tremble and they began to graze as the sun came up over the hill where the star had been.

"For sheep," said Amos to himself, "the angels shine too much. A shepherd is better."

With the morning the others came up the road from Bethlehem, and they told Amos of the manger and of the wise men who had mingled there with shepherds. And they described to him the gifts: gold, frankincense and myrrh. And when they were done they said, "And did you see wonders here in the fields with the sheep?"

Amos told them, "Now my hundred are one hundred and one," and he showed them a lamb which had been born just before the dawn.

"Was there for this a great voice out of heaven?" asked the eldest of the shepherds.

Amos shook his head and smiled, and there was upon his face that which seemed to the shepherds a wonder even in a night of wonders.

"To my heart," he said, "there came a whisper."

ROBERT P. TRISTRAM COFFIN

ఊ§ §ప

Christmas in Maine

IF YOU want to have a Christmas like the one we had on Paradise Farm when I was a boy, you will have to hunt up a saltwater farm on the Maine coast, with bays on both sides of it, and a road that goes around all sorts of bays, up over Misery Hill and down, and through the fir trees so close together that they brush you and your horse on both cheeks. That is the only kind of place a Christmas like that grows. You must have a clear December night, with blue Maine stars snapping like sapphires with the cold, and the big moon flooding full over Misery, and lighting up the snowy spruce boughs like crushed diamonds. You ought to be wrapped in a buffalo robe to your nose, and be sitting in a family pung, and have your breath trailing along with you as you slide over the dry, whistling snow. You will have to sing the songs we sang, "God Rest You Merry, Gentlemen" and "Joy to the World," and you will be able to see your songs around you in the air like blue smoke. That's the only way to come to a Paradise Christmas.

And you really should cross over at least one broad bay on the ice, and feel the tide rifts bounce you as the runners slide over them. And if the whole bay booms out, every now and then, and the sound echoes around the wooded islands for miles, you will be having the sort of ride we loved to take from town, the night before Christmas.

I won't insist on your having a father like ours to drive you home to your Christmas. One with a wide moustache full of icicles, and eyes like the stars of the morning. That would be impossible, anyway, for there has been only one of him in the world. But it is too bad, just the same. For you won't have the stories we had by the fireplace. You won't hear about Kitty Wells who died beautifully in song just as the

39

sun came over the tops of the eastern mountains and just after her
lover had named the wedding day, and you will not hear how Kitty's
departure put an end to his mastering the banjo:

> *"But death came in my cabin door*
> *And took from me my joy, my pride,*
> *And when they said she was no more,*
> *I laid my banjo down and cried."*

But you will be able to have the rooms of the farmhouse banked
with emerald jewels clustered on bayberry boughs, clumps of ever-
lasting roses with gold spots in the middle of them, tree evergreens,
and the evergreen that runs all over the Maine woods and every so
often puts up a bunch of palm leaves. And there will be rose-hips
stuck in pine boughs. And caraway seeds in every crust and cookie in
the place.

An aunt should be on hand, an aunt who believes in yarrow tea and
the Bible as the two things needed to keep children well. She will
read the Nativity story aloud to the family, hurrying over the really
exciting parts that happened at the stable, and bearing down hard on
what the angels had to say and the more edifying points that might
be supposed to improve small boys who like to lie too long abed in
the mornings. She will put a moral even into Christmas greens, and
she will serve well as a counterirritant to the over-eating of mince pies.
She will insist on all boys washing behind their ears, and that will
keep her days full to the brim.

The Christmas tree will be there, and it will have a top so high
that it will have to be bent over and run along the ceiling of the sitting
room. It will be the best fir tree of the Paradise forests, picked from
ten thousand almost perfect ones, and every bough on it will be like
old-fashioned fans wide open. You will have brought it home that very
morning, on the sled, from Dragonfly Spring.

Dragonfly Spring was frozen solid to the bottom, and you could
look down into it and see the rainbows where you dented it with
your copper-toed boots, see whole ferns caught motionless in the
crystal deeps, and a frog, too, down there, with hands just like a baby's
on him. Your small sister—the one with hair like new honey laid open
—in the middle of a honeycomb—had cried out, "Let's dig him up and
take him home and warm his feet!" (She is the same sister who ate up

all your more vivid pastel crayons when you were away at school, and then ate up all the things you had been pretty sure were toadstools in Bluejay Woods, when you were supposed to be keeping an eye on her, but were buried so deep in "Mosses from an Old Manse" that you couldn't have been dug up with horses and oxen.)

Your dog, Snoozer, who is a curious and intricate combination of many merry pugs and many mournful hound-dogs, was snuffling all the time, hot on the feather-stitching the mice had made from bush to bush while you were felling the Christmas tree. A red squirrel was taking a white-pine cone apart on a hemlock bough, and telling Snoozer what he thought of him and all other dogs, the hour or so you were there.

There will be a lot of aunts in the house besides the Biblical one. Aunts of every complexion and cut. Christmas is the one time that even the most dubious of aunts take on value. One of them can make up wreaths, another can make rock candy that puts a tremble on the heart, and still another can steer your twelve-seater bobsled—and turn it over, bottom up, with you all in just the right place for a fine spill.

There will be uncles, too, to hold one end of the molasses taffy you will pull sooner or later, yanking it out till it flashes and turns into cornsilk that almost floats in the air, tossing your end of it back and probably lassoing your uncle around his neck as you do it, and pulling out a new rope of solid honey.

The uncles will smoke, too, and that will be a help to all the younger brothers who have been smoking their acorn-pipes out in the wood-shed, and who don't want their breaths to give them away. The uncles will make themselves useful in other ways. They will rig up schooners no bigger than your thumb, with shrouds like cobwebs; they will mend the bob-sled, tie up cut fingers, and sew on buttons after you shin up to the cupola in the barn; and—if you get on the good side of them— they will saw you up so much birch wood that you won't have to lay hand to a bucksaw till after New Year's.

There will be cousins by the cart load. He-ones and she-ones. The size you can sit on, and the size that can sit on you. Enough for two armies, on Little Round Top and on Big, up in the haymow. You will play Gettysburg there till your heads are full of hay chaff that will keep six aunts busy cleaning it out. And then you will come in to the house and down a whole crock of molasses cookies—the kind that go up in peaks in the middle—which somebody was foolish enough to leave the cover off.

Every holiday that came along, in my father's house, was the gathering of an Anglo-Saxon clan. My father was built for lots of people 'round him. But Christmas was a whole assembly of the West Saxons! My father wanted people in squads. There were men with wide moustaches and men with smooth places on top of their heads, women wide and narrow. Cousins of the second and third water, even, were there. Hired men, too. They were special guests and had to be handled with kid gloves, as New England hired men must. They had to have the best of everything, and you could not find fault with them, as you could with uncles, if they smacked you for upsetting their coffee into their laps. Babies were underfoot in full cry. The older children hunted in packs. The table had to be pieced out with flour barrels and bread boards and ironing boards. It was a house's length from the head of the table, where your father sat and manufactured the roast up into slivers, to your mother dishing out the pork gravy. Whole geese disappeared on the way down. The Christmas cake, which had been left sweetly to itself for a month to age into a miracle, was a narrow isthmus when it got to Mother. But Mother always said that Christmas, to her, was watching other people eat. She was the kind of mother who claimed that the neck and the back of the chicken were the tastiest parts.

The prize goose, whom you had brought up by hand and called Oliver Cromwell, Old Ironsides, or some such distinguished title, was duly carved. And Father found his wishbone snow-white and you all applauded, for that meant lots of snow and two more months of coasting on your sleds. There were mince pies by the legion. And if Uncle Tom were there, a whole raccoon baked just for him and girt around with browned sweet potatoes. Mother's wild strawberry jam was there on deck, winking at you like rubies from the holes in tarts that melted away like bubbles in the mouth. That dinner was three hours in Beulah Land!

Of course, there will be an apple pudding at such a season. Steamed in a lard bucket, and cut open with a string. A sauce of oranges and lemons to make an ocean around each steaming volcano of suet and russet apples as it falls crumbling from the loop of twine. It will have to be steamed in the boiler, if your Christmas is to be the size of ours, and cooked in a ten-pound lard pail. Better use a cod line instead of the twine of other holidays, to parcel it out to the members of the clan.

The whole nation of you in the house will go from one thing to another. The secret of the best Christmases is everybody doing the same things all at the same time. You will all fall to and string cranberries and popcorn for the tree, and the bright lines each of you has a hold on will radiate from the tree like ribbons on a maypole. Everybody will have needles and thread in the mouth, you will all get in each other's way, but that is the art of doing Christmas right. You will all bundle up together for a ride in the afternoon. You had better take the horse-sled, as the pung will not begin to hold you. And even then a dozen or so of assorted uncles and aunts and cousins will have to come trooping after through the deep snow, and wait for their turn on the straw in the sled. Smaller cousins will fall off over the sides in great knots and never be missed, and the hullabaloo will roar on and send the rabbits flying away through the woods, showing their bobbing scuts.

Everybody will hang presents on the tree at once, when the sun has dipped down into the spruces in the west and you are back home in the sitting-room. There will be no nonsense of tiptoeing up and edging a package on when nobody is looking. Everybody knows who is giving him what. There is no mystery about it. Aunt Ella has made rag dinahs for all hands and the cook—for all under fourteen years of age—and she does not care who knows it. The dinahs are all alike, except that those for the children whose lower garments are forked have forked red-flannel pants instead of red-flannel petticoats. They all have pearl button eyes and stocking toes for faces. There will be so many hands at work on the tree at once that the whole thing will probably go over two or three times, and it will be well to make it fast with a hawser or so.

And then you will turn right around and take the presents off again, the minute you have got them all on and have lighted the candles up. There will be no waiting, with small children sitting around with aching hearts. The real candles will be a problem, in all that mass of spills. Boughs will take fire here and there. But there will be plenty of uncles around to crush out the small bonfires in their big brown hands. All the same, it would be well to have an Uncle Thomas who can take up a live coal in his thumb and finger, and light his pipe from it, cool as a cucumber. Better turn the extinguishing of the tree over to him.

There will be boughten presents, to be sure—a turtle of cardboard in a glassed, dainty box, hung on springs and swimming for dear life with all four feet, and popguns with their barrels ringed and streaked with red and yellow lines. Why popguns should be painted like broomsticks is one of the mysteries, along with the blue paint you always find on Maine cartwheels. Somebody will probably get one of those Swiss music-boxes that will eke out a ghostly "Last Rose of Summer," if tenderly cranked. There should be those little bottles of transparent candies, with real syrup in them, which I used to live for through the years. And there must be a German doll for every last girl, with mountains of yellow hair and cheeks looking as if life were a continuous blowing of bubbles. Boughten things are all right.

But if it is going to be our kind of Christmas, most of the presents will be home-made. Socks knit by the aunt who swears only by useful gifts. You have seen those socks growing up from their white toes for the last two weeks. Wristers, always red. A box of Aunt Louise's candied orange peel that she will never let on to anybody how she makes. Your father will have made a sled for every mother's son and daughter of you, with a bluebird, or robin redbreast, more real than life, painted on each one and your name underneath. You will never have another present to match that, though you grow up and become Midases. Popcorn balls, big as muskmelons, will be common ware. They will be dripping with molasses, and will stick your wristers and socks and other treasures together.

But the pith of the party is not reached until the whole nation of you sits down in rocking chairs, or lies down on their bellies in front of the six-foot gulf of the fireplace. The presents are all stowed, heaped and tucked away, stuck fast with cornballs. The last lamps are out. The firelight dances on the ceiling. It lights up the steel engraving of Major McCullock leaping from Kentucky to Ohio, with ten thousand mounted redskins yelling and reining in their steeds behind him. It lights up Daniel Boone's daughters as they lean away towards their boat's end and scream their silent screams and drop their water lilies, while Indian head after Indian head grins up at them from the river of the Dark and Bloody Ground.

All the babies will be hushed and put away. All the younger fry will be more than half asleep. The toasted cheese and red herring will go 'round. The herring, by the way—if you are worthy to wear my shoes after me—which you yourself have smoked with green oak, and have gotten your own two eyes so that they looked like two burnt holes in a blanket while doing it, and have hugely enjoyed every hour of it all.

Then you had best find a fair substitute for my father. Give him the best chair in the house—and the way to find *that* is to push the cat out of it—and let him tear! He will begin by telling you about such people as the brilliant young ladies of Philadelphia who had a piano too big to fit their house, so they put it on the porch and played on it through the open window. Then he will sit back and work his way to the Caliph of Bagdad, who had a daughter so homely that she had to wear a sack on her head when her suitors came awooing, and how she fell down a well and made herself a great fortune, and won the handsomest husband that ever wore a turban. That story, by the way, you will not find in the "Arabian Nights" even though you look for it, as I have done, till you have gray hairs in your head.

The firelight will get into your father's eyes and on his hair. He will move on from Bagdad to Big Bethel, and tell you all how the Yankee campfires looked like the high Milky Way itself, all night long before the battle; how the dew silvered every sleeping soldier's face and the stacked rifles, as the dawn came up with the new day and death. And you will hug your knees and hear the wind outside going its rounds among the snowy pines, and you will listen on till the story you are hearing becomes a part of the old winds of the world and the motion of the bright stars. And probably it will take two uncles at least to carry you to bed.

CHARLES DICKENS

<§>

A Christmas Carol

IN FOUR STAVES

Stave One: Marley's Ghost

MARLEY was dead, to begin with. There is no doubt whatever about that. The register of his burial was signed by the clergyman, the clerk, the undertaker, and the chief mourner. Scrooge signed it. And Scrooge's name was good upon 'Change for anything he chose to put his hand to.

Old Marley was as dead as a door-nail.

Scrooge knew he was dead? Of course he did. How could it be otherwise? Scrooge and he were partners for I don't know how many years. Scrooge was his sole executor, his sole administrator, his sole assign, his sole residuary legatee, his sole friend, his sole mourner.

Scrooge never painted out old Marley's name, however. There it yet stood, years afterwards, above the warehouse door—Scrooge and Marley. The firm was known as Scrooge and Marley. Sometimes people new to the business called Scrooge Scrooge, and sometimes Marley. He answered to both names. It was all the same to him.

Oh! But he was a tight-fisted hand at the grindstone, was Scrooge! a squeezing, wrenching, grasping, scraping, clutching, covetous old sinner! External heat and cold had little influence on him. No warmth could warm, no cold could chill him. No wind that blew was bitterer than he, no falling snow was more intent upon its purpose, no pelting rain less open to entreaty. Foul weather didn't know where to have him. The heaviest rain and snow and hail and sleet could boast of the

EDITOR'S NOTE: This is the shortened version of the *Carol*, made by Dickens himself for use in his public readings.

46

advantage over him in only one respect,—they often "came down" handsomely, and Scrooge never did.

Nobody ever stopped him in the street to say, with gladsome looks, "My dear Scrooge, how are you? When will you come to see me?" No beggars implored him to bestow a trifle, no children asked him what it was o'clock, no man or woman ever once in all his life inquired the way to such and such a place, of Scrooge. Even the blind men's dogs appeared to know him, and when they saw him coming on, would tug their owners into doorways and up courts; and then would wag their tails as though they said, "No eyes at all is better than an evil eye, dark master!"

But what did Scrooge care! It was the very thing he liked. To edge his way along the crowded paths of life, warning all human sympathy to keep its distance, was what the knowing ones call "nuts" to Scrooge.

Once upon a time—of all the good days in the year, upon a Christmas eve—old Scrooge sat busy in his counting-house. It was cold, bleak, biting, foggy weather; and the city clocks had only just gone three, but it was quite dark already.

The door of Scrooge's counting-house was open, that he might keep his eye upon his clerk, who, in a dismal little cell beyond, a sort of tank, was copying letters. Scrooge had a very small fire, but the clerk's fire was so very much smaller that it looked like one coal. But he couldn't replenish it, for Scrooge kept the coal-box in his own room; and so surely as the clerk came in with the shovel, the master predicted that it would be necessary for them to part. Wherefore the clerk put on his white comforter, and tried to warm himself at the candle; in which effort, not being a man of a strong imagination, he failed.

"A Merry Christmas, uncle! God save you!" cried a cheerful voice. It was the voice of Scrooge's nephew, who came upon him so quickly that this was the first intimation Scrooge had of his approach.

"Bah!" said Scrooge; "humbug!"

"Christmas a humbug, uncle! You don't mean that, I am sure?"

"I do. Out upon merry Christmas! What's Christmas time to you but a time for paying bills without money; a time for finding yourself a year older, and not an hour richer; a time for balancing your books and having every item in 'em through a round dozen of months presented dead against you? If I had my will, every idiot who goes about with 'Merry Christmas' on his lips should be boiled with his own pudding, and buried with a stake of holly through his heart. He should!"

"Uncle!"

"Nephew, keep Christmas in your own way, and let me keep it in mine."

"Keep it! But you don't keep it."

"Let me leave it alone, then. Much good may it do you! Much good it has ever done you!"

"There are many things from which I might have derived good, by which I have not profited, I dare say, Christmas among the rest. But I am sure I have always thought of Christmas time, when it has come round—apart from the veneration due to its sacred origin, if anything belonging to it *can* be apart from that—as a good time; a kind, forgiving, charitable, pleasant time; the only time I know of, in the long calendar of the year, when men and women seem by one consent to open their shut-up hearts freely, and to think of people below them as if they really were fellow-travellers to the grave, and not another race of creatures bound on other journeys. And therefore, uncle, though it has never put a scrap of gold or silver in my pocket, I believe that it *has* done me good, and *will* do me good; and I say, God bless it!"

The clerk in the tank involuntarily applauded.

"Let me hear another sound from *you*," said Scrooge, "and you'll keep your Christmas by losing your situation! You're quite a powerful speaker, sir," he added, turning to his nephew. "I wonder you don't go into Parliament."

"Don't be angry, uncle. Come! Dine with us to-morrow."

Scrooge said that he would see him—yes, indeed he did. He went the whole length of the expression, and said that he would see him in that extremity first.

"But why?" cried Scrooge's nephew. "Why?"

"Why did you get married?"

"Because I fell in love."

"Because you fell in love!" growled Scrooge, as if that were the only one thing in the world more ridiculous than a merry Christmas. "Good afternoon!"

"Nay, uncle, but you never came to see me before that happened. Why give it as a reason for not coming now?"

"Good afternoon."

"I want nothing from you; I ask nothing of you; why cannot we be friends?"

"Good afternoon."

"I am sorry, with all my heart, to find you so resolute. We have never had any quarrel, to which I have been a party. But I have made the trial in homage to Christmas, and I'll keep my Christmas humour to the last. So A Merry Christmas, uncle!"

"Good afternoon!"

"And A Happy New-Year!"

"Good afternoon!"

His nephew left the room without an angry word, notwithstanding. The clerk, in letting Scrooge's nephew out, had let two other people in. They were portly gentlemen, pleasant to behold, and now stood, with their hats off, in Scrooge's office. They had books and papers in their hands, and bowed to him.

"Scrooge and Marley's, I believe," said one of the gentlemen, referring to his list. "Have I the pleasure of addressing Mr. Scrooge or Mr. Marley?"

"Mr. Marley has been dead these seven years. He died seven years ago, this very night."

"At this festive season of the year, Mr. Scrooge," said the gentleman, taking up a pen, "it is more than usually desirable that we should make some slight provision for the poor and destitute, who suffer greatly at the present time. Many thousands are in want of common necessaries; hundreds of thousands are in want of common comforts, sir."

"Are there no prisons?"

"Plenty of prisons. But under the impression that they scarcely furnish Christian cheer of mind or body to the unoffending multitude, a few of us are endeavouring to raise a fund to buy the poor some meat and drink, and means of warmth. We choose this time, because it is a time, of all others, when Want is keenly felt, and Abundance rejoices. What shall I put you down for?"

"Nothing!"

"You wish to be anonymous?"

"I wish to be left alone. Since you ask me what I wish, gentlemen, that is my answer. I don't make merry myself at Christmas, and I can't afford to make idle people merry. I help to support the prisons and the workhouses,—they cost enough,—and those who are badly off must go there."

"Many can't go there; and many would rather die."

"If they would rather die, they had better do it, and decrease the surplus population."

At length the hour of shutting up the counting-house arrived. With an ill-will Scrooge, dismounting from his stool, tacitly admitted the fact to the expectant clerk in the tank, who instantly snuffed his candle out, and put on his hat.

"You want all day to-morrow, I suppose?"

"If quite convenient, sir."

"It's not convenient, and it's not fair. If I was to stop half a crown for it, you'd think yourself mightily ill-used, I'll be bound?"

"Yes, sir."

"And yet you don't think *me* ill-used, when I pay a day's wages for no work."

"It's only once a year, sir."

"A poor excuse for picking a man's pocket every twenty-fifth of December! But I suppose you must have the whole day. Be here all the earlier *next* morning."

The clerk promised that he would, and Scrooge walked out with a growl. The office was closed in a twinkling, and the clerk, with the long ends of his white comforter dangling below his waist (for he boasted no great-coat), went down a slide, at the end of a lane of boys, twenty times, in honour of its being Christmas eve, and then ran home as hard as he could pelt, to play at blindman's buff.

Scrooge took his melancholy dinner in his usual melancholy tavern; and having read all the newspapers, and beguiled the rest of the evening with his banker's book, went home to bed. He lived in chambers which had once belonged to his deceased partner. They were a gloomy suite of rooms, in a lowering pile of building up a yard. The building was old enough now, and dreary enough, for nobody lived in it but Scrooge, the other rooms being all let out as offices.

Now it is a fact, that there was nothing at all particular about the knocker on the door of this house, except that it was very large; also, that Scrooge had seen it, night and morning, during his whole residence in that place; also, that Scrooge had as little of what is called fancy about him as any man in the city of London. And yet Scrooge, having his key in the lock of the door, saw in the knocker, without its undergoing any intermediate process of change, not a knocker, but Marley's face.

Marley's face, with a dismal light about it, like a bad lobster in a dark cellar. It was not angry or ferocious, but it looked at Scrooge as Marley used to look,—ghostly spectacles turned up upon its ghostly forehead.

As Scrooge looked fixedly at this phenomenon, it was a knocker again. He said, "Pooh, pooh!" and closed the door with a bang.

The sound resounded through the house like thunder. Every room above, and every cask in the wine-merchant's cellars below, appeared to have a separate peal of echoes of its own. Scrooge was not a man to be frightened by echoes. He fastened the door, and walked across the hall, and up the stairs. Slowly too, trimming his candle as he went.

Up Scrooge went, not caring a button for its being very dark. Darkness is cheap, and Scrooge liked it. But before he shut his heavy door, he walked through his rooms to see that all was right. He had just enough recollection of the face to desire to do that.

Sitting-room, bedroom, lumber-room, all as they should be. Nobody under the table, nobody under the sofa; a small fire in the grate; spoon and basin ready; and the little saucepan of gruel (Scrooge had a cold in his head) upon the hob. Nobody under the bed; nobody in the closet; nobody in his dressing-gown, which was hanging up in a suspicious attitude against the wall. Lumber-room as usual. Old fire-guards, old shoes, two fish-baskets, washing-stand on three legs, and a poker.

Quite satisfied, he closed his door, and locked himself in; double-locked himself in, which was not his custom. Thus secured against surprise, he took off his cravat, put on his dressing-gown and slippers and his nightcap, and sat down before the very low fire to take his gruel.

As he threw his head back in the chair, his glance happened to rest upon a bell, a disused bell, that hung in the room, and communicated, for some purpose now forgotten, with a chamber in the highest story of the building. It was with great astonishment, and with a strange, inexplicable dread, that, as he looked, he saw this bell begin to swing. Soon it rang out loudly, and so did every bell in the house.

This was succeeded by a clanking noise, deep down below as if some person were dragging a heavy chain over the casks in the wine-merchant's cellar.

Then he heard the noise much louder, on the floors below; then coming up the stairs; then coming straight towards his door.

It came on through the heavy door, and a spectre passed into the room before his eyes. And upon its coming in, the dying flame leaped up, as though it cried, "I know him! Marley's ghost!"

The same face, the very same. Marley in his pigtail, usual waistcoat, tights, and boots. His body was transparent; so that Scrooge, observing him, and looking through his waistcoat, could see the two buttons on his coat behind.

Scrooge had often heard it said that Marley had no bowels, but he had never believed it until now.

No, nor did he believe it even now. Though he looked the phantom through and through, and saw it standing before him,—though he felt the chilling influence of its death-cold eyes, and noticed the very texture of the folded kerchief bound about its head and chin,—he was still incredulous.

"How now!" said Scrooge, caustic and cold as ever. "What do you want with me?"

"Much!"—Marley's voice, no doubt about it.

"Who are you?"

"Ask me who I *was*."

"Who *were* you then?"

"In life I was your partner, Jacob Marley."

"Can you—can you sit down?"

"I can."

"Do it, then."

Scrooge asked the question, because he didn't know whether a ghost so transparent might find himself in a condition to take a chair; and felt that, in the event of its being impossible, it might involve the necessity of an embarrassing explanation. But the ghost sat down on the opposite side of the fireplace, as if he were quite used to it.

"You don't believe in me."

"I don't."

"What evidence would you have of my reality beyond that of your senses?"

"I don't know."

"Why do you doubt your senses?"

"Because a little thing affects them. A slight disorder of the stomach makes them cheats. You may be an undigested bit of beef, a blot of mustard, a crumb of cheese, a fragment of an underdone potato. There's more of gravy than of grave about you, whatever you are!"

Scrooge was not much in the habit of cracking jokes, nor did he feel in his heart by any means waggish then. The truth is, that he tried to be smart, as a means of distracting his own attention, and keeping down his horror.

But how much greater was his horror when, the phantom taking off the bandage round its head, as if it were too warm to wear indoors, its lower jaw dropped down upon its breast!

"Mercy! Dreadful apparition, why do you trouble me? Why do spirits walk the earth, and why do they come to me?"

"It is required of every man that the spirit within him should walk abroad among his fellow-men, and travel far and wide; and if that spirit goes not forth in life, it is condemned to do so after death. I cannot tell you all I would. A very little more is permitted to me. I cannot rest, I cannot stay, I cannot linger anywhere. My spirit never walked beyond our counting-house—mark me!—in life my spirit never roved beyond the narrow limits of our money-changing hole; and weary journeys lie before me!"

"Seven years dead. And travelling all the time? You travel fast?"

"On the wings of the wind."

"You might have got over a great quantity of ground in seven years."

"O blind man, blind man! not to know that ages of incessant labour by immortal creatures for this earth must pass into eternity before the good of which it is susceptible is all developed. Not to know that any Christian spirit working kindly in its little sphere, whatever it may be, will find its mortal life too short for its vast means of usefulness. Not to know that no space of regret can make amends for one life's opportunities misused! Yet I was like this man; I once was like this man!"

"But you were always a good man of business, Jacob," faltered Scrooge, who now began to apply this to himself.

"Business!" cried the Ghost, wringing its hands again. "Mankind was my business. The common welfare was my business; charity, mercy, forbearance, benevolence, were all my business. The dealings of my trade were but a drop of water in the comprehensive ocean of my business!"

Scrooge was very much dismayed to hear the spectre going on at this rate, and began to quake exceedingly.

"Hear me! My time is nearly gone."

"I will. But don't be hard upon me! Don't be flowery, Jacob! Pray!"

"I am here to-night to warn you that you have yet a chance and hope of escaping my fate. A chance and hope of my procuring, Ebenezer."

"You were always a good friend to me. Thank'ee!"

"You will be haunted by Three Spirits."

"Is that the chance and hope you mentioned, Jacob? I—I think I'd rather not."

"Without their visits, you cannot hope to shun the path I tread. Expect the first to-morrow night, when the bell tolls One. Expect the second on the next night at the same hour. The third, upon the next night, when the last stroke of Twelve has ceased to vibrate. Look to see me no more; and look that, for your own sake, you remember what has passed between us!"

It walked backward from him; and at every step it took, the window raised itself a little, so that, when the apparition reached it, it was wide open.

Scrooge closed the window, and examined the door by which the Ghost had entered. It was double-locked, as he had locked it with his own hands, and the bolts were undisturbed. Scrooge tried to say, "Humbug!" but stopped at the first syllable. And being, from the emotion he had undergone, or the fatigues of the day, or his glimpse of the invisible world, or the dull conversation of the Ghost, or the lateness of the hour, much in need of repose, he went straight to bed, without undressing, and fell asleep on the instant.

Stave Two: The First of the Three Spirits

When Scrooge awoke, it was so dark, that, looking out of bed, he could scarcely distinguish the transparent window from the opaque walls of his chamber, until suddenly the church clock tolled a deep, dull, hollow, melancholy ONE.

Light flashed up in the room upon the instant, and the curtains of his bed were drawn aside by a strange figure,—like a child; yet not so like a child as like an old man, viewed through some supernatural medium, which gave him the appearance of having receded from the view, and being diminished to a child's proportions. Its hair, which hung about its neck and down its back, was white as if with age; and yet the face had not a wrinkle in it, and the tenderest bloom was on the skin. It held a branch of fresh green holly in its hand; and, in singular contradiction of that wintry emblem, had its dress trimmed with summer flowers. But the strangest thing about it was, that from the crown of its head there sprung a bright clear jet of light, by which all this was visible; and which was doubtless the occasion of its using, in its duller moments, a great extinguisher for a cap, which it now held under its arm.

"Are you the Spirit, sir, whose coming was foretold to me?"

"I am!"

"Who and what are you?"

"I am the Ghost of Christmas Past."

"Long Past?"

"No. Your past. The things that you will see with me are shadows of the things that have been; they will have no consciousness of us."

Scrooge then made bold to inquire what business brought him there.

"Your welfare. Rise and walk with me!"

It would have been in vain for Scrooge to plead that the weather and the hour were not adapted to pedestrian purposes; that bed was warm, and the thermometer a long way below freezing; that he was clad but lightly in his slippers, dressing-gown, and night-cap; and that he had a cold upon him at that time. The grasp, though gentle as a woman's hand, was not to be resisted. He rose; but finding that the Spirit made towards the window, clasped its robe in supplication.

"I am a mortal, and liable to fall."

"Bear but a touch of my hand *there*," said the Spirit, laying it upon his heart, "and you shall be upheld in more than this!"

As the words were spoken, they passed through the wall, and stood in the busy thoroughfares of a city. It was made plain enough by the dressing of the shops that here, too, it was Christmas time. The Ghost stopped at a certain warehouse door, and asked Scrooge if he knew it.

"Know it! I was apprenticed here!"

They went in. At sight of an old gentleman in a Welsh wig, sitting behind such a high desk that, if he had been two inches taller, he must have knocked his head against the ceiling, Scrooge cried in great excitement: "Why, it's old Fezziwig! Bless his heart, it's Fezziwig, alive again!"

Old Fezziwig laid down his pen, and looked up at the clock, which pointed to the hour of seven. He rubbed his hands; adjusted his capacious waistcoat; laughed all over himself, from his shoes to his organ of benevolence; and called out in a comfortable, oily, rich, fat, jovial voice: "Yo ho, there! Ebenezer! Dick!"

A living and moving picture of Scrooge's former self, a young man, came briskly in, accompanied by his fellow-apprentice.

"Dick Wilkins, to be sure!" said Scrooge to the Ghost. "My old fellow-prentice, bless me, yes. There he is. He was very much attached to me, was Dick. Poor Dick! Dear, dear!"

"Yo ho, my boys!" said Fezziwig. "No more work to-night. Christmas eve, Dick. Christmas, Ebenezer! Let's have the shutters up, before a man can say Jack Robinson! Clear away, my lads, and let's have lots of room here!"

Clear away! There was nothing they wouldn't have cleared away, or couldn't have cleared away, with old Fezziwig looking on. It was done in a minute. Every movable was packed off, as if it were dismissed from public life for evermore; the floor was swept and watered, the lamps were trimmed, fuel was heaped upon the fire; and the warehouse was as snug and warm and dry and bright a ballroom as you would desire to see on a winter's night.

In came a fiddler with a music-book, and went up to the lofty desk, and made an orchestra of it, and tuned like fifty stomach-aches. In came Mrs. Fezziwig, one vast substantial smile. In came the three Miss Fezziwigs, beaming and lovable. In came the six young followers whose hearts they broke. In came all the young men and women employed in the business. In came the housemaid, with her cousin the baker. In came the cook, with her brother's particular friend the milkman. In they all came one after another; some shyly, some boldly, some gracefully, some awkwardly, some pushing, some pulling; in they all came, anyhow and everyhow. Away they all went, twenty couples at once; hands half round and back again the other way; down the middle and up again; round and round in various stages of affectionate grouping; old top couple always turning up in the wrong place; new top couple starting off again, as soon as they got there; all top couples at last, and not a bottom one to help them. When this result was brought about, old Fezziwig, clapping his hands to stop the dance, cried out, "Well done"; and the fiddler plunged his hot face into a pot of porter especially provided for that purpose.

There were more dances, and there were forfeits, and more dances, and there was cake, and there was negus, and there was a great piece of Cold Roast, and there was a great piece of Cold Boiled, and there were mince-pies, and plenty of beer. But the great effect of the evening came after the Roast and Boiled, when the fiddler struck up "Sir Roger de Coverley." Then old Fezziwig stood out to dance with Mrs. Fezziwig. Top couple, too; with a good stiff piece of work cut out for them; three or four and twenty pair of partners; people who were not to be trifled with; people who *would* dance, and had no notion of walking.

But if they had been twice as many—four times—old Fezziwig would have been a match for them, and so would Mrs. Fezziwig. As to *her*, she was worthy to be his partner in every sense of the term. A positive light appeared to issue from Fezziwig's calves. They shone in every part of the dance. You couldn't have predicted, at any given time, what would become of 'em next. And when old Fezziwig and Mrs. Fezziwig had gone all through the dance,—advance and retire, turn your partner, bow and courtesy, corkscrew, thread the needle, and back again to your place,—Fezziwig "cut,"—cut so deftly, that he appeared to wink with his legs.

When the clock struck eleven this domestic ball broke up. Mr. and Mrs. Fezziwig took their stations, one on either side the door, and, shaking hands with every person individually as he or she went out, wished him or her a Merry Christmas. When everybody had retired but the two 'prentices, they did the same to them; and thus the cheerful voices died away, and the lads were left to their beds, which were under a counter in the back shop.

"A small matter," said the Ghost, "to make these silly folks so full of gratitude. He has spent but a few pounds of your mortal money,—three or four perhaps. Is that so much that he deserves this praise?"

"It isn't that," said Scrooge, heated by the remark, and speaking unconsciously like his former, not his latter self,—"it isn't that, Spirit. He has the power to render us happy or unhappy; to make our service light or burdensome; a pleasure or a toil. Say that his power lies in words and looks; in things so slight and insignificant that it is impossible to add and count 'em up: what then? The happiness he gives is quite as great as if it cost a fortune."

He felt the Spirit's glance, and stopped.

"What is the matter?"

"Nothing particular."

"Something, I think?"

"No, no. I should like to be able to say a word or two to my clerk just now. That's all."

"My time grows short," observed the Spirit. "Quick!"

This was not addressed to Scrooge, or to any one whom he could see, but it produced an immediate effect. For again he saw himself. He was older now; a man in the prime of life.

He was not alone, but sat by the side of a fair young girl in a black dress, in whose eyes there were tears.

"It matters little," she said softly to Scrooge's former self. "To you very little. Another idol has displaced me; and if it can comfort you in time to come, as I would have tried to do, I have no just cause to grieve."

"What idol has displaced you?"

"A golden one. You fear the world too much. I have seen your nobler aspirations fall off one by one, until the master-passion, Gain, engrosses you. Have I not?"

"What then? Even if I have grown so much wiser, what then? I am not changed towards you. Have I ever sought release from our engagement?"

"In words, no. Never."

"In what, then?"

"In a changed nature; in an altered spirit; in another atmosphere of life; another Hope as its great end. If you were free to-day, to-morrow, yesterday, can even I believe that you would choose a dowerless girl; or, choosing her, do I not know that your repentance and regret would surely follow? I do; and I release you. With a full heart, for the love of him you once were."

"Spirit! remove me from this place."

"I told you these were shadows of the things that have been," said the Ghost. "That they are what they are, do not blame me!"

"Remove me!" Scrooge exclaimed. "I cannot bear it! Leave me! Take me back. Haunt me no longer!"

As he struggled with the Spirit he was conscious of being exhausted, and overcome by an irresistible drowsiness; and, further, of being in his own bedroom. He had barely time to reel to bed before he sank into a heavy sleep.

Stave Three: The Second of the Three Spirits

Scrooge awoke in his own bedroom. There was no doubt about that. But it and his own adjoining sitting-room, into which he shuffled in his slippers, attracted by a great light there, had undergone a surprising transformation. The walls and ceiling were so hung with living green, that it looked a perfect grove. The leaves of holly, mistletoe, and ivy reflected back the light, as if so many little mirrors had been scattered there; and such a mighty blaze went roaring up the chimney, as that petrifaction of a hearth had never known in Scrooge's time, or Marley's, or for many and many a winter season gone. Heaped upon the floor, to form a kind of throne, were turkeys, geese, game, brawn, great joints of meat, sucking pigs, long wreaths of sausages, mince-pies, plum-puddings, barrels of oysters, red-hot chestnuts, cherry-cheeked apples, juicy oranges, luscious pears, immense twelfth-cakes, and great bowls of punch. In easy state upon this couch there sat a Giant glorious to see; who bore a glowing torch, in shape not unlike Plenty's horn, and who raised it high to shed its light on Scrooge, as he came peeping round the door.

"Come in,—come in! and know me better, man! I am the Ghost of Christmas Present. Look upon me! You have never seen the like of me before."

"Never."

"Have never walked forth with the younger members of my family;

meaning (for I am very young) my elder brothers born in these later years?" pursued the Phantom.

"I don't think I have, I am afraid I have not. Have you had many brothers, Spirit?"

"More than eighteen hundred."

"A tremendous family to provide for! Spirit, conduct me where you will. I went forth last night on compulsion, and I learnt a lesson which is working now. To-night, if you have aught to teach me, let me profit by it."

"Touch my robe!"

Scrooge did as he was told, and held it fast.

The room and its contents all vanished instantly, and they stood in the city streets upon a snowy Christmas morning.

Scrooge and the Ghost passed on, invisible, straight to Scrooge's clerk's; and on the threshold of the door the Spirit smiled, and stopped to bless Bob Cratchit's dwelling with the sprinklings of his torch. Think of that! Bob had but fifteen "bob" a week himself; he pocketed on Saturdays but fifteen copies of his Christian name; and yet the Ghost of Christmas Present blessed his four-roomed house!

Then up rose Mrs. Cratchit, Cratchit's wife, dressed out but poorly in a twice-turned gown, but brave in ribbons, which are cheap and make a goodly show for sixpence; and she laid the cloth, assisted by Belinda Cratchit, second of her daughters, also brave in ribbons; while Master Peter Cratchit plunged a fork into the saucepan of potatoes, and, getting the corners of his monstrous shirt-collar (Bob's private property, conferred upon his son and heir in honour of the day) into his mouth, rejoiced to find himself so gallantly attired, and yearned to show his linen in the fashionable Parks. And now two smaller Cratchits, boy and girl, came tearing in, screaming that outside the baker's they had smelt the goose, and known it for their own; and, basking in luxurious thoughts of sage and onion, these young Cratchits danced about the table, and exalted Master Peter Cratchit to the skies, while he (not proud, although his collars nearly choked him) blew the fire, until the slow potatoes, bubbling up, knocked loudly at the saucepan-lid to be let out and peeled.

"What has ever got your precious father then?" said Mrs. Cratchit. "And your brother Tiny Tim! And Martha warn't as late last Christmas day by half an hour!"

"Here's Martha, mother!" said a girl, appearing as she spoke.

"Here's Martha, mother!" cried the two young Cratchits. "Hurrah! There's *such* a goose, Martha!"

"Why, bless your heart alive, my dear, how late you are!" said Mrs. Cratchit, kissing her a dozen times, and taking off her shawl and bonnet for her.

"We'd a deal of work to finish up last night," replied the girl, "and had to clear away this morning, mother!"

"Well! Never mind so long as you are come," said Mrs. Cratchit. "Sit ye down before the fire, my dear, and have a warm, Lord bless ye!"

"No, no! There's father coming," cried the two young Cratchits, who were everywhere at once. "Hide, Martha, hide!"

So Martha hid herself, and in came little Bob, the father, with at least three feet of comforter, exclusive of the fringe, hanging down before him; and his threadbare clothes darned up and brushed, to look seasonable; and Tiny Tim upon his shoulder. Alas for Tiny Tim, he bore a little crutch, and had his limbs supported by an iron frame!

"Why, where's our Martha?" cried Bob Cratchit, looking round.

"Not coming," said Mrs. Cratchit.

"Not coming!" said Bob, with a sudden declension in his high spirits; for he had been Tim's blood-horse all the way from church, and had come home rampant,—"not coming upon Christmas day!"

Martha didn't like to see him disappointed, if it were only in joke; so she came out prematurely from behind the closet door, and ran into his arms, while the two young Cratchits hustled Tiny Tim, and bore him off into the wash-house, that he might hear the pudding singing in the copper.

"And how did little Tim behave?" asked Mrs. Cratchit, when she had rallied Bob on his credulity, and Bob had hugged his daughter to his heart's content.

"As good as gold," said Bob, "and better. Somehow he gets thoughtful, sitting by himself so much, and thinks the strangest things you ever heard. He told me, coming home, that he hoped the people saw him in the church, because he was a cripple, and it might be pleasant to them to remember, upon Christmas day, who made lame beggars walk and blind men see."

Bob's voice was tremulous when he told them this, and trembled more when he said that Tiny Tim was growing strong and hearty.

His active little crutch was heard upon the floor, and back came Tiny Tim before another word was spoken, escorted by his brother and sister to his stool beside the fire; and while Bob, turning up his cuffs,—as if, poor fellow, they were capable of being made more shabby,—compounded some hot mixture in a jug with gin and lemons, and stirred it round and round, and put it on the hob to simmer, Master Peter and the two ubiquitous young Cratchits went to fetch the goose, with which they soon returned in high procession.

Mrs. Cratchit made the gravy (ready beforehand in a little saucepan) hissing hot; Master Peter mashed the potatoes with incredible vigour; Miss Belinda sweetened up the apple-sauce; Martha dusted the hot plates; Bob took Tiny Tim beside him in a tiny corner at the table; the two young Cratchits set chairs for everybody, not forgetting themselves, and mounting guard upon their posts, crammed spoons into their mouths, lest they should shriek for goose before their turn came to be helped. At last the dishes were set on, and grace was said. It was succeeded by a breathless pause, as Mrs. Cratchit, looking slowly all along the carving-knife, prepared to plunge it in the breast; but when she did, and when the long-expected gush of stuffing issued forth, one murmur of delight arose all round the board, and even Tiny Tim, excited by the two young Cratchits, beat on the table with the handle of his knife, and feebly cried, Hurrah!

There never was such a goose. Bob said he didn't believe there ever was such a goose cooked. Its tenderness and flavour, size and cheapness, were the themes of universal admiration. Eked out by apple-sauce and mashed potatoes, it was a sufficient dinner for the whole family; indeed, as Mrs. Cratchit said with great delight (surveying one small atom of a bone upon the dish) they hadn't ate it all at last! Yet every one had had enough, and the youngest Cratchits in particular were steeped in sage and onion to the eyebrows! But now, the plates being changed by Miss Belinda, Mrs. Cratchit left the room alone,—too nervous to bear witnesses,—to take the pudding up, and bring it in.

Suppose it should not be done enough! Suppose it should break in turning out! Suppose somebody should have got over the wall of the back yard, and stolen it, while they were merry with the goose,—a supposition at which the two young Cratchits became livid! All sorts of horrors were supposed.

Hallo! A great deal of steam! The pudding was out of the copper. A smell like a washing-day! That was the cloth. A smell like an eating-house and a pastry-cook's next door to each other, with a laundress's next door to that! That was the pudding! In half a minute Mrs. Cratchit entered,—flushed but smiling proudly,—with the pudding, like a speckled cannon-ball, so hard and firm, blazing in half of half a quartern of ignited brandy, and bedight with Christmas holly stuck into the top.

Oh, a wonderful pudding! Bob Cratchit said, and calmly too, that he regarded it as the greatest success achieved by Mrs. Cratchit since their marriage. Mrs. Cratchit said that now the weight was off her mind, she would confess she had had her doubts about the quantity of flour. Everybody had something to say about it, but nobody said or thought it was at all a small pudding for a large family. Any Cratchit would have blushed to hint at such a thing.

At last the dinner was all done, the cloth was cleared, the hearth swept, and the fire made up. The compound in the jug being tasted, and considered perfect, apples and oranges were put upon the table, and a shovelful of chestnuts on the fire.

Then all the Cratchit family drew round the hearth, in what Bob Cratchit called a circle, and at Bob Cratchit's elbow stood the family display of glass,—two tumblers, and a custard-cup without a handle.

These held the hot stuff from the jug, however, as well as golden goblets would have done; and Bob served it out with beaming looks, while the chestnuts on the fire spluttered and crackled noisily. Then Bob proposed:—

"A Merry Christmas to us all, my dears. God bless us!"

Which all the family re-echoed.

"God bless us every one!" said Tiny Tim, the last of all.

He sat very close to his father's side, upon his little stool. Bob held his withered little hand in his, as if he loved the child, and wished to keep him by his side, and dreaded that he might be taken from him.

Scrooge raised his head speedily, on hearing his own name.

"Mr. Scrooge!" said Bob; "I'll give you Mr. Scrooge, the Founder of the Feast!"

"The Founder of the Feast indeed!" cried Mrs. Cratchit, reddening. "I wish I had him here. I'd give him a piece of my mind to feast upon, and I hope he'd have a good appetite for it."

"My dear," said Bob, "the children! Christmas day."

"It should be Christmas day, I am sure," said she, "on which one drinks the health of such an odious, stingy, hard, unfeeling man as Mr. Scrooge. You know he is, Robert! Nobody knows it better than you do, poor fellow!"

"My dear," was Bob's mild answer, "Christmas day."

"I'll drink his health for your sake and the day's," said Mrs. Cratchit, "not for his. Long life to him! A merry Christmas and a happy New Year! He'll be very merry and very happy, I have no doubt!"

The children drank the toast after her. It was the first of their proceedings which had no heartiness in it. Tiny Tim drank it last of all, but he didn't care twopence for it. Scrooge was the Ogre of the family. The mention of his name cast a dark shadow on the party, which was not dispelled for full five minutes.

After it had passed away, they were ten times merrier than before, from the mere relief of Scrooge the Baleful being done with. Bob Cratchit told them how he had a situation in his eye for Master Peter, which would bring him, if obtained, full five and sixpence weekly. The two young Cratchits laughed tremendously at the idea of Peter's being a man of business; and Peter himself looked thoughtfully at the fire from between his collars, as if he were deliberating what particular investments he should favour when he came into the receipt of that bewildering income. Martha, who was a poor apprentice at a milliner's, then told them what kind of work she had to do, and how many hours she worked at a stretch, and how she meant to lie abed to-morrow morning for a good long rest; to-morrow being a holiday she passed at home. Also how she had seen a countess and a lord some days before, and how the lord "was much about as tall as Peter;" at which Peter pulled up his collars so high that you couldn't have seen his head if you had been there. All this time the chestnuts and the jug went round and round; and by and by they had a song, about a lost child travelling in the snow, from Tiny Tim, who had a plaintive little voice, and sang it very well indeed.

There was nothing of high mark in this. They were not a handsome family; they were not well dressed; their shoes were far from being waterproof; their clothes were scanty; and Peter might have known, and very likely did, the inside of a pawnbroker's. But they were happy, grateful, pleased with one another, and contented with the time; and when they faded, and looked happier yet in the bright sprinklings of the Spirit's torch at parting, Scrooge had his eye upon them, and especially on Tiny Tim, until the last.

It was a great surprise to Scrooge, as this scene vanished, to hear a hearty laugh. It was a much greater surprise to Scrooge to recognize it as his own nephew's, and to find himself in a bright, dry, gleaming room, with the Spirit standing smiling by his side, and looking at that same nephew.

It is a fair, even-handed, noble adjustment of things, that while there is infection in disease and sorrow, there is nothing in the world so irresistibly contagious as laughter and good-humour. When Scrooge's nephew laughed, Scrooge's niece by marriage laughed as heartily as he. And their assembled friends, being not a bit behind-hand, laughed out lustily.

"He said that Christmas was a humbug, as I live!" cried Scrooge's nephew. "He believed it too!"

"More shame for him, Fred!" said Scrooge's niece, indignantly. Bless those women! they never do anything by halves. They are always in earnest.

She was very pretty; exceedingly pretty. With a dimpled, surprised-looking, capital face; a ripe little mouth that seemed made to be kissed,—as no doubt it was; all kinds of good little dots about her chin, that melted into one another when she laughed; and the sunniest pair of eyes you ever saw in any little creature's head. Altogether she was what you would have called provoking, but satisfactory, too. Oh, perfectly satisfactory.

"He's a comical old fellow," said Scrooge's nephew, "that's the truth; and not so pleasant as he might be. However, his offences carry their own punishment, and I have nothing to say against him. Who suffers by his ill whims? Himself, always. Here he takes it into his head to dislike us, and he won't come and dine with us. What's the consequence? He don't lose much of a dinner."

"Indeed, I think he loses a very good dinner," interrupted Scrooge's niece. Everybody else said the same, and they must be allowed to have been competent judges, because thy had just had dinner; and, with the dessert upon the table, were clustered round the fire, by lamplight.

"Well, I am very glad to hear it," said Scrooge's nephew, "because I haven't any great faith in these young housekeepers. What do *you* say, Topper?"

Topper clearly had his eye on one of Scrooge's niece's sisters, for he answered that a bachelor was a wretched outcast, who had no right to express an opinion on the subject. Whereat Scrooge's niece's sister—the plump one with the lace tucker; not the one with the roses —blushed.

After tea they had some music. For they were a musical family, and knew what they were about, when they sung a Glee or Catch, I can assure you,—especially Topper, who could growl away in the bass like a good one, and never swell the large veins in his forehead, or get red in the face over it.

But they didn't devote the whole evening to music. After a while they played at forfeits; for it is good to be children sometimes, and never better than at Christmas, when its mighty Founder was a child himself. There was first a game at blindman's buff though. And I no more believe Topper was really blinded than I believe he had eyes in his boots. Because the way in which he went after that plump sister in the lace tucker was an outrage on the credulity of human nature. Knocking down the fire-irons, tumbling over the chairs, bumping up against the piano, smothering himself among the curtains, wherever she went there went he! He always knew where the plump sister was. He wouldn't catch anybody else. If you had fallen up against him, as some of them did, and stood there, he would have made a feint of endeavouring to seize you, which would have been an affront to your understanding, and would instantly have sidled off in the direction of the plump sister.

"Here is a new game," said Scrooge. "One half-hour, Spirit, only one!"

It was a Game called Yes and No, where Scrooge's nephew had to think of something, and the rest must find out what; he only answering to their questions yes or no, as the case was. The fire of questioning to which he was exposed elicited from him that he was thinking of an animal, a live animal, rather a disagreeable animal, a savage animal, an animal that growled and grunted sometimes, and talked sometimes, and lived in London, and walked about the streets, and wasn't made a show of, and wasn't led by anybody, and didn't live in a menagerie, and was never killed in a market, and was not a horse, or an ass, or a cow, or a bull, or a tiger, or a dog, or a pig, or a cat, or a bear. At every new question put to him, this nephew burst into a fresh roar of laughter; and was so inexpressibly tickled, that he was obliged to get up off the sofa and stamp. At last the plump sister cried out:—

"I have found it out! I know what it is, Fred! I know what it is!"

"What is it?" cried Fred.

"It's your uncle Scro-o-o-o-oge!"

Which it certainly was. Admiration was the universal sentiment, though some objected that the reply to "Is it a bear?" ought to have been "Yes."

Uncle Scrooge had imperceptibly become so gay and light of heart, that he would have drank to the unconscious company in an inaudible speech. But the whole scene passed off in the breath of the last word spoken by his nephew; and he and the Spirit were again upon their travels.

Much they saw, and far they went, and many homes they visited, but always with a happy end. The Spirit stood beside sick-beds, and they were cheerful; on foreign lands, and they were close at home; by struggling men, and they were patient in their greater hope; by poverty, and it was rich. In almshouse, hospital, and jail, in misery's every refuge, where vain man in his little brief authority had not made fast the door, and barred the Spirit out, he left his blessing, and taught Scrooge his precepts. Suddenly, as they stood together in an open place, the bell struck twelve.

Scrooge looked about him for the Ghost, and saw it no more. As the last stroke ceased to vibrate, he remembered the prediction of old Jacob Marley, and, lifting up his eyes, beheld a solemn Phantom, draped and hooded, coming like a mist along the ground towards him.

Stave Four: *The Last of the Spirits*

The Phantom slowly, gravely, silently approached. When it came near him, Scrooge bent down upon his knee; for in the air through which this Spirit moved it seemed to scatter gloom and mystery.

It was shrouded in a deep black garment, which concealed its head, its face, its form, and left nothing of it visible save one outstretched hand. He knew no more, for the Spirit neither spoke nor moved.

"I am in the presence of the Ghost of Christmas Yet to Come? Ghost of the Future! I fear you more than any spectre I have seen. But as I know your purpose is to do me good, and as I hope to live to be another man from what I was, I am prepared to bear you company, and do it with a thankful heart. Will you not speak to me?"

It gave him no reply. The hand was pointed straight before them.

"Lead on! Lead on! The night is waning fast, and it is precious time to me, I know. Lead on, Spirit!"

They scarcely seemed to enter the city; for the city rather seemed to spring up about them. But there they were in the heart of it; on 'Change, amongst the merchants.

The Spirit stopped beside one little knot of business men. Observing that the hand was pointed to them, Scrooge advanced to listen to their talk.

"No," said a great fat man with a monstrous chin. "I don't know much about it either way. I only know he's dead."

"When did he die?" inquired another.

"Last night, I believe."

"Why, what was the matter with him? I thought he'd never die."

"God knows," said the first, with a yawn.

"What has he done with his money?" asked a red-faced gentleman.

"I haven't heard," said the man with the large chin. "Company, perhaps. He hasn't left it to me. That's all I know. By, by."

Scrooge was at first inclined to be surprised that the Spirit should attach importance to conversation apparently to trivial; but feeling assured that it must have some hidden purpose, he set himself to consider what it was likely to be. It could scarcely be supposed to have any bearing on the death of Jacob, his old partner, for that was Past, and this Ghost's province was the Future.

He looked about in that very place for his own image; but another man stood in his accustomed corner, and though the clock pointed to his usual time of day for being there, he saw no likeness of himself amongst the multitudes that poured in through the Porch. It gave him little surprise, however; for he had been revolving in his mind a change of life, and he thought and hoped he saw his newborn resolutions carried out in this.

They left this busy scene, and went into an obscure part of the town, to a low shop where iron, old rags, bottles, bones, and greasy offal were bought. A grey-haired rascal, of great age, sat smoking his pipe. Scrooge and the Phantom came into the presence of this man, just as a woman with a heavy bundle slunk into the shop. But she had scarcely entered, when another woman, similarly laden, came in too; and she was closely followed by a man in faded black. After a short period of blank astonishment, in which the old man with the pipe had joined them, they all three burst into a laugh.

"Let the charwoman alone to be the first!" cried she who had entered first. "Let the laundress alone to be the second; and let the undertaker's man alone to be the third. Look here, old Joe, here's a chance! If we haven't all three met here without meaning it!"

"You couldn't have met in a better place. You were made free of it long ago, you know; and the other two ain't strangers. What have you got to sell? What have you got to sell?"

"Half a minute's patience, Joe, and you shall see."

"What odds then! What odds, Mrs. Dilber?" said the woman. "Every person has a right to take care of themselves. *He* always did! Who's the worse for the loss of a few things like these? Not a dead man, I suppose."

Mrs. Dilber, whose manner was remarkable for general propitiation, said, "No, indeed, ma'am."

"If he wanted to keep 'em after he was dead, a wicked old screw, why wasn't he natural in his lifetime? If he had been, he'd have had somebody to look after him when he was struck with Death, instead of lying gasping out his last there, alone by himself."

"It's the truest word that ever was spoke, it's a judgment on him."

"I wish it was a little heavier judgment, and it should have been, you may depend upon it, if I could have laid my hands on anything else. Open that bundle, old Joe, and let me know the value of it. Speak out plain. I'm not afraid to be the first, nor afraid for them to see it."

Joe went down on his knees for the greater convenience of opening the bundle, and dragged out a large and heavy roll of some dark stuff.

"What do you call this? Bed-curtains!"

"Ah! Bed-curtains! Don't drop that oil upon the blankets, now."

"*His* blankets?"

"Whose else's do you think? He isn't likely to take cold without 'em, I dare say. Ah! You may look through that shirt till your eyes ache; but you won't find a hole in it, nor a threadbare place. It's the best he had, and a fine one too. They'd have wasted it by dressing him up in it, if it hadn't been for me."

Scrooge listened to this dialogue in horror.

"Spirit! I see, I see. The case of this unhappy man might be my own. My life tends that way, now. Merciful Heaven, what is this!"

The scene had changed, and now he almost touched a bare, un-curtained bed. A pale light, rising in the outer air, fell straight upon this bed; and on it, unwatched, unwept, uncared for, was the body of this plundered unknown man.

"Spirit, let me see some tenderness connected with a death, or this dark chamber, Spirit, will be for ever present to me."

The Ghost conducted him to poor Bob Cratchit's house,—the dwelling he had visited before,—and found the mother and the children seated round the fire.

Quiet. Very quiet. The noisy little Cratchits were as still as statues in one corner, and sat looking up at Peter, who had a book before him. The mother and her daughters were engaged in needlework. But surely they were very quiet!

" 'And he took a child, and set him in the midst of them.' "

Where had Scrooge heard those words? He had not dreamed them. The boy must have read them out, as he and the Spirit crossed the threshold. Why did he not go on?

The mother laid her work upon the table, and put her hand up to her face. "The colour hurts my eyes," she said.

The colour? Ah, poor Tiny Tim!

"They're better now again. It makes them weak by candle-light; and I wouldn't show weak eyes to your father when he comes home, for the world. It must be near his time."

"Past it rather," Peter answered, shutting up his book. "But I think he has walked a little slower than he used, these few last evenings, mother."

"I have known him walk with—I have known him walk with Tiny Tim upon his shoulder, very fast indeed."

"And so have I," cried Peter. "Often."

"And so have I," exclaimed another. So had all.

"But he was very light to carry, and his father loved him so, that it was no trouble,—no trouble. And there is your father at the door!"

She hurried out to meet him; and little Bob in his comforter—he had need of it, poor fellow—came in. His tea was ready for him on the hob, and they all tried who should help him to it most. Then the two young Cratchits got upon his knees and laid, each child, a little cheek against his face, as if they said, "Don't mind it, father. Don't be grieved!"

Bob was very cheerful with them, and spoke pleasantly to all the family. He looked at the work upon the table, and praised the industry and speed of Mrs. Cratchit and the girls. They would be done long before Sunday, he said.

"Sunday! You went to-day, then, Robert?"

"Yes, my dear," returned Bob. "I wish you could have gone. It would have done you good to see how green a place it is. But you'll see it often. I promised him that I would walk there on a Sunday. My little, little child! My little child!"

He broke down all at once. He couldn't help it. If he could have helped it, he and his child would have been farther apart, perhaps, than they were.

"Spectre," said Scrooge, "something informs me that our parting moment is at hand. I know it, but I know not how. Tell me what man that was, with the covered face, whom we saw lying dead?"

The Ghost of Christmas Yet to Come conveyed him to a dismal, wretched, ruinous churchyard.

The Spirit stood amongst the graves, and pointed down to One.

"Before I draw nearer to that stone to which you point, answer me one question. Are these the shadows of the things that Will be, or are they shadows of the things that May be only?"

Still the Ghost pointed downward to the grave by which it stood.

"Men's courses will foreshadow certain ends, to which, if persevered in, they must lead. But if the courses be departed from, the ends will change. Say it is thus with what you show me!"

The Spirit was immovable as ever.

Scrooge crept towards it, trembling as he went; and, following the

finger, read upon the stone of the neglected grave his own name—
EBENEZER SCROOGE.

"Am *I* that man who lay upon the bed? No, Spirit! Oh no, no!
Spirit! hear me! I am not the man I was. I will not be the man I
must have been but for this intercourse. Why show me this, if I am
past all hope? Assure me that I yet may change these shadows you
have shown me by an altered life."

For the first time the kind hand faltered.

"I will honour Christmas in my heart, and try to keep it all the
year. I will live in the Past, the Present, and the Future. The Spirits
of all three shall strive within me. I will not shut out the lessons that
they teach. Oh, tell me I may sponge away the writing on this stone!"

Holding up his hands in one last prayer to have his fate reversed,
he saw an alteration in the Phantom's hood and dress. It shrunk,
collapsed, and dwindled down into a bedpost.

Yes, and the bedpost was his own. The bed was his own, the room
was his own. Best and happiest of all, the Time before him was his
own, to make amends in!

He was checked in his transports by the churches ringing out the
lustiest peals he had ever heard.

Running to the window, he opened it, and put out his head. No
fog, no mist, no night; clear, bright, stirring, golden day.

"What's to-day?" cried Scrooge, calling downward to a boy in Sunday clothes, who perhaps had loitered in to look about him.

"*Eh?*"

"What's to-day, my fine fellow?"

"To-day! Why *Christmas day.*"

"It's Christmas day! I haven't missed it. Hallo, my fine fellow!"

"Hallo!"

"Do you know the Poulterer's, in the next street but one, at the
corner?"

"I should hope I did."

"An intelligent boy! A remarkable boy! Do you know whether
they've sold the prize Turkey that was hanging up there? Not the
little prize Turkey,—the big one?"

"What, the one as big as me?"

"What a delightful boy! It's a pleasure to talk to him. Yes, my
buck!"

"It's hanging there now."

"Is it? Go and buy it."

"Walk-*er!*" exclaimed the boy.

"No, no, I am in earnest. Go and buy it, and tell 'em to bring it here, that I may give them the direction where to take it. Come back with the man, and I'll give you a shilling. Come back with him in less than five minutes, and I'll give you half a crown!"

The boy was off like a shot.

"I'll send it to Bob Cratchit's! He sha'n't know who sends it. It's twice the size of Tiny Tim. Joe Miller never made such a joke as sending it to Bob's will be!"

The hand in which he wrote the address was not a steady one; but write it he did, somehow, and went down stairs to open the street door, ready for the coming of the poulterer's man.

It *was* a Turkey! He never could have stood upon his legs, that bird. He would have snapped 'em short off in a minute, like sticks of sealing-wax.

Scrooge dressed himself "all in his best," and at last got out into the streets. The people were by this time pouring forth, as he had seen them with the Ghost of Christmas Present; and, walking with his hands behind him, Scrooge regarded every one with a delighted smile. He looked so irresistibly pleasant, in a word, that three or four good-humoured fellows said, "Good morning, sir! A merry Christmas to you!" And Scrooge said often afterwards, that, of all the blithe sounds he had ever heard, those were the blithest in his ears.

In the afternoon, he turned his steps towards his nephew's house.

He passed the door a dozen times, before he had the courage to go up and knock. But he made a dash, and did it.

"Is your master at home, my dear?" said Scrooge to the girl. Nice girl! Very.

"Yes, sir."

"Where is he, my love?"

"He's in the dining-room, sir, along with mistress."

"He knows me," said Scrooge, with his hand already on the dining-room lock. "I'll go in here, my dear."

"Fred!"

"Why, bless my soul!" cried Fred, "who's that?"

"It's I. Your uncle Scrooge. I have come to dinner. Will you let me in, Fred?"

Let him in! It is a mercy he didn't shake his arm off. He was at home in five minutes. Nothing could be heartier. His niece looked just the same. So did Topper when *he* came. So did the plump sister when *she* came. So did every one when *they* came. Wonderful party, wonderful games, wonderful unanimity, won-derful happiness!

But he was early at the office next morning. Oh, he was early there. If he could only be there first, and catch Bob Cratchit coming late! That was the thing he had set his heart upon.

And he did it. The clock struck nine. No Bob. A quarter past. No Bob. Bob was full eighteen minutes and a half behind his time. Scrooge sat with his door wide open, that he might see him come into the tank.

Bob's hat was off before he opened the door; his comforter too. He was on his stool in a jiffy; driving away with his pen, as if he were trying to overtake nine o'clock.

"Hallo!" growled Scrooge, in his accustomed voice, as near as he could feign it. "What do you mean by coming here at this time of day?"

"I am very sorry, sir. I *am* behind my time."

"You are? Yes. I think you are. Step this way if you please."

"It's only once a year, sir. It shall not be repeated. I was making rather merry yesterday, sir."

"Now, I'll tell you what, my friend. I am not going to stand this sort of thing any longer. And therefore," Scrooge continued, leaping from his stool, and giving Bob such a dig in the waistcoat that he staggered back into the tank again,—"and therefore I am about to raise your salary!"

Bob trembled, and got a little nearer to the ruler.

"A merry Christmas, Bob!" said Scrooge, with an earnestness that could not be mistaken, as he clapped him on the back. "A merrier Christmas, Bob, my good fellow, than I have given you for many a year! I'll raise your salary, and endeavour to assist your struggling family, and we will discuss your affairs this very afternoon, over a Christmas bowl of smoking bishop, Bob! Make up the fires, and buy a second coal-scuttle before you dot another i, Bob Cratchit!"

Scrooge was better than his word. He did it all, and infinitely more;

and to Tiny Tim, who did NOT die, he was a second father. He became as good a friend, as good a master, and as good a man as the good old city knew, or any other good old city, town, or borough in the good old world. Some people laughed to ese the alteration in him; but his own heart laughed, and that was quite enough for him.

He had no further intercourse with Spirits, but lived in that respect upon the Total Abstinence Principle ever afterwards; and it was always said of him that he knew how to keep Christmas well, if any man alive possessed the knowledge. May that be truly said of us, and all of us! And so, as Tiny Tim observed, God Bless Us, Every One!

RACHEL FIELD

⊷⧽⧼⊶

Christmas in London

LITTLE DOG Toby traveled with his master and a Punch and Judy show. They traveled a great many roads, from Land's End to Yorkshire.

Now it was London again and a little room under the gables of an old house in High Holborn.

London seemed strange to Toby who had once known its streets so well. He had to begin learning his way about all over again. He wondered more than he had in his earlier days, wondered about the houses and who lived in them; about the shops, what they sold and whether business was good; most of all he wondered about the people who passed him, where they were going and why, and if any of them knew Miss Patty and Fufu, her little white French poodle. It seemed probable that some must, since there were such hundreds and hundreds of them. It warmed his heart to see so many, for out of them all surely he must come across the two he had been looking for so long.

"Perhaps by Christmas I shall meet them," he told himself, as that jolly season approached.

That week before the holiday the weather turned nipping cold with ice in all the gutters and sometimes sleet that froze as it fell and made the street slippery as glass. The sun set almost before you knew it was up and the hot gingerbread and Muffin-men did a thriving business at tea-time. Street lamps burned early and late and shop and house windows were bright with flaring gas-jets. Even the poorest tradesmen hung up bunches of holly and mistletoe, or strings of colored mottoes in honor of the season. Streets were a jumble of Christmas trees and greens, of penny-toymen with their trays and crowds of hurrying, bundle-laden people. Toby thought it a very fine time to be up and about even if it was sometimes hard to find space on the pavements to set up the show wagon.

The coppers did not drop into the hat so fast as they had before and there were no sixpences to speak of. People were too busy buying gifts to hang on children's Christmas trees or to put in their stockings.

"Still, h'it's not 'alf bad, eh Toby?" Master would say, blowing on his fingers to limber them up between performances and buttoning Toby tighter into his red plush jacket. He would thump his tail and stare down at all the people hurrying by, with high hopes that he might catch a glimpse of a small white poodle and a Mistress in the latest fashion of muff and tippet and shiny topped boots.

The day before Christmas was raw and windy with sudden blinding flurries of snow that made them hurry to take shelter in doorways and under arcades. As they waited in one of these Toby fell into conversation with a Blindman's dog.

"And how is business with you today?" asked the other, who was a shaggy little fellow with a tail like a banner just off the field of battle. "We've tried all the corners from Hyde Park to St. Paul's, and it's bad, very bad."

"But it might be worse," Toby reminded him, "it might be a fog and then no one would see us at all."

"Ah," said the Blindman's dog, "I see you look on the bright side of things. So did I when I was your age, but lately what with all these upstarts crowding us off the very pavements, I confess I get a little low in my mind."

"Still, Christmas is Christmas," persisted Toby.

"Well, no one can deny that," admitted the other, "and it only comes once a year too."

"And there's always the smell of the evergreens and the pies and the plum puddings in the shops when you go by," added Toby, "and the little boys and girls always *want* to give you pennies even if they have spent all theirs."

"A penny that clinks in your cup is worth two in other people's pockets, though," said the Blindman's dog, with a solemn headshake, as they moved on.

"Merry Christmas just the same," Toby barked after him and followed Master to a place just at the entrance of a large toyshop where he was already setting up the Punch and Judy Show.

They played there all the rest of the day and Toby was careful to watch all the children and dogs who passed. In the times between his own special part he had a fine chance to look over the audience and whoever entered or left the topshop. It had two big windows, packed full of the most wonderful dolls and wooden animals; Noah's Arks and doll houses; ships and skates and queer carved boxes that played the prettiest tinkling tunes. Whenever the doors opened or shut on customers Toby could hear snatches of music and it made him feel almost like a puppy again, it sounded so gay.

Pennies were still rather scanty. Toby was an artist, however, and went through his part with just as much spirit and as many barks and wags and paw-givings as if business were at its best. The little boys and girls were as delighted as ever over his antics and several of them reached up and gave him bits of their own gingerbread which he ate with pleasure while Mr. Punch and the rest were acting. He liked to see the children go into the toyshop and come out later on with enormous knobby looking parcels held very tight. Sometimes he could tell what was inside the wrappings, dolls and Noah's Arks were easy. Once he was very much flattered to have a little girl in a shabby dress and shawl lift up a queerly shaped pink plush dog for him to see. She evidently thought it as good as real, and though Toby couldn't honestly feel much enthusiasm for it, he looked down as if he did and she ran off as pleased and proud as could be.

It must have been about the middle of the afternoon when Toby noticed the Little Boy in kilts and Scotch cap. He was standing alone at the edge of the crowd and Toby thought he had never seen any child enjoy the show quite so much. He laughed and clapped and hopped up and down and he never once took his eyes off Toby. Now Toby was used to this sort of thing by that time, but there was something about this Little Boy that made you notice him. It wasn't just his clothes, though they were handsomer than most of the others. It was the way his blue eyes shone and the set of his head and shoulders when he stood watching with his hands in his pockets.

Toby fairly outdid himself to please the Little Boy and each time he could manage to look his way he saw him squeezing in nearer to the front, his eyes very round and his cap all on one side, with ex-

cited interest. Then, just as things were going their best and Toby
was getting ready for the nose-nipping part, there was a commotion
in the crowd. Toby had to keep his mind on business, not to miss any
barks or bites, and he dared not look to see what was the matter, but
he felt it in his bones that it had something to do with the Little
Boy. He was right, for when he was able at last to turn his eyes that
way, it was to see a worried looking lady and a tall man in uniform
leading him off between them. It was plain from the Little Boy's
shoulders and the way he hung back that he did not want to leave the
Punch and Judy Show. Indeed Toby could hear his protests even
above Mr. Punch's squeakings. Everyone was staring after the three
in a curious sort of way and the Proprietor of the toyshop stood in
the door, bowing long after they had passed out of sight.

Master, of course, saw nothing of all this, being behind the little
stage and busy putting the puppets through their paces. He grumbled
a good deal when he came out to pass the hat round and found so
many people had gone away, and Toby couldn't tell him the reason.

The Lamplighters made their rounds early that evening. It was
barely tea-time and yet it might have been midnight from the darkness and all the lighted windows. People still hurried by jostling each
other off the pavements and looking like bumpy gnomes with their
mufflers and great-coats and queer-shaped bundles. Snow powdered
their caps and shoulders and frosted the stage of the Punch and Judy
Show. Toby's paws made little prints in it and whenever he had to
come to the front to do his part his whiskers grew white with the
clinging flakes. The plush coat did not seem nearly as warm as usual.

Then, suddenly there was a great clattering of horse's hoofs. A
soldier in magnificent scarlet coat and bushy black helmet was reining up beside them. The Punch and Judy wagon shook on its wheels
as the horse pawed and stamped impatiently.

"Hi, you there!" cried the rider, beckoning to Mr. Hicks, who was
peering from between the curtains in amazement. "Come over here
and be quick about it!"

Mr. Hicks hurried to do so. Indeed he did not even stop to hang
Mr. Punch back on his hook, but kept him still on one hand. Toby
tried hard to hear what the soldier was saying, but he was too far
away on his perch and besides, such a lot of people ran out from
nearby doorways, and they made such a noise, that he couldn't make

out more than a word or two. He saw the rider give Master a bit of paper that seemed to please him greatly. Master nodded his head a great many times and kept pulling at his forelock and grinning in a queer kind of way.

"Remember now," the soldier said as he wheeled his horse about smartly, "half after three and mind you're there on the dot."

"'Alf after three," Mr. Hicks repeated after him, his mouth still gaping open in astonishment. "We'll be there, Toby'n me."

When the last clatter of the horse's hoofs had died away Mr. Hicks began to recover a little and to say things under his breath that showed how astonished he was. Toby couldn't make them out and he was already completely dazed by what had happened. He knew that it was something extraordinarily fine and in some mysterious way concerned him too. The keeper of the toyshop and the man who sold hot chestnuts both clapped him on the back and all the rest crowded round eagerly.

"Talk about your luck," Toby heard one of them say, "and 'by command.' Well, I never."

"H'it's fair took me off my feet," said Mr. Hicks, though Toby noticed that he still seemed to be standing on them as well as ever. "Can't 'ardly credit my senses. Well, Toby boy, you'n me 'ave got a sight to do afore this time tomorrow. Time we was gettin' 'ome."

There were plenty of hands to help Mr. Hicks fold up the stage and pack it in the barrow that night and the toyshop man insisted upon their both coming in to warm themselves a bit before his fire. Toby was so excited at finding himself among the toys he had stared at so long from a distance that he hardly knew how to behave. Indeed he did almost disgrace himself when an ugly Jack-in-the-Box flew out at him and if it had been within reach he would surely have treated it as he did Mr. Punch's hooked nose. How beautiful the dolls looked so near, even more lovely than from the other side of the window. Those with golden curls and ruffles made him think of Miss Patty, and there was a beautiful little wax figure in pink who danced on her toes on the top of one music box and a yellow old mandarin who nodded his head in time to the tune on another. The toyshop man's wife came out from a back room and when she heard that Mr. Hicks and Toby were going to play "by command" next day, she flung up both hands in wonder.

"And to think they was right here in my shop and I didn't know it," her husband kept repeating. "Well, Hicks, I don't begrudge you your luck and just so no one shall say I'm small I'm going to make your Toby there a present of the finest red ribbon bow a dog ever wore around his neck."

They had collected a great many things besides the ribbon by the time they reached home. First Master changed the paper the soldier had given him for a great many shillings and sixpences and even several half crowns. After that he bought a whole bottle of beer, not just a mug as he usually did, and some tobacco and a whole platter of roast beef and onions and the biggest bone Toby had ever had. Toby was more pleased with this than the cake of soap and the scrubbing brush which was the last purchase. He somehow felt that they were to concern him intimately before the evening was over, and he was right.

First it was beef and bones and onions. Then Master called to the Landlady to bring him another scuttleful of coal and a kettle for heating water. He also asked for the loan of her wooden wash-tub, and carried it himself up the five long flights of stairs. Toby had to be dragged from under the bed by his tail. By the time the water was hot enough to make suds, it was well on towards midnight and the Christmas waits already going about singing in the streets below. Their voices rose shrill and clear on the frosty air. Toby could hear snatches of their carols between the splashings and sloshings of the soap and water as Mr. Hicks gave him the most thorough washing he had ever had.

> *"God rest you, merry Gentlemen,*
> *Let nothing you dismay——"*

Scrub. Scrub. Scrub.

> *"Remember Christ, the Saviour,*
> *Was born on Christmas Day——"*

Scrub. Scrub. Scrub.

Then scrub again. It was soap in the eyes and ears and nose. More rinsing, with water enough to drown him, it seemed, and then more soap again. Toby thought it would be the death of him and he felt very sorry to think that he might never know what would be happening next day that Master made such a to-do about. The washing did finally end and he shook himself till the fire hissed with the drops he spattered. Then Master rubbed and dried him with an old piece of flannel and polished him off by a combing with his own comb. Toby thought there would surely be nothing left of him in the end, but there still seemed to be, for Mr. Hicks sat back and surveyed him with great approval.

"Toby," he said solemnly, "you're clean for once't in your life an' may it last you for good an' all!"

Toby agreed with him perfectly.

Master was away all the next morning. He would not take Toby with him for fear he might spoil his fine looks before afternoon. Three o'clock found them out on the streets, Toby riding a-top the show wagon as Master pushed it along before him. He had on the new red ribbon and his best ruff and the hole in his plush coat had been neatly darned the night before. Even Master was all smartened up for the holiday in a new muffler, with a big blue glass stick pin in the middle. They did not stop to set the show up, no matter what good corners they came to, but went on and on.

Just as Toby was beginning to wonder if they would ever reach their destination, they came to a high gate with gold lions above it and another soldier in a red coat standing at attention by a queer little house just big enough to hold him if it should happen to rain. Toby felt rather awed as they came alongside and Master pulled a card out of his pocket and handed it over. Another soldier now joined the first one and they both looked at the card and asked Mr. Hicks some questions which Toby was too excited to hear. Next thing he knew they were following the second soldier through the gate and up a driveway towards the most enormous stone house he had ever seen. It seemed to Toby that it must be almost as big as St. Paul's and the Tower of London put together only it didn't look in the least like either of them.

Master was making a queer hoarse sound in his throat, as if he, too, didn't quite know what to make of all this.

"Keep your 'ead up, Toby boy," he said softly as they came up to the great carved doors. "Don't you go and let Bucking'am Palace take the stuffin' out o' you!"

Buckingham Palace! Toby's head began to reel so he didn't know what was happening next. In fact he didn't know when or how they got inside. Then they were in an enormous room with so much gold and red velvet Toby scarcely dared look beyond his own nose. Servants in livery were hurrying to and fro, arranging chairs and tables and hanging trinkets on a tall Christmas tree that stood at the far end of the room; others were lighting hundreds of candles in great crystal chandeliers that hung from the ceiling, and Mr. Hicks was setting up the Punch and Judy Show behind a high carved screen. Nobody paid any attention to Toby and so he gathered up courage enough to do a little exploring on his own account.

Here a new surprise awaited him. As he trotted out over the miraculously soft carpet he beheld a dog advancing to meet him. It came nearer and nearer and the queer thing about it was that it, too, wore a ruff and a red ribbon and a plush coat. He turned about uncertainly and there beside him was another exactly like the first. He flew in another direction, nearly colliding with a servant bearing a great tray of cakes, only to catch glimpses of more Toby dogs, and still more, little yellow dogs in ruffs in every direction. He forgot his awe of Buckingham Palace and flew at the nearest one, teeth bared and ears up. His claws slid against something smooth and his nose went bang against a cool something. Then one of the servants laughed and carried him back to Master.

"Tryin' to fight 'imself in the mirrors, the little chap was," he explained, while Toby grinned sheepishly and tried to make a joke of it.

Still, it was a relief to find there weren't really all those other Dog Tobys to be his rivals.

Now Master lifted him up to his place on the stage and they waited for the party to begin. Toby knew it was a party, for he had heard the word pass from one footman to another. He felt almost as scared and excited as the time he had first played his part, and it seemed as if the great gold doors would never open. He could peer through a carved place in the screen and see all that was going on. The Christmas tree was a blaze of light now and all the tinsel and colored balls shone like fairy fruits. Now a music box began to play the sweetest tunes and the doors opened wide to let in a company of children—little girls in sashes and curls and stiffly starched dresses and little boys in velvet jackets and round white collars. All the mouths were smiling and all the eyes held little bright glints from the Christmas tree candles and all the feet began to skip and caper.

Then someone was lifting the screen away from the show wagon and Toby suddenly saw that the children were all hurrying after a lady with smoothly parted hair and rustling skirts, and a tall gentleman in whiskers and a soldier's coat with medals and yards and yards of gold braid. Between them were two children and Toby could hardly keep from barking for joy when he saw that one was the Little Boy of yesterday afternoon. There was no mistaking him even if he had not worn his gay Scotch kilts. His fair hair shone in the candle light and when he saw what was standing behind the screen he dropped the lady's hand and ran straight up to the show wagon. Toby was so glad to see him again that he stood right up and barked, though he knew it wasn't the right time for that, but nobody seemed to mind his doing that at all.

"Here is your surprise, Eddie," said the lady, "the very same Punch and Judy Show that you saw by the arcade yesterday, only you must remember never to run away from Mademoiselle to see one again."

"Yes," said the Little Boy, drawing a long breath, "it's the same Little Dog Toby. Please can't it begin?"

So Toby and the puppets and Mr. Hicks played their parts and all the children pressed as close and squealed and laughed and clapped as hard as those at any street corner or country fair. Toby had never barked or growled or bitten and shaken Mr. Punch so beautifully. He wasn't afraid any longer. He even took pleasure in turning to look at himself in all the long mirrors on the walls. Over and over they acted it and the candles burnt out on the tree and the cakes and jellies and tarts waited untasted on the tables. The Little Boy could never have enough and his eyes never left the painted stage.

"Come," said the lady, bending over him, "Dog Toby must be tired now, and the others want to open their presents and have their tea."

The Little Boy would not go till the gentleman in whiskers had lifted him up so that he could pat Dog Toby himself. It was a proud moment and Mr. Hicks came out and stood grinning nearby. The Little Boy's hand was very clean and soft as he stroked him. Toby suddenly felt very glad that Master had given him that hard scrubbing last night. He put out his pink tongue and gave the plump fingers several licks.

"I wish he were my Little Dog Toby," he said.

Mr. Hicks looked rather serious at this, but the tall man only smiled and set the child on his feet.

By the time Master had folded the stage up, all the children were busy eating cakes and drinking their cambric tea.

"Come along, Toby," he said moving towards the door which two servants were opening for them, "we can go 'ome now."

They went back to High Holborn stuffed full of roast goose and plum pudding from the servants' hall. Master's pockets bulged with oranges and nuts and raisins and gingerbread, and Toby had a royal beef bone to take home. Surely no dog ever had such a Christmas!

Tired as they were after it all, Master sat up late painting a gold crown to go with the moon and stars above the Punch and Judy Stage. He printed red letters on a big placard for Toby to wear round his neck, and this is what they said:—

"Dog Toby,
by Special Appointment to
His Royal Highness, Prince of Wales."

ANATOLE FRANCE

Our Lady's Juggler

IN THE DAYS of King Louis there was a poor juggler in France, a native of Compiègne, Barnaby by name, who went about from town to town performing feats of skill and strength.

On fair days he would unfold an old worn-out carpet in the public square, and when by means of a jovial address, which he had learned of a very ancient juggler, and which he never varied in the least, he had drawn together the children and loafers, he assumed extraordinary attitudes, and balanced a tin plate on the tip of his nose. At first the crowd would feign indifference.

But when, supporting himself on his hands face downwards, he threw into the air six copper balls, which glittered in the sunshine, and caught them again with his feet; or when throwing himself backwards until his heels and the nape of the neck met, giving his body the form of a perfect wheel, he would juggle in this posture with a dozen knives, a murmur of admiration would escape the spectators, and pieces of money rain down upon the carpet.

Nevertheless, like the majority of those who live by their wits, Barnaby of Compiègne had a great struggle to make a living.

Earning his bread in the sweat of his brow, he bore rather more than his share of the penalties consequent upon the misdoings of our father Adam.

Again, he was unable to work as constantly as he would have been willing to do. The warmth of the sun and the broad daylight were as necessary to enable him to display his brilliant parts as to the trees if flower and fruit should be expected of them. In winter time he was nothing more than a tree stripped of its leaves, and as it were dead. The frozen ground was hard to the juggler, and, like the grasshopper

86

of which Marie de France tells us, the inclement season caused him to suffer both cold and hunger. But as he was simple-natured he bore his ills patiently.

He had never meditated on the origin of wealth, nor upon the inequality of human conditions. He believed firmly that if this life should prove hard, the life to come could not fail to redress the balance, and this hope upheld him. He did not resemble those thievish and miscreant Merry Andrews who sell their souls to the devil. He never blasphemed God's name; he lived uprightly, and although he had no wife of his own, he did not covet his neighbour's, since woman is ever the enemy of the strong man, as it appears by the history of Samson recorded in the Scriptures.

In truth, his was not a nature much disposed to carnal delights, and it was a greater deprivation to him to forsake the tankard than the Hebe who bore it. For whilst not wanting in sobriety, he was fond of a drink when the weather waxed hot. He was a worthy man who feared God, and was very devoted to the Blessed Virgin.

Never did he fail on entering a church to fall upon his knees before the image of the Mother of God, and offer up this prayer to her:

"Blessed Lady, keep watch over my life until it shall please God that I die, and when I am dead, ensure to me the possession of the joys of paradise."

II

Now on a certain evening after a dreary wet day, as Barnaby pursued his road, sad and bent, carrying under his arm his balls and knives wrapped up in his old carpet, on the watch for some barn where, though he might not sup, he might sleep, he perceived on the road, going in the same direction as himself, a monk, whom he saluted courteously. And as they walked at the same rate they fell into conversation with one another.

"Fellow traveller," said the monk, "how comes it about that you are clothed all in green? Is it perhaps in order to take the part of a jester in some mystery play?"

"Not at all, good father," replied Barnaby. "Such as you see me, I am called Barnaby, and for my calling I am a juggler. There would be no pleasanter calling in the world if it would always provide one with daily bread."

"Friend Barnaby," returned the monk, "be careful what you say. There is no calling more pleasant than the monastic life. Those who lead it are occupied with the praises of God, the Blessed Virgin, and the saints; and, indeed, the religious life is one ceaseless hymn to the Lord."

Barnaby replied—

"Good father, I own that I spoke like an ignorant man. Your calling cannot be in any respect compared to mine, and although there may be some merit in dancing with a penny balanced on a stick on the tip of one's nose, it is not a merit which comes within hail of your own. Gladly would I, like you, good father, sing my office day by day, and especially, the office of the most Holy Virgin, to whom I have vowed a singular devotion. In order to embrace the monastic life I would willingly abandon the art by which from Soissons to Beauvais I am well known in upwards of six hundred towns and villages."

The monk was touched by the juggler's simplicity, and as he was not lacking in discernment, he at once recognized in Barnaby one of those men of whom it is said in the Scriptures: Peace on earth to men of good will. And for this reason he replied—

"Friend Barnaby, come with me, and I will have you admitted into the monastery of which I am Prior. He who guided St. Mary of Egypt in the desert set me upon your path to lead you into the way of salvation."

It was in this manner, then, that Barnaby became a monk. In the monastery into which he was received the religious vied with one another in the worship of the Blessed Virgin, and in her honour each employed all the knowledge and all the skill which God had given him.

The prior on his part wrote books dealing according to the rules of scholarship with the virtues of the Mother of God.

Brother Maurice, with a deft hand copied out these treatises upon sheets of vellum.

Brother Alexander adorned the leaves with delicate miniature paintings. Here were displayed the Queen of Heaven seated upon Solomon's throne, and while four lions were on guard at her feet, around the nimbus which encircled her head hovered seven doves, which are the seven gifts of the Holy Spirit, the gifts, namely, of Fear, Piety,

Knowledge, Strength, Counsel, Understanding, and Wisdom. For her companions she had six virgins with hair of gold, namely, Humility, Prudence, Seclusion, Submission, Virginity, and Obedience.

At her feet were two little naked figures, perfectly white, in an attitude of supplication. These were souls imploring her all-powerful intercession for their soul's health, and we may be sure not imploring in vain.

Upon another page facing this, Brother Alexander represented Eve, so that the Fall and the Redemption could be perceived at one and the same time—Eve the Wife abased, and Mary the Virgin exalted.

Furthermore, to the marvel of the beholder, this book contained presentments of the Well of Living Waters, the Fountain, the Lily, the Moon, the Sun, and the Garden enclosed of which the Song of Songs tells us, the Gate of Heaven and the City of God, and all these things were symbols of the Blessed Virgin.

Brother Marbode was likewise one of the most loving children of Mary.

He spent all his days carving images in stone, so that his beard, his eyebrows, and his hair were white with dust, and his eyes continually swollen and weeping; but his strength and cheerfulness were not diminished, although he was now well gone in years, and it was clear that the Queen of Paradise still cherished her servant in his old age. Marbode represented her seated upon a throne, her brow encircled with an orb-shaped nimbus set with pearls. And he took care that the folds of her dress should cover the feet of her, concerning whom the prophet declared: My beloved is as a garden enclosed.

Sometimes, too, he depicted her in the semblance of a child full of grace, and appearing to say, "Thou art my God, even from my mother's womb."

In the priory, moreover, were poets who composed hymns in Latin, both in prose and verse, in honour of the Blessed Virgin Mary, and amongst the company was even a brother from Picardy who sang the miracles of Our Lady in rhymed verse and in the vulgar tongue.

III

Being a witness of this emulation in praise and the glorious harvest of their labours, Barnaby mourned his own ignorance and simplicity.

"Alas!" he sighed, as he took his solitary walk in the little shelter-less garden of the monastery, "wretched wight that I am, to be unable, like my brothers, worthily to praise the Holy Mother of God, to whom I have vowed my whole heart's affection. Alas! alas! I am but a rough man and unskilled in the arts, and I can render you in service, blessed Lady, neither edifying sermons, nor treatises set out in order according to rule, nor ingenious paintings, nor statues truthfully sculptured, nor verses whose march is measured to the beat of feet. No gift have I, alas!"

After this fashion he groaned and gave himself up to sorrow. But one evening, when the monks were spending their hour of liberty in conversation, he heard one of them tell the tale of a religious man who could repeat nothing other than the Ave Maria. This poor man was despised for his ignorance; but after his death there issued forth from his mouth five roses in honour of the five letters of the name Mary (Marie), and thus his sanctity was made manifest.

Whilst he listened to this narrative Barnaby marvelled yet once again at the loving kindness of the Virgin; but the lesson of that blessed death did not avail to console him, for his heart overflowed with zeal, and he longed to advance the glory of his Lady, who is in heaven.

How to compass this he sought but could find no way, and day by day he became the more cast down, when one morning he awakened filled full with joy, hastened to the chapel, and remained there alone for more than an hour. After dinner he returned to the chapel once more.

And, starting from that moment, he repaired daily to the chapel at such hours as it was deserted, and spent within it a good part of the time which the other monks devoted to the liberal and mechanical arts. His sadness vanished, nor did he any longer groan.

A demeanour so strange awakened the curiosity of the monks.

These began to ask one another for what purpose Brother Barnaby could be indulging so persistently in retreat.

The prior, whose duty it is to let nothing escape him in the behaviour of his children in religion, resolved to keep a watch over Barnaby during his withdrawals to the chapel. One day, then, when he was shut up there after his custom, the prior, accompanied by two of the older monks, went to discover through the chinks in the door what was going on within the chapel.

They saw Barnaby before the altar of the Blessed Virgin, head downwards, with his feet in the air, and he was juggling with six balls of copper and a dozen knives. In honour of the Holy Mother of God he was performing those feats, which aforetime had won him most renown. Not recognizing that the simple fellow was thus placing at the service of the Blessed Virgin his knowledge and skill, the two old monks exclaimed against the sacrilege.

The prior was aware how stainless was Barnaby's soul, but he concluded that he had been seized with madness. They were all three preparing to lead him swiftly from the chapel, when they saw the Blessed Virgin descend the steps of the altar and advance to wipe away with a fold of her azure robe the sweat which was dropping from her juggler's forehead.

Then the prior, falling upon his face upon the pavement, uttered these words—

"Blessed are the simple-hearted, for they shall see God."

"Amen!" responded the old brethren, and kissed the ground.

LUCRETIA P. HALE

<s>≈§ §≈</s>

The Peterkins' Christmas-Tree

EARLY in the autumn the Peterkins began to prepare for their Christ-mas-tree. Everything was done in great privacy, as it was to be a surprise to the neighbors, as well as to the rest of the family. Mr. Peterkin had been up to Mr. Bromwick's wood-lot, and with his consent, selected the tree. Agamemnon went to look at it occasionally after dark, and Solomon John made frequent visits to it mornings, just after sunrise. Mr. Peterkin drove Elizabeth Eliza and her mother that way, and pointed furtively to it with his whip; but none of them ever spoke of it aloud to each other. It was suspected that the little boys had been to see it Wednesday and Saturday afternoons. But they came home with their pockets full of chestnuts, and said nothing about it.

At length Mr. Peterkin had it cut down and brought secretly into the Larkins' barn. A week or two before Christmas a measurement was made of it with Elizabeth Eliza's yard-measure. To Mr. Peterkin's great dismay it was discovered that it was too high to stand in the back parlor.

This fact was brought out at a secret council of Mr. and Mrs. Peterkin, Elizabeth Eliza, and Agamemnon.

Agamemnon suggested that it might be set up slanting; but Mrs. Peterkin was very sure it would make her dizzy, and the candles would drip.

But a brilliant idea came to Mr. Peterkin. He proposed that the ceiling of the parlor should be raised to make room for the top of the tree.

Elizabeth Eliza thought the space would need to be quite large. It must not be like a small box, or you could not see the tree.

92

"Yes," said Mr. Peterkin, "I should have the ceiling lifted all across the room; the effect would be finer."

Elizabeth Eliza objected to having the whole ceiling raised, because her room was over the back parlor, and she would have no floor while the alteration was going on, which would be very awkward. Besides, her room was not very high now, and, if the floor were raised, perhaps she could not walk in it upright.

Mr. Peterkin explained that he didn't propose altering the whole ceiling, but to lift up a ridge across the room at the back part where the tree was to stand. This would make a hump, to be sure, in Elizabeth Eliza's room; but it would go across the whole room.

Elizabeth Eliza said she would not mind that. It would be like the cuddy thing that comes upon the deck of a ship, that you sit against, only here you would not have the sea-sickness. She thought she should like it, for a rarity. She might use it for a divan.

Mrs. Peterkin thought it would come in the worn place of the carpet, and might be a convenience in making the carpet over.

Agamemnon was afraid there would be trouble in keeping the matter secret, for it would be a long piece of work for a carpenter; but Mr. Peterkin proposed having the carpenter for a day or two, for a number of other jobs.

One of them was to make all the chairs in the house of the same height, for Mrs. Peterkin had nearly broken her spine by sitting down in a chair that she had supposed was her own rocking-chair, and it had proved to be two inches lower. The little boys were now large enough to sit in any chair; so a medium was fixed upon to satisfy all the family, and the chairs were made uniformly of the same height.

On consulting the carpenter, however, he insisted that the tree could be cut off at the lower end to suit the height of the parlor, and demurred at so great a change as altering the ceiling. But Mr. Peterkin had set his mind upon the improvement, and Elizabeth Eliza had cut her carpet in preparation for it.

So the folding-doors into the back parlor were closed, and for nearly a fortnight before Christmas there was great litter of fallen plastering, and laths, and chips, and shavings; and Elizabeth Eliza's carpet was taken up, and the furniture had to be changed, and one night she had to sleep at the Bromwicks', for there was a long hole in her floor that might be dangerous.

All this delighted the little boys. They could not understand what was going on. Perhaps they suspected a Christmas-tree, but they did not know why a Christmas-tree should have so many chips, and were still more astonished at the hump that appeared in Elizabeth Eliza's room. It must be a Christmas present, or else the tree in a box.

Some aunts and uncles, too, arrived a day or two before Christmas, with some small cousins. These cousins occupied the attention of the little boys, and there was a great deal of whispering and mystery, behind doors, and under the stairs, and in the corners of the entry.

Solomon John was busy, privately making some candles for the tree. He had been collecting some bayberries, as he understood they made very nice candles, so that it would not be necessary to buy any.

The elders of the family never all went into the back parlor together, and all tried not to see what was going on. Mrs. Peterkin would go in with Solomon John, or Mr. Peterkin with Elizabeth Eliza, or Elizabeth Eliza and Agamemnon and Solomon John. The little boys and the small cousins were never allowed even to look inside the room.

Elizabeth Eliza meanwhile went into town a number of times. She wanted to consult Amanda as to how much ice-cream they should need, and whether they could make it at home, as they had cream and ice. She was pretty busy in her own room; the furniture had to be changed, and the carpet altered. The "hump" was higher than she expected. There was danger of bumping her own head whenever she crossed it. She had to nail some padding on the ceiling for fear of accidents.

The afternoon before Christmas, Elizabeth Eliza, Solomon John, and their father collected in the back parlor for a council. The carpenters had done their work, and the tree stood at its full height at the back of the room, the top stretching up into the space arranged for it. All the chips and shavings were cleared away, and it stood on a neat box.

But what were they to put upon the tree?

Solomon John had brought in his supply of candles; but they proved to be very "stringy" and very few of them. It was strange how many bayberries it took to make a few candles! The little boys had helped him, and he had gathered as much as a bushel of bayberries. He had put them in water, and skimmed off the wax, according to the directions; but there was so little wax!

Solomon John had given the little boys some of the bits sawed off from the legs of the chairs. He had suggested that they should cover them with gilt paper, to answer for gilt apples, without telling them what they were for.

These apples, a little blunt at the end, and the candles, were all they had for the tree!

After all her trips into town Elizabeth Eliza had forgotten to bring anything for it.

"I thought of candies and sugar-plums," she said; "but I concluded if we made caramels ourselves we should not need them. But, then, we have not made caramels. The fact is, that day my head was full of my carpet. I had bumped it pretty badly, too."

Mr. Peterkin wished he had taken, instead of a fir-tree, an apple-tree he had seen in October, full of red fruit.

"But the leaves would have fallen off by this time," said Elizabeth Eliza.

"And the apples, too," said Solomon John.

"It is odd I should have forgotten, that day I went in on purpose to get the things," said Elizabeth Eliza, musingly. "But I went from shop to shop, and didn't know exactly what to get. I saw a great many gilt things for Christmas-trees; but I knew the little boys were making the gilt apples; there were plenty of candles in the shops, but I knew Solomon John was making the candles."

Mr. Peterkin thought it was quite natural.

Solomon John wondered if it were too late for them to go into town now.

Elizabeth Eliza could not go in the next morning, for there was to be a grand Christmas dinner, and Mr. Peterkin could not be spared, and Solomon John was sure he and Agamemnon would not know what to buy. Besides, they would want to try the candles to-night.

Mr. Peterkin asked if the presents everybody had been preparing would not answer. But Elizabeth Eliza knew they would be too heavy.

A gloom came over the room. There was only a flickering gleam from one of Solomon John's candles that he had lighted by way of trial.

Solomon John again proposed going into town. He lighted a match to examine the newspaper about the trains. There were plenty of trains coming out at that hour, but none going in except a very late one. That would not leave time to do anything and come back.

"We could go in, Elizabeth Eliza and I," said Solomon John, "but we should not have time to buy anything."

Agamemnon was summoned in. Mrs. Peterkin was entertaining the uncles and aunts in the front parlor. Agamemnon wished there was time to study up something about electric lights. If they could only have a calcium light! Solomon John's candle sputtered and went out.

At this moment there was a loud knocking at the front door. The little boys, and the small cousins, and the uncles and aunts, and Mrs. Peterkin, hastened to see what was the matter.

The uncles and aunts thought somebody's house must be on fire. The door was opened, and there was a man, white with flakes, for it was beginning to snow, and he was pulling in a large box.

Mrs. Peterkin supposed it contained some of Elizabeth Eliza's purchases, so she ordered it to be pushed into the back parlor, and hastily called back her guests and the little boys into the other room. The little boys and the small cousins were sure they had seen Santa Claus himself.

Mr. Peterkin lighted the gas. The box was addressed to Elizabeth Eliza. It was from the lady from Philadelphia! She had gathered a hint from Elizabeth Eliza's letters that there was to be a Christmas-tree, and had filled this box with all that would be needed.

It was opened directly. There was every kind of gilt hanging-thing, from gilt pea-pods to butterflies on springs. There were shining flags and lanterns, and bird-cages, and nests with birds sitting on them, baskets of fruit, gilt apples and bunches of grapes, and, at the bottom of the whole, a large box of candles and a box of Philadelphia bonbons!

Elizabeth Eliza and Solomon John could scarcely keep from screaming. The little boys and the small cousins knocked on the folding-doors to ask what was the matter.

Hastily Mr. Peterkin and the rest took out the things and hung them on the tree, and put on the candles.

When it was all done, it looked so well that Mr. Peterkin exclaimed:—

"Let us light the candles now, and send to invite all the neighbors to-night, and have the tree on Christmas Eve!"

And so it was the Peterkins had their Christmas-tree the day before, and on Christmas night could go and visit their neighbors.

LORD HALIFAX

ᥒᡃ᠍᠍ᡀᢆᢒᥕ

Childhood Christmas

FROM "FULLNESS OF DAYS"

I T WAS the same family party that assembled at Hickleton for Christmas year after year—my grandfather Devon, as long as he lived,
and our great-Aunt Georgiana Grey, daughter of Lord Grey of the
Reform Bill, all the other uncles, aunts and cousins who were not
claimed elsewhere, and a few old friends. Queen Victoria had been
pleased to give Aunt Georgiana a set of rooms in the Palace of
Hampton Court, where she had made for herself a position of authority that appeared to be generally accepted by the officials and
other residents. From the operation of this benevolent autocracy
the Chapel was not exempt, and Aunt Georgiana had clear views as
to what might and might not be appropriately read from the Old
Testament. For instance, she judged the story of Jacob with the con-
niving assistance of his mother deceiving his father, and so supplant-
ing his brother Esau in getting the paternal blessing, as a thoroughly
unedifying narrative, which could do nobody any good, and she
would not therefore allow it to be read. We all thought her rather
alarming and she lived to be ninety-nine, being greatly grieved, as we
were always told, to have fallen short of the hundred. She always
came with presents for the family (the presents having been selected
immediately after the preceding Christmas in case she should die in
the meanwhile), to be distributed in due course with great solemnity.

Such was the party that altered little unless someone died, or until
a further generation of children made its appearance. One of our
great interests when we were little used to be to go into the kitchen
and watch the joints being roasted before a huge open fire and having

gravy ladled over them by one of the kitchen maids, as the joints revolved on spits by some kind of clockwork. There would be about twenty for dinner, and everybody combined to make it look gay. The gardeners came in after tea to do the table, the flowers being chosen so far as might be to match the silver or silver gilt plate; all the plate that could be used was produced; and dinner was a serious affair of six or seven courses—soup, fish, entrée, joint, possibly game, vegetables, sweet, savoury, toast and butter, and dessert; most of it off silver plates on hot water containers which must have weighed a ton to carry up and down from the pantry. People from the village, stables and gardens used to come in to help in the carrying (very necessary, as there were two flights of stairs and a long passage from the kitchen) and washing up; and no doubt ate a good deal that came out of the dining-room. There was, I believe, in addition a regular spread in the servants' hall when the work was finished, washed down with plenty of Hickleton beer. But it must have been a formidable labour problem none-the-less.

As one recalls the habits of fifty years ago, it is the labour picture that is the most surprising. All this dining-room work; no bathrooms and every guest therefore having cans of hot and cold water carried up to their bedrooms for a hipbath in front of a coal fire, and the bath water emptied with slop pails; lamps for the sitting-rooms and passages when it got dark, taken away by the footmen when the bell was rung to signal that everybody was going to bed, which they did taking one of the silver hand candlesticks set in rows at the foot of the stairs; wicks of lamps and bedroom candlesticks to be trimmed and cleaned next morning; no wonder it had to be a pretty considerable household to cope with it all.

When I was of 'being at Oxford' age, it had become traditional that we always had champagne on Christmas Eve, and toasted cheese and spiced beer; but whether this had always gone on, I do not know. As children, we used to come down for dessert, and be given a chocolate or some fruit, and then retire to bed, except on Christmas Day when we were allowed to dine. On Christmas Eve too there was the ritual of the house carpenter bringing round the Yule log. We would generally be in my father's room being read to, and the log would be solemnly brought in, the performance being repeated for every room in the house. All these were equipped with old-fashioned steel grates, in which blazed a lovely coal fire which was most cosy and luxurious. But on Christmas Eve members of the family used sometimes to practise self-denial for the benefit of the housemaids by not having a fire; for the business of doing forty or fifty grates was not negligible.

I do not remember any great attention being paid to stockings on Christmas Eve night, though there was always much wondering as to what time Father Christmas might come and whether we should see him. A few years later, the great preoccupation that I shared with my sister Agnes was whether or not we should wake up to hear the Waits singing round the house on Christmas morning. These were eight or ten of the men from the village who used to come and sing "Christians Awake," "Hark the Herald Angels sing," "O come all ye faithful" and "While Shepherds watched" about five o'clock in the morning at each side of the house. Among my earliest memories is that of shivering as we got out of nice warm beds and showed a light in the windows to tell the singers that their efforts were not in vain. I believe that the old custom used to be that when they had done their singing they adjourned into the servants' hall for beer—home-brewed of course—and cake. But this, I fancy, was gradually discouraged on grounds of church order and came to an end.

There was never any midnight Mass at Hickleton, so far as I recall, while my father was alive, except once when the chaplain celebrated in the chapel, not the church. Everybody went to church at seven or eight o'clock, or both, on Christmas morning. Breakfast was quite an affair, with a certain amount of present-giving, and a large bowl of firmity, rather like sweet porridge, made of cream and barley among other things, that you were supposed by Yorkshire, as by Scottish, custom to eat standing up. What the origin of this was I do not know, but I remember firmity being very nasty. Church happened again at ten o'clock, sung Mattins with the Athanasian Creed, before the sung celebration. My mother always played the organ, supported by two or three of the village with fiddle, cello and flute, William Ball, the head mason, led the procession, every candle that could be lit was lit, and it was a pretty long service both for children and grown-ups; so that I think we were all thankful when it became the practice for the celebrant to preach no sermon, but merely to wish everybody a happy Christmas. And after church there was the

Christmas tree to be decorated, already set up on its dust sheet in the hall. This did not take very long with a lot of helpers, and one of the uncles, generally Uncle Henry Corry, on some steps to put the flags at the very top, children being deflected from the hall till they were allowed in for the regular showing of the tree after tea. There was drawing-room tea for the elders and schoolroom tea, over which our governess, Miss Hilder, presided of her own right so long as she was governess, and when she had ceased to be governess by continuing convention. Tea had to be finished by the time the school children from the village were ready for the tree, illuminated meanwhile by the elders. To this the house servants came and were given their presents. The upper servants got what you might call personal presents; the humbler maids in their lace caps all got a length of print for a cotton frock.

Meanwhile the children walked round the tree, and generally a carol party from the neighbouring mining village would be heard outside the front door and my father would thank them and give them 10s. or £1 for whatever their good cause might be. But sometimes there would be a sudden and terrifying diversion—my father coming in, hobbling with a stick and dressed up as a witch, and the word passing round that this was indeed Gagool from *King Solomon's Mines*, which was being read aloud to us at the time. Or there was another memorable occasion much later when William Ballinger, the coachman, was encouraged to pretend with others to be a raiding party of gipsies, whom we had actually seen that afternoon on the roadside, when we had all been out for a walk with the children. I remember it as if it was yesterday—a great banging at the front door, my father telling James, the butler, to go and see what it was, and James going to the door and coming back—an awful silence having overtaken the company inside the hall—to say that there were a lot of rough gipsies, who as far as he could make out said they wanted a little boy and were coming in to fetch him; and on his heels came in four or five of the biggest ruffians you ever saw, who were William and some of the gardeners, and William shouting rather bolshie sentiments about rich and poor and the half-starved gipsies, and how they wanted a fat little boy they had seen and had brought a sack to take him away in. My father furious, "I won't have people like you speaking to me in that way—get out, at once." "We must take the little boy with us" from the gipsies—and absolute panic among the children; some fleeing upstairs, others screaming and hiding behind grown-ups, until order had to be restored by the gipsy withdrawal and a general pacification, induced by the normal proceeding of crackers and carols, after which the school children filed out past my mother who gave them a present, and an orange and a bag of sweets.

On Christmas Day, as I have said, the children were allowed to dine, and after dinner the traditional practice was to play Pounce Commerce round a large table in the library. This was a card game at which any number could play and in which one only survived as victor. It was really rather a difficult game—a great deal of play and a good deal of luck—and the younger children used to be shepherded through its mazes and mysteries. Excitement rose as the field of survival narrowed and my father used presently to disappear, to reappear with an object that was to be the prize of victory, generally a box of sugar plums or something of the sort. Some of the grown-ups used to get very cross with others of the grown-ups, whom they thought to be playing an unsporting game and following more than was proper dog-in-the-manger principles.

If there was snow and frost, as there then seemed to be much more often than nowadays, we used to have great battles in the snow, divided into sides, who occupied opposing forts on the croquet ground. Or if there was skating, activity on the round pond ranging from hockey for the more skilled to the safer pastime for the beginners of being impelled round the pond on a wooden chair from the kitchen by the excellent Smith, who had begun life fifty years earlier as my mother's pony boy and had become butler. When it was open weather, we went out hunting on our ponies if the meet was at Hickleton or within reach, and thought this always rather an adventure. I was almost invariably acutely conscious, as I think Siegfried Sassoon said somewhere that he was too, that my breeches and gaiters and boots were never as compact or secure an outfit as those of other boys I saw. Mine used to show gaps, or turn round on my leg, or someone had put the wrong gaiter on the wrong leg, or a button would have come off, and this gave me a lasting inferiority complex about the business. Thus inadvertently do the elders inflict minor miseries upon the young.

Our two principal indoor delights as children are associated in my mind with the time after tea. Then we came down into the hall, and my mother would vamp away at the piano for us to play some sort of game to, or dance, or perhaps occasionally sing. But much better were the exciting games we used to play, with Uncle Henry Wood a principal figure, of a kind of Tom Tiddler, which we called "Friar" and involved getting across the floor without being caught. The two big bear skins that used to be in the hall, a grizzly and a polar bear, came into it and the game always aroused much noise and intense excitement. The other enjoyment was being read to by my father in his room, sometimes Walter Scott, sometimes Robert Louis Stevenson, and sometimes a ghost story. The last was what we loved the best with its element of fearful mystery when it was finished, so that we looked over our shoulders as we ran upstairs, with the not too well-lit passages and landings to get through, before we reached the security of our own rooms. The baize door of the hall on the backstairs used to function as a kind of automatic measure of the occult threat and a magic shield against it. As we passed the door we would throw it open saying something like "Catch me if you can, devil, ghost or man," and scamper up the stairs as fast as we could. If we got to the top of the first flight, which in fact we could always do, before the door swung to, we were safe. But it introduced a thrilling and delicious spice of imaginative danger. And sometimes after dinner the big leather Ghost book would be produced, from which many of the stories were later published in *Lord Halifax's Ghost Book*, and my father would read aloud. And I remember, but I think he usually came in either summer or autumn, Augustus Hare making all our flesh creep with his story of the vampire at Croglin Grange, which he could only tell when he wore a very much ribbed shirt, so that picking his shirt with his nail, he could represent the vampire picking the mortar from the window pane to get in. We used to be terrified when we went up to bed. I suppose all this would nowadays fall into the category of 'horror comics' and be condemned; but I don't think it did us any harm, and my father always said it was very good for our imaginations.

Quite often, but not every year, there would be a servants' dance, to which each servant was allowed to invite a friend, and for which in addition there were certain 'corporate' invitations, such as any young people in the village not otherwise covered, the principal farmers and their wives, Doncaster tradesmen, and a selection of servants from the neighbouring houses. When the party was assembled, either in the dining-room or hall, the parents sailed in, with us following behind, and after they had said a word or two and shaken hands with the principal visitors, the Master of Ceremonies, who used to be Smith, the butler, would invite everybody to take partners for "The Triumph," a rather stately country dance, which my father danced with the housekeeper and my mother with Smith. Polkas, Valses, Schottisches, Lancers and the Ribbon dance, to the tune of 'Pop goes the Weasel,' pretty much made the programme, twosteps and glides and Paul Jones's not being yet invented. We went to bed about eleven, but the entertainment went on into the small hours with supper about midnight in the servants' hall. The housemaids, we used to be told, generally made a night of it, and started doing their early morning work as soon as they had changed out of their dance-clothes. However smart these last might be, they were always expected to wear their caps.

Indeed the ritual of 'below stairs' must have been quite strict. Ladies' maids and valets normally took the same precedence as their masters and mistresses. All joined for the first course of the midday dinner in the servants' hall, but the upper servants left the hall after the first course was over, adjourning to the 'Room' (housekeeper's room) with their glass of beer in their hands for the pudding. Whether the origin of this was merely a social distinction, or because the uppers had a second course and the others did not, I don't know. But that is what regularly happened.

Occasionally, but not as a regular event, and somewhere about New Year's Day, there was a snap-dragon. This consisted of an enormous dish of raisins, liberally sprinkled with brandy, and with flaming brandy flowing around the raisins well heaped up in the middle. We were encouraged to dab through the flames and pick out a raisin, and it was gloriously dangerous and exciting. There was no other light in the room, but this rather garish and flickering illumination, made much more bizarre by salt being thrown in, turning everybody and everything green and ghastly. It must have been extravagant with brandy.

So would end the regular Christmas celebrations, and the party would gradually melt. A little later there would sometimes be another party for the Hunt ball at Pontefract and for the Infirmary ball in Doncaster, which the parents used to think it their duty to support. I doubt whether driving in to Doncaster for three-quarters of an hour after dinner and driving out for the same time at two or three in the morning in an old omnibus and brougham would be tolerated by a modern generation. But speed had not succeeded in establishing the mastery over life that it has since acquired, and we thought no more of driving six miles behind a pair of horses then than people would think of driving thirty in a fast car now. Life, in comparison with that of to-day, was sedate, unhurried and traditional. The charms of novelty were not more alluring than those of tried and proved enjoyments. So, when the excitements of one Christmas gathering were over, it did not seem too difficult to settle down again to the customary tempo and order with the relish of a comfortable if subconscious feeling that the next Christmas could be safely relied upon to be as much fun as the last.

O. HENRY

The Gift of the Magi

THE GIFT OF THE MAGI, *first published in 1907, is probably the most famous story that O. Henry ever wrote. When we consider that at the time it was written $20 a week was thought to be a decent salary, this tender story becomes all the more touching.*

ONE DOLLAR and eighty-seven cents. That was all. And sixty cents of it was in pennies. Pennies saved one and two at a time by bulldozing the grocer and the vegetable man and the butcher until one's cheeks burned with the silent imputation of parsimony that such close dealing implied. Three times Della counted it. One dollar and eighty-seven cents. And the next day would be Christmas.

There was clearly nothing to do but flop down on the shabby little couch and howl. So Della did it. Which instigates the moral reflection that life is made up of sobs, sniffles, and smiles, with sniffles predominating.

While the mistress of the home is gradually subsiding from the first stage to the second, take a look at the home. A furnished flat at $8 per week. It did not exactly beggar description, but it certainly had that word on the lookout for the mendicancy squad.

In the vestibule below was a letter-box into which no letter would go, and an electric button from which no mortal finger could coax a ring. Also appertaining thereunto was a card bearing the name "Mr. James Dillingham Young."

The "Dillingham" had been flung to the breeze during a former period of prosperity when its possessor was being paid $30 per week. Now, when the income was shrunk to $20, the letters of "Dillingham" looked blurred, as though they were thinking seriously of contracting to a modest and unassuming D. But whenever Mr. James Dillingham Young came home and reached his flat above he was called "Jim" and greatly hugged by Mrs. James Dillingham Young, already introduced to you as Della. Which is all very good.

Della finished her cry and attended to her cheeks with the powder rag. She stood by the window and looked out dully at a gray cat walking a gray fence in a gray backyard. Tomorrow would be Christmas Day, and she had only $1.87 with which to buy Jim a present. She had been saving every penny she could for months, with this result. Twenty dollars a week doesn't go far. Expenses had been greater than she had calculated. They always are. Only $1.87 to buy a present for Jim. Her Jim. Many a happy hour she had spent planning for something nice for him. Something fine and rare and sterling—something just a little bit near to being worthy of the honour of being owned by Jim.

There was a pier-glass between the windows of the room. Perhaps you have seen a pier-glass in an $8 flat. A very thin and very agile person may, by observing his reflection in a rapid sequence of longitudinal strips, obtain a fairly accurate conception of his looks. Della, being slender, had mastered the art.

Suddenly she whirled from the window and stood before the glass. Her eyes were shining brilliantly, but her face had lost its color within twenty seconds. Rapidly she pulled down her hair and let it fall to its full length.

Now, there were two possessions of the James Dillingham Youngs, in which they both took a mighty pride. One was Jim's gold watch that had been his father's and his grandfather's. The other was Della's hair. Had the Queen of Sheba lived in the flat across the airshaft, Della would have let her hair hang out the window some day to dry just to depreciate Her Majesty's jewels and gifts. Had King Solomon been the janitor, with all his treasures piled up in the basement, Jim would have pulled out his watch every time he passed, just to see him pluck at his beard from envy.

So now Della's beautiful hair fell about her rippling and shining like a cascade of brown waters. It reached below her knee and made itself almost a garment for her. And then she did it up again nervously and quickly. Once she faltered for a minute and stood still while a tear or two splashed on the worn red carpet.

On went her old brown jacket; on went her old brown hat. With a whirl of skirts and with the brilliant sparkle still in her eyes, she fluttered out the door and down the stairs to the street.

Where she stopped the sign read: "Mme. Sofronie. Hair Goods of All Kinds." One flight up Della ran, and collected herself, panting. Madame, large, too white, chilly, hardly looked the "Sofronie."

"Will you buy my hair?" asked Della.

"I buy hair," said Madame. "Take yer hat off and let's have a sight at the looks of it."

Down rippled the brown cascade.

"Twenty dollars," said Madame, lifting the mass with a practised hand.

"Give it to me quick," said Della.

Oh, and the next two hours tripped by on rosy wings. Forget the hashed metaphor. She was ransacking the stores for Jim's present.

She found it at last. It surely had been made for Jim and no one else. There was no other like it in any of the stores, and she had turned all of them inside out. It was a platinum fob chain simple and chaste in design, properly proclaiming its value by substance alone and not by meretricious ornamentation—as all good things should do. It was even worthy of The Watch. As soon as she saw it she knew that it must be Jim's. It was like him. Quietness and value —the description applied to both. Twenty-one dollars they took from her for it, and she hurried home with the 87 cents. With that chain on his watch Jim might be properly anxious about the time in any company. Grand as the watch was, he sometimes looked at it on the sly on account of the old leather strap that he used in place of a chain.

When Della reached home her intoxication gave way a little to prudence and reason. She got out her curling irons and lighted the gas and went to work repairing the ravages made by generosity added to love. Which is always a tremendous task, dear friends—a mammoth task.

Within forty minutes her head was covered with tiny, close-lying curls that made her look wonderfully like a truant schoolboy. She looked at her reflection in the mirror long, carefully, and critically.

"If Jim doesn't kill me," she said to herself, "before he takes a second look at me, he'll say I look like a Coney Island chorus girl.

But what could I do—oh! what could I do with a dollar and eighty-seven cents?"

At 7 o'clock the coffee was made and the frying-pan was on the back of the stove hot and ready to cook the chops.

Jim was never late. Della doubled the fob chain in her hand and sat on the corner of the table near the door that he always entered. Then she heard his step on the stair way down on the first flight, and she turned white for just a moment. She had a habit of saying little silent prayers about the simplest everyday things, and now she whispered: "Please God, make him think I am still pretty."

The door opened and Jim stepped in and closed it. He looked thin and very serious. Poor fellow, he was only twenty-two—and to be burdened with a family! He needed a new overcoat and he was without gloves.

Jim stopped inside the door, as immovable as a setter at the scent of quail. His eyes were fixed upon Della, and there was an expression in them that she could not read, and it terrified her. It was not anger, nor surprise, nor disapproval, nor horror, nor any of the sentiments that she had been prepared for. He simply stared at her fixedly with that peculiar expression on his face.

Della wriggled off the table and went for him.

"Jim, darling," she cried, "don't look at me that way. I had my hair cut off and sold it because I couldn't have lived through Christmas without giving you a present. It'll grow out again—you won't mind, will you? I just had to do it. My hair grows awfully fast. Say 'Merry Christmas,' Jim, and let's be happy. You don't know what a nice—what a beautiful, nice gift I've got for you."

"You've cut off your hair?" asked Jim, laboriously, as if he had not arrived at that patent fact yet even after the hardest mental labor.

"Cut it off and sold it," said Della. "Don't you like me just as well, anyhow? I'm me without my hair, ain't I?"

Jim looked about the room curiously.

"You say your hair is gone?" he said, with an air almost of idiocy.

"You needn't look for it," said Della. "It's sold, I tell you—sold and gone, too. It's Christmas Eve, boy. Be good to me, for it went for you. Maybe the hairs of my head were numbered," she went on with a sudden serious sweetness, "but nobody could ever count my love for you. Shall I put the chops on, Jim?"

Out of his trance Jim seemed quickly to wake. He enfolded his Della. For ten seconds let us regard with discreet scrutiny some inconsequential object in the other direction. Eight dollars a week or a million a year—what is the difference? A mathematician or a wit would give you the wrong answer. The magi brought valuable gifts, but that was not among them. This dark assertion will be illuminated later on.

Jim drew a package from his overcoat pocket and threw it upon the table.

"Don't make any mistake, Dell," he said, "about me. I don't think there's anything in the way of a haircut or a shave or a shampoo that could make me like my girl any less. But if you'll unwrap that package you may see why you had me going a while at first."

White fingers and nimble tore at the string and paper. And then an ecstatic scream of joy; and then, alas! a quick feminine change to hysterical tears and wails, necessitating the immediate employment of all the comforting power of the lord of the flat.

For there lay The Combs—the set of combs, side and back, that Della had worshipped for long in a Broadway window. Beautiful combs, pure tortoise shell, with jewelled rims—just the shade to wear in the beautiful vanished hair. They were expensive combs, she knew, and her heart had simply craved and yearned over them without the least hope of possession. And now, they were hers, but the tresses that should have adorned the coveted adornments were gone.

But she hugged them to her bosom, and at length she was able to look up with dim eyes and a smile and say: "My hair grows so fast, Jim!"

And then Della leaped up like a little singed cat and cried, "Oh, oh!"

Jim had not yet seen his beautiful present. She held it out to him eagerly upon her open palm. The dull precious metal seemed to flash with a reflection of her bright and ardent spirit.

"Isn't it a dandy, Jim? I hunted all over town to find it. You'll have to look at the time a hundred times a day now. Give me your watch. I want to see how it looks on it."

Instead of obeying, Jim tumbled down on the couch and put his hands under the back of his head and smiled.

"Dell," said he, "let's put our Christmas presents away and keep 'em a while. They're too nice to use just at present. I sold the watch to get the money to buy your combs. And now suppose you put the chops on."

The magi, as you know, were wise men—wonderfully wise men—who brought gifts to the Babe in the manger. They invented the art of giving Christmas presents. Being wise, their gifts were no doubt wise ones, possibly bearing the privilege of exchange in case of duplication. And here I have lamely related to you the uneventful chronicle of two foolish children in a flat who most unwisely sacrificed for each other the greatest treasures of their house. But in a last word to the wise of these days let it be said that of all who give gifts these two were the wisest. Of all who give and receive gifts, such as they are wisest. Everywhere they are wisest. They are the magi.

A. M. HOPKINS

❧

Recollections of a Boyhood Christmas Visit to a Neighboring Farm

A LETTER

FOR YEARS I have written to friends and acquaintances a "Christmas Letter," written it with joy in my heart and from the sacred spot where blessed memories are stored; written until the annual contribution has become an institution, and the happiest task that comes my way. You may be one of those who feel that all the songs dealing with the world's holiday have been sung, but if this is so, you, my friend, are a thousand times wrong, for Christmas is light and laughter, love and tenderness, sympathy and good impulses; dedicated for the ages of ages to the well being of all of us. Giving! It is pure gold, and while love lasts, must endure.

The changing world, with its luxuries and its faster pace; its multitude of inventions; its higher standard of living; its departure from old ways and the simple life of other times, has never outstripped human kindness. The things within us; the gold in our breasts, that make us human, can never change, please God.

There is a generation today that has never known hardship and privation; that has never been forced to make its own pleasures and to do without a thousand luxuries, that are now a part of every home; and for their good, and because, as I write in front of a crackling wood fire I am surrounded by kindly ghosts who demand recognition, I'm going back to the blustering Christmas of 1874, and that, to most of you, is a long, long time ago.

There was snow everywhere, blizzards and gusts of snow, that hung

111

to the trees and covered the fences, and the little cottage that was my home looked like unto a great white mound with a thin volume of smoke issuing from the brick chimney. I had dug a path to the barn only to see it filling up behind me, and, as was my daily "chore," had gone to the wood pile by the west fence to beat out of its icy covering enough hard maple wood to fill the yawning woodbox that stood behind the kitchen stove. There was a trample of feet, a loud, "Whoa," a ripping and ploughing of snowdrifts, and there were two great steaming black horses, frost hanging to their muzzles. Albert Herick had delivered a load of wood and was pounding his mittens and blowing smoky breath on his hands in an effort to get warm.

How was I to know, as I stood there in my copper toed boots, wishing that I could drive a black team and deliver wood to people who needed it, that I was on the threshold of adventure and romance? I had never been ten miles from home. The horizon covered my world, and all that I lived and hoped for and enjoyed, existed under the roof of a six-room cottage that contained not one item of luxury that you find so essential now. Even my mittens and the red comforter around my neck, and the trousers that encased my slim legs, were home made and with a great deal of love worked into the making.

The door squeaked frostily and there was Mother asking Mr. Herick to come in and thaw out, and his face was red with cold and he laughed like a blessed Santa Claus as he said, "Glad to see you all and I have just two things to be done; first unload this wood, and the other is to borrow a boy for Christmas. Amanda told me to get him even if I had to steal him, and I'll have him back bright and early Christmas morning ready to see what is in his stocking."

I do not think that Columbus, when he sighted America, received the thrill that was mine at that moment. The Herick home was a little cottage on a little farm and the Hericks, brother and sister, not forgetting Uncle Cyrus with his squeaky voice, were all the Heaven that I could ask, for there was the urge of adventure in my breast; and I had never slept even one night farther from my good mother than the next room. "Can I go?" and she smiled and nodded and told me to come in and get my face washed, and in ten minutes I was sitting on the front seat, holding the lines and Mr. Herick was clucking to the horses, and you can keep your Rolls-Royce and your

Twentieth Century Limiteds because I know what is the best in the world.

How shall I describe the cottage and the welcome; the one weatherbeaten and the other love raised to the heights. Here were brother and sister, unmarried, struggling for an existence, poor in money all of their lives, happy in their fine impulses, and lonesome, for had they not borrowed a boy for Christmas?

I can see every corner of that home. There was the fireplace with blazing logs; a canary bird that sang beautifully; some mottoes on the wall, worked with colored worsteds: "God Bless Our Home," and I'm sure that He did bless it; "Peace Be Unto This Household," I don't believe that a harsh word was ever spoken under that roof. Over in the corner there was a melodeon, old even then, and there were some house plants, and a rag carpet on the floor, and Uncle Cyrus had a splint bottomed rocker where he sat and rocked and smoked his pipe and told me the most charming stories of the time when he was a little boy; and when we reached the scary places, he let me hold his rough hand to sort of tide me over. No automobile in the barn; no radio in the living room; no telephone on the wall; no furnace in the basement; no gas or hot water or electric lights; no cement walks; no mail delivery; no street lights; no aeroplanes buzzing overhead; no talking machine; no bath room; not even a neighbor nearer than half a mile up the snow drifted road; but hospitality, contentment, consideration and a determination to do one's duty and make the best of things; these were everywhere.

We had the blue dishes on the table, and I had the seat of honor, a big book labelled in gold letters, "Diseases of the Horse," under me to raise my head above my plate, and Albert Herick asked the blessing that contained not one word about poverty and hard work, but was a plea to the Almighty that all of us might be properly grateful for the benefits and blessings that had reached us; for life and health and the power to do good, and there was a special plea for the boy who had been borrowed for Christmas and that he might grow up to become a useful citizen, and Uncle Cyrus squeaked "Amen" and we ate a Christmas dinner that was home cooked and home produced and home consumed, and no chef with his twenty-five thousand a year ever concocted finer food.

The sweet face of Amanda Herick is with me as I write. She always smiled. Her grey hair was smoothed back over her well shaped head, and ever there seemed to be a bit of sadness in her eyes. She was soft voiced and when I remember it, I seem to hear the notes of a flute. In my child way I loved her deeply, and I could not keep my eyes off her face, and she caught my gaze and asked the borrowed boy over the coffee pot: "Why do you look at me?", and I stammered because I was ashamed, "Because I love you and you are so good."

What had I done! What had I done! For tears leaped to her eyes and she came around the table with love, I guess for all children, glowing, and placed her arms about me and kissed me, while Uncle Cyrus grunted and said: "Amanda, you ort to have had a dozen of your own."

And then evening came and the lamp was lighted, and the fire was stirred until the sparks leaped up the chimney, and Amanda Herick found an old book and sang in her sweet voice, "Flow Gently Sweet Afton," and the little melodeon wheezed delightfully and even the canary awoke on its perch and trilled a few bars; and Uncle Cyrus let me sit close to him by the fire and told me some bear stories, and about the fight his big dog had with a wolf; and the one about the deer he killed in the back lot; and there was the grateful smell of wood smoke, and the wind zoomed harmony in the chimney, and it was still snowing. Peace! Peace! The great noisy world shut out, just as it is today in the back counties; and fine people doing their best to make happiness and to be happy in their own way.

Hickory nuts were cracked and eaten. A bag of red apples was laid aside for the borrowed boy to take home to his mother; my Christmas was laid before me: A cup of fragile china with "To a Good Boy" on its surface, from Amanda, and it was and is my most treasured possession; a large cake of maple sugar from Albert Herick, and Uncle Cyrus gave me his wonderful staghorn handled jackknife and it served me for long years.

They talked and the fire crackled and the world seemed slipping away, and I was carried to a soft bed in Amanda's room, and I heard a voice saying, "Be sure and put plenty of kiver over that boy," and I was away into dreamland.

I'm almost to the end of my simple story. I have not tried to do any fine writing about those blessed and heart hungry people, or to set down the delights of a season that must always be devoted to children.

There was the getting up in a cold house; the sound of a rooster crowing frostily; Albert Herick shoveling snow to get to the barn and feed the stock; the warm breakfast and the still warmer good-bye; Amanda Herick coming out to the big farm sleigh to wrap her shawl about me, and the ride home and then the dash into the kitchen and a hug from Mother and the cry, "Oh, I had such a good time."

And so I plead for memories of olden times, and simple pleasures, and the making of the most delightful music in the world, the laughter of happy children, and devoutly repeat Albert Herick's bene-diction: "God bless us all and make us contented."

"MERRY CHRISTMAS"

A. M. HOPKINS

CINCINNATI, *December* 24, 1927.

W. D. HOWELLS

Christmas Every Day

THE LITTLE GIRL came into her papa's study, as she always did Saturday morning before breakfast, and asked for a story. He tried to beg off that morning, for he was very busy, but she would not let him. So he began:

"Well, once there was a little pig—"

She put her hand over his mouth and stopped him at the word. She said she had heard little pig stories till she was perfectly sick of them.

"Well, what kind of story *shall* I tell, then?"

"About Christmas. It's getting to be the season. It's past Thanksgiving already."

"It seems to me," argued her papa, "that I've told as often about Christmas as I have about little pigs."

"No difference! Christmas is more interesting."

"Well!" Her papa roused himself from his writing by a great effort. "Well, then, I'll tell you about the little girl that wanted it Christmas every day in the year. How would you like that?"

"First-rate!" said the little girl; and she nestled into comfortable shape in his lap, ready for listening.

"Very well, then, this little pig—Oh, what are you pounding me for?"

"Because you said little pig instead of little girl."

"I should like to know what's the difference between a little pig and a little girl that wanted it Christmas every day!"

"Papa," said the little girl, warningly, "if you don't go on, I'll *give* it to you!" And at this her papa darted off like lightning, and began to tell the story as fast as he could.

116

Well, once there was a little girl who liked Christmas so much that she wanted it to be Christmas every day in the year; and as soon as Thanksgiving was over she began to send postal cards to the old Christmas Fairy to ask if she mightn't have it. But the old Fairy never answered any of the postals; and, after a while, the little girl found out that the Fairy was pretty particular, and wouldn't notice anything but letters, not even correspondence cards in envelopes; but real letters on sheets of paper, and sealed outside with a mono-gram—or your initial, any way. So, then, she began to send her letters; and in about three weeks—or just the day before Christmas, it was—she got a letter from the Fairy, saying she might have it Christmas every day for a year, and then they would see about hav-ing it longer.

The little girl was a good deal excited already, preparing for the old-fashioned, once-a-year Christmas that was coming the next day, and perhaps the Fairy's promise didn't make such an impression on her as it would have made at some other time. She just resolved to keep it to herself, and surprise everybody with it as it kept coming true; and then it slipped out of her mind altogether.

She had a splendid Christmas. She went to bed early, so as to let Santa Claus have a chance at the stockings, and in the morning she was up the first of anybody and went and felt them, and found hers all lumpy with packages of candy, and oranges and grapes and pocketbooks and rubber balls and all kinds of small presents and her big brother's with nothing but the tongs in them, and her young lady sister's with a new silk umbrella, and her papa's and mamma's with potatoes and pieces of coal wrapped up in tissue paper, just as they always had every Christmas. Then she waited around till the rest of the family were up, and she was the first to burst into the library, when the doors were opened, and look at the large presents laid out on the library-table—books, and portfolios and boxes of stationery, and breast pins, and dolls, and little stoves and dozens of handkerchiefs, and ink-stands, and skates, and snow-shovels, and photograph-frames, and little easels, and boxes of water-colors, and Turkish paste, and nougat, and candied cherries, and dolls' houses, and waterproofs—and the big Christmas-tree, lighted and standing in a wastebasket in the middle.

She had a splendid Christmas all day. She ate so much candy

that she did not want any breakfast; and the whole forenoon the presents kept pouring in that the expressman had not had time to deliver the night before; and she went 'round giving the presents she had got for other people, and came home and ate turkey and cranberry for dinner, and plum-pudding and nuts and raisins and oranges and more candy, and then went out and coasted and came in with a stomach-ache, crying; and her papa said he would see if his house was turned into that sort of fool's paradise another year; and they had a light supper, and pretty early everybody went to bed cross.

Here the little girl pounded her papa in the back, again.

"Well, what now? Did I say pigs?"

"You made them *act* like pigs."

"Well, didn't they?"

"No matter; you oughtn't to put it into a story."

"Very well, then, I'll take it all out."

Her father went on:

The little girl slept very heavily, and she slept very late, but she was wakened at last by the other children dancing 'round her bed with their stockings full of presents in their hands.

"What is it?" said the little girl, and she rubbed her eyes and tried to rise up in bed.

"Christmas! Christmas! Christmas!" they all shouted, and waved their stockings.

"Nonsense! It was Christmas yesterday."

Her brothers and sisters just laughed. "We don't know about that. It's Christmas to-day, any way. You come into the library and see."

Then all at once it flashed on the little girl that the Fairy was keeping her promise, and her year of Christmases was beginning. She was dreadfully sleepy, but she sprang up like a lark—a lark that had overeaten itself and gone to bed cross—and darted into the library. There it was again! Books, and portfolios, and boxes of stationery, and breast pins—

"You needn't go over it all, Papa; I guess I can remember just what was there," said the little girl.

Well, and there was the Christmas-tree blazing away, and the family picking out their presents, but looking pretty sleepy, and her father perfectly puzzled, and her mother ready to cry. "I'm sure I don't see how I'm to dispose of all these things," said her mother, and her father said it seemed to him they had had something just like it the day before, but he supposed he must have dreamed it. This struck the little girl as a kind of a joke; and so she ate so much candy she didn't want any breakfast, and went 'round carrying presents, and had turkey and cranberry for dinner, and then went out and coasted, and came in with a—

"Papa!"

"Well, what now?"

"What did you promise, you forgetful thing?"

"Oh! oh, yes!"

Well, the next day, it was just the same thing over again, but everybody getting crosser; and at the end of a week's time so many people had lost their tempers that you could pick up lost tempers everywhere; they perfectly strewed the ground. Even when people tried to recover their tempers they usually got somebody else's, and it made the most dreadful mix.

The little girl began to get frightened, keeping the secret all to herself; she wanted to tell her mother, but she didn't dare to; and she was ashamed to ask the Fairy to take back her gift, it seemed ungrateful and ill-bred, and she thought she would try to stand it, but she hardly knew how she could, for a whole year. So it went on and on, and it was Christmas on St. Valentine's Day, and Washington's Birthday just the same as any day, and it didn't skip even the First of April, though everything was counterfeit that day, and that was some *little* relief.

After a while, coal and potatoes began to be awfully scarce, so many had been wrapped up in tissue paper to fool papas and mammas with. Turkeys got to be a thousand dollars apiece—

"Papa!"

"Well, what?"

"You're beginning to fib."

"Well, *two* thousand, then."

And they got to passing off almost anything for turkeys,—half-grown humming-birds, and even rocs out of the *Arabian Nights*—the real turkeys were so scarce. And cranberries—well, they asked a diamond apiece for cranberries. All the woods and orchards were cut down for Christmas-trees, and where the woods and orchards used to be, it looked just like a stubble-field, with the stumps. After a while they had to make Christmas-trees out of rags, and stuff them with bran, like old-fashioned dolls; but there were plenty of rags, because people got so poor, buying presents for one another, that they couldn't get any new clothes, and they just wore their old ones to tatters. They got so poor that everybody had to go to the poor-house, except the confectioners, and the fancy storekeepers, and the picture-book sellers, and the expressmen; and *they* all got so rich and proud that they would hardly wait upon a person when he came to buy; it was perfectly shameful!

Well, after it had gone on about three or four months, the little girl, whenever she came into the room in the morning and saw those great ugly lumpy stockings dangling at the fire-place, and the disgusting presents around everywhere, used to just sit down and burst out crying. In six months she was perfectly exhausted; she couldn't even cry any more; she just lay on the lounge and rolled her eyes and panted. About the beginning of October she took to sitting down on dolls, wherever she found them—French dolls, or any kind—she hated the sight of them so; and by Thanksgiving she was crazy, and just slammed her presents across the room.

By that time people didn't carry presents around nicely any more. They flung them over the fence, or through the window, or anything; and, instead of running their tongues out and taking great pains to write "For dear Papa," or "Mamma," or "Brother," or "Sister," or "Susie," or "Sammie," or "Billie," or "Bobby," or "Jimmie," or "Jennie," or whoever it was, and troubling to get the spelling right, and then signing their names, and "Xmas, 188——,' they used to write in the gift-books, "Take it, you horrid old thing!" and then go and bang it against the front door. Nearly everybody had built barns to hold their presents, but pretty soon the barns overflowed, and then they used to let them lie out in the rain, or anywhere. Sometimes the police used to come and tell them to shovel their presents off the sidewalk, or they would arrest them.

"I thought you said everybody had gone to the poor-house," interrupted the little girl.

"They did go, at first," said her papa; "but after a while the poor-houses got so full that they had to send the people back to their own houses. They tried to cry, when they got back, but they couldn't make the least sound."

"Why couldn't they?"

"Because they had lost their voices, saying 'Merry Christmas' so much. Did I tell you how it was on the Fourth of July?"

"No; how was it?" And the little girl nestled closer, in expectation of something uncommon.

Well, the night before, the boys stayed up to celebrate, as they always do, and fell asleep before twelve o'clock, as usual, expecting to be wakened by the bells and cannon. But it was nearly eight o'clock before the first boy in the United States woke up, and then he found out what the trouble was. As soon as he could get his clothes on, he ran out of the house and smashed a big cannon-torpedo down on the pavement; but it didn't make any more noise than a damp wad of paper, and, after he tried about twenty or thirty more, he began to pick them up and look at them. Every single torpedo was a big raisin! Then he just streaked it upstairs, and examined his fire-crackers and toy-pistol and two-dollar collection of fireworks, and found they they were nothing but sugar and candy painted up to look like fireworks! Before ten o'clock, every boy in the United States found out that his Fourth of July things had turned into Christmas things; and then they just sat down and cried—they were so mad. There are about twenty million boys in the United States, and so you can imagine what a noise they made. Some men got together before night, with a little powder that hadn't turned into purple sugar yet, and they said they would fire off *one* cannon, any way. But the cannon burst into a thousand pieces, for it was nothing but rock-candy, and some of the men nearly got killed. The Fourth of July orations all turned into Christmas carols, and when anybody tried to read the Declaration, instead of saying, "When in the course of human events it becomes necessary," he was sure to sing, "God rest you merry, gentlemen." It was perfectly awful.

The little girl drew a deep sigh of satisfaction.

"And how was it at Thanksgiving?" she asked.

Her papa hesitated. "Well, I'm almost afraid to tell you. I'm afraid you'll think it's wicked."

"Well, tell any way," said the little girl.

Well, before it came Thanksgiving, it had leaked out who had caused all these Christmases. The little girl had suffered so much that she had talked about it in her sleep; and after that, hardly anybody would play with her. People just perfectly despised her, because if it had not been for her greediness, it wouldn't have happened, and now, when it came Thanksgiving, and she wanted them to go to church, and have a squash pie and turkey, and show their gratitude, they said that all the turkeys had been eaten up for her old Christmas dinners, and if she would stop the Christmases, they would see about the gratitude. Wasn't it dreadful? And the very next day the little girl began to send letters to the Christmas Fairy, and then telegrams, to stop it. But it didn't do any good; and then she got to calling at the Fairy's house, but the girl that came to the door always said "Not at home," or "Engaged," or "At dinner," or something like that; and so it went on till it came to the old once-a-year Christmas Eve. The little girl fell asleep, and when she woke up in the morning—

"She found it was all nothing but a dream," suggested the little girl.

"No, indeed!" said her papa. "It was all every bit true!"

"Well, what did she find out then?"

"Why, that it wasn't Christmas at last, and wasn't ever going to be, any more. Now it's time for breakfast."

The little girl held her papa fast around the neck.

"You shan't go if you're going to leave it so!"

"How do you want it left?"

"Christmas once a year."

"All right," said her papa; and he went on again.

Well, there was the greatest rejoicing all over the country, and it extended clear up into Canada. The people met together everywhere, and kissed and cried for joy. The city carts went around and gathered up all the candy and raisins and nuts, and dumped them into the river; and it made the fish perfectly sick; and the whole United States, as far out as Alaska, was one blaze of bonfires, where the children were burning up their gift-books and presents of all kinds. They had the greatest *time!*

The little girl went to thank the old Fairy because she had stopped its being Christmas, and she said she hoped she would keep her promise, and see that Christmas never, never came again. Then the Fairy frowned, and asked her if she was sure she knew what she meant; and the little girl asked her, why not? and the old Fairy said that now she was behaving just as greedily as ever, and she'd better look out. This made the little girl think it all over carefully again, and she said she would be willing to have it Christmas about once in a thousand years; and then she said a hundred, and then she said ten, and at last she got down to one. Then the Fairy said that was the good old way that had pleased people ever since Christmas began, and she was agreed. Then the little girl said, "What're your shoes made of?" And the Fairy said, "Leather." And the little girl said, "Bargain's done forever," and skipped off, and hippity-hopped the whole way home, she was so glad.

"How will that do?" asked the papa.

"First-rate!" said the little girl; but she hated to have the story stop, and was rather sober. However, her mamma put her head in at the door, and asked her papa:

"Are you never coming to breakfast? What have you been telling that child?"

"Oh, just a moral tale."

The little girl caught him around the neck again.

"*We* know! Don't you tell *what*, Papa! Don't you tell *what!*"

FANNIE HURST

❧ ❦

White Christmas

IT WAS a white December twenty-fourth, and because in the city a white Christmas is difficult to keep that way, you felt like wrapping it up before it became tire-streaked and putting it away in a cake box.

During a gray forenoon which had smelled and tasted of snow, the flakes began to come down in purposeful lines. They were big and efficient, apparently intent upon laying heavy carpet. Almost immediately park statues, the dome of the Capitol, and the branches of trees became decked out in what, to a Southern town, was strange finery.

In Washington there is always a proportion of the very young and of migrants from still more southerly zones who have never seen snow.

Children kick delightedly through the stuff and stretch out their palms to catch stars which die at the touch. The runners of their sleds are apt to be rusty, and their short, inquisitive hands clumsy at fashioning balls. The sounds of such children at play are lovely. A year previous they would have lured Elsa to one of the double windows of the large room she shared with her husband in Mrs. Guthrie's boardinghouse on H Street, N.W.

Now, however, she sat beside the single window of the single room she occupied on another floor of that same boardinghouse, her gaze broody and not even aware of the tossing youngsters who were cleaving first paths down terraces as they flung themselves belly-buster on their seldom-used sleds.

It was the gaze of one who is terribly intent within, so much so, that, as she watched, Elsa was conscious, only in a secondary fashion, that the impending Christmas was about to be thickly white and

124

that already against its whiteness holly wreaths in the windows opposite seemed rounder and greener, berries redder.

Elsa, who was expert at fine-fingered catering and the making of party favors, could have reproduced the scene in whipped cream and icing on a cake. She could have outlined, in chocolate, a thatched cottage with chocolate smoke emerging from its chimney and "Merry Christmas" in chocolate script.

Back in the days (only one Christmas removed) when she and Kurt had run their catering establishment, she used effectively to flank such cakes with a pair of silver angels. Some of Washington's best homes, and one or two of the embassies, had created quite a little demand for these silver angels of her handicraft.

Ah me, only a year ago, when the first order from the Swedish Embassy had come, Kurt, so eager for diplomatic accounts, had exclaimed: "A little bird must have told them that my parents were born in Gothenburg and that my wife has a silver thumb."

"Silly-Billy," she had said, fixing her lips in a manner that she knew prompted him to want to kiss them. "What actually must have happened is that the Ambassador's wife attended Mrs. Spreckel's reception and asked her what genius could have made those perfectly magnificent sunshine cakes decorated in silver angels! The answer, in case you need to be reminded again, my spouse, is me, Elsa, your bride, your genius!"

Ah me, ah me, ah me, the lovely nonsense of one short year ago.

This was not the first white Christmas Elsa had seen, nor the second, nor the tenth. Before she had come to Washington to accept a position with "Kurt Johnsson, Inc., Caterer," she had spent all twenty-four of her winters in Trenton, where the snows fly frequently and hard.

As a matter of fact, there had been dry, creaking snow on the ground the afternoon they had been married back in Elsa's home town, where with spick-and-span attention to the proprieties the ceremony had taken place in the presence of her sole surviving relative, an aged aunt who had been only two months away from her death.

That Christmas they had honeymooned in Lakewood, where the New Jersey pinewoods had also been laid over with the magic of snow. They had washed each other's faces in it, tobogganed, walked miles of trails under cold white sunlight and cold white moonlight.

Fierce stars had come out at them, so big and defined that she had told Kurt they must have been cut with one of her cooky molds. She had been kissed beneath those stars, the fur about her neck crushed down by Kurt's strong, clean lips.

His death had made all that remote as a dream. Could there actually have been, only one Christmas ago, two such people as Kurt and herself, prospering in their small business, facing their lives with the high expectancy of the young, founding their future?

The dead look in Elsa's eyes was for the deadness of Kurt. Sometimes the hot tears that stung her eyes were tincture of rebelliousness. He had been too young and too vital and too full of good to die by such a small force as an explosion in the pastry kitchen. Sitting out in her cashier's cage, fashioning decorations during slack hours while his doom took shape, she had smelled the escaping gas, but too idly to do anything about it. She, who was usually so prophetic of things to come, had remained there unreached by so much as the premonition of a chill down her spine.

She used to say to Kurt: "Whenever anything good is going to happen, I can tell it by the delicious way I feel down my spine."

"You must have had some chill down it the day before we met."

"No kidding, I did, dear! For weeks, before I ever dreamed I'd follow my Trenton firm to Washington, and then get into yours after they liquidated, I had spells of feeling myself ring like a bell with premonition."

"And I heard you ringing and let you in."

Thank God for that.

And then, premonition apparently at rest beneath the hush of her complacency, she had sat in her cashier's cage unreached while the angel of death moved through the wintry afternoon.

He had been too young, too like a tree felled while in happy leaf and with the sap running high. A child was now about to be born who would never know its father. And what a father!

In the loneliness, the broody thoughts of Elsa, sluiced with inner tears, floundered about.

Here she sat, one Christmas Eve removed from the ecstatic one of their honeymoon, his widow, carrying his child who would never know the father who had been shattered to his death because a pocket of gas and a flame had met in an oven.

How further ironic that upon that same day an exciting new account had come in from the home of a high government official who did much entertaining, and which was likely to lead to more contacts in official Washington. Kurt had been all agog. It had all been so gay and so promising and he had been terrific with new energies. Plans ahead for three!

The flakes fell along the high terraces of the houses across the street, while children, wild with the novelty of them, shouted and coasted, belly-busting in high tension. Kurt's large galoshes were still standing on her closet shelf. Having them on hand for weather such as this had been one thing; getting him to wear them, another.

The day deepened, and Mrs. Guthrie, who had been an angel of solicitude during these months while Elsa was selling a business she could no longer endure, came knocking at the door.

She was an ample woman of friendly solicitudes, tiered chins, immense hips; the black sweater, which she wore next to her skin, containing her fulsomeness as if it had been a cheese bag.

It took so long for the sound of her knocking at her door to penetrate the dozy kind of listlessness that had Elsa in its grip that finally the landlady burst in.

"God rest my soul, sitting brooding again, and no heat on! You'd think from the look and feel of this room that you had a scrimpy landlady freezing you out."

Day in and day out Mrs. Guthrie made what amounted to this identical speech. Huddling herself thus in a room in which she had not even troubled to turn on the heat had become drearily characteristic of Elsa.

"I've been trimming the tree," said Mrs. Guthrie. "I had a mind to bring the little table fir Mr. Delahanty of the third-floor back sent in, up here in your room, but on second thought decided I'd set it up for you downstairs, so you won't have an excuse for not joining us."

"That's lovely of you, Mrs. Guthrie."

"Bless my soul, what's that on the table, a Christmas present? My, that's pretty work!"

"Yes, isn't it? It's a bed jacket which Mrs. Paterno knitted for me."

"The lady whose husband is buying out your business? Say, that's something. Sort of a herringbone stitch, isn't it? And pink! Well, you'll soon be needing either a lot of pink or a lot of blue. I ain't saying the color of the little booties I'm knitting."

"The Paternos are such nice people. So kind to me. I wonder if I'll ever be able to repay half. I pray they make good in our business. They are a team at it too—the way Kurt and I were."

"Say, don't you bother your head. It's up to them from now on. They're getting a mighty fine, spanking little business, and you could have held out for even more than they paid, and they know it."

"It *is* a nice, spanking little business, Mrs. Guthrie. Kurt built it up into that out of care and honesty."

"You should have kept it yourself."

"No. I haven't the heart left in me."

"Nonsense. I give you until your child is a few years old to be right back in again."

"Kurt loved that business so while he was alive. I loved it too—"

"Now, now, no brooding! You've no idea, dearie, how those silver angels you made for me dress up the tree. I saw some at Sherman's, not half as pretty, for eighty-nine cents apiece."

"I've lost my knack. My fingers are thumbs these days."

"I'd like to see the body whose fingers wouldn't slow down her eighth month. Did you go over to the hospital this morning for your checkup? It's your day. Don't forget, dearie, we've all got responsibility in this world, if not to ourselves, then to God."

"I know it, Mrs. Guthrie. His way, no matter how hard it may be to see it, is bound to be the right way. On the other hand, I keep feeling it's my responsibility to protect a child from coming into a world that doesn't contain the finest father a child could ever have had."

"Why, Mrs. Johnsson, that's downright sinful, and on Christmas Eve too! It's just because your husband was such a fine, upstanding man that you have to make up to your child by being both father and mother to it."

"Please, Mrs. Guthrie. Please don't! When you and the doctor and that nice nurse at the hospital get to talking that way, I appreciate it and all, but I get hard inside of me. Funny, isn't it, but I just freeze up."

"No, 'tisn't funny, it's natural. When I was carrying my poor Eddie, God rest his soul, his father, God rest his soul even if he was such a holy terror for drink, used to say to me that I got lower in my mind than his shoe ties. Nobody can't tell me the eighth month isn't as bad as the first, because it is. But this is Christmas Eve, dearie, and what's more, just look out there, will you? It's going to be a white Christmas!"

Elsa dropped her face into her hands, her tearless voice dry as a bone.

"I just can't want to face this Christmas, Mrs. Guthrie," she said down into her hands; "I want to be all the things you and the others say I should be and that I know I should be. But without Kurt it's just not left in me——"

"Sh-h-h. God comes back very close to the earth on Christmas. It's the time of birth and hope and joy. It's God's own day. Come Christmas, I always feel Him in my bones, and I'm not much of a one to feel thataway in my bones, the way you do."

"Yes, I'm a feeler of things in my bones, Mrs. Guthrie. But I didn't feel what was going to happen to Kurt——"

"It's only the good things you feel with your premonition, dearie. But if a tired old woman on her calluses can get this way, come Christmas, you with a baby coming should be able to feel God. The miracle of Christmas was a baby."

"Oh, dear Mrs. Guthrie, don't," cried Elsa, drawing back from her kindness as if it stung; "don't, please!"

The telephone in the lower hall rang then, and on the calloused feet that day and night did endless mileage of stair service Mrs. Guthrie hove in the direction of the dictatorial buzz, her voice floating back almost immediately.

"It's Mrs. Paterno."

"Coming! I'll be right there."

Going down the stairs to the hall telephone, Elsa, more from fear than weakness, felt along the walls with her hand. What if the Paternos had changed their minds? The last papers were not to be signed until January second. What if Mrs. Paterno, after a few days' trial at the store with her husband, had decided—wives, after all, were so often the bosses in such matters—what if she had decided against!

"Hello?"

"The strangest thing," Elsa said faintly, hanging up the receiver and turning toward Mrs. Guthrie, who was hovering discreetly out of hearing. "The strangest thing," she kept repeating softly; "something Kurt has always wanted so very much. A White House account!"

"White House?"

"Yes. A children's party is being held there this afternoon. It seems the First Lady has suddenly asked in about ninety extra little girls from some orphanage that had a fire last night. They need someone to rush over and make up favors and do table decorations in a hurry. It seems they have several large iced cakes on hand but no time to do Christmas decorations on them. The Paternos are new at all this. Poor dear, I wish I could help. She is almost out of her mind. They wanted me to go there and do the favors and decorate the cakes. Kurt always wanted that account so much! If it weren't for this——"

"If it wasn't for what? You mean you said no?"

"How could I say anything else, Mrs. Guthrie? Me—like this?"

"Like what?"

"So—clumsy——"

"Why, you're beautiful! You've got that kind of strange burning look in your face. I was saying only last night to Mrs. Delahanty, you look like a woman who is being whispered to and the message seems too good to be true."

"But——"

"You mean to tell me—after wishing there was something you could do for Mrs. Paterno, seeing how kind she has been to you— you mean to tell me you're not going to help out at the White House, just when the Paternos have got their chance to jump in on an emergency help out! You said, 'No' to Mrs. Paterno!"

"But——"

"No 'buts.' There's nothing the matter with your looks that any woman wouldn't be proud to have wrong with hers."

"But——"

"You're going to the White House if I've got to carry you there. Hand me that telephone. This is where your old landlady gets rough."

The snow lay on the ground like a thick white turf and through its continuing fall White House lights burned in the gray of early afternoon.

Workmen, hanging strings of colored electric bulbs on the tall Christmas tree on the Pennsylvania Avenue lawn, flashed them experimentally on and off.

To Elsa, arriving in a taxicab with her small valise of paraphernalia of silver paper and pastry tubes, with which she squeezed whipped-cream sentiments on cake tops, the scene was a Christmas card.

These winding whitened drives which the wheels beneath her were now desecrating with tire tracks; the colonial façade of the White House, its pillars giving it that leisurely look of a Southern mansion, had been wistfully viewed by herself and Kurt on many a Sunday afternoon when they had taken what they used to call their "constitutional."

"Darling Kurt," said Elsa aloud in the taxicab, clutching the card of directions the Paternos had given her.

"Did you say something, miss?" inquired the driver, sliding back his glass window.

"No, thank you."

"Big kids' party here today. They've a lot of children and grandchildren of their own, this Administration. As I used to tell my wife, when she was always rubbing against the window with a wet rag, 'A kid's smear on the pane is God's autograph on a house.'"

"That's a pretty thought."

" 'Tain't mine. I'm joking. I ain't got no kids. A fare said it to me when I brought him here last Christmas, and I keep remembering it. 'God's autograph.' Here we are! Watch your step, lady. Merry Christmas!"

Even in a great roomy kitchen with plenty of table surface and helpful gadgets, it meant working under intense pressure to turn out about eight dozen of the silver angels and to squeeze Christmas greetings across cake tops in the elegant whipped-cream chirography of pastry tubes.

For all the opportunity she had to so much as look about her Elsa might have been in the kitchen of any old-fashioned, well-preserved mansion. Submerged for the time being in her old-time zest for the job, her fingers flew with the hours before the last silver angel and the last whipped-cream signature of Christmas were accomplished.

The white-haired Negress to whom she had presented herself, a

Mrs. Worley, of scrupulous dignity and consideration, was so kind that as Elsa emerged from her period of complete absorption she wondered, with embarrassment, if her condition could be as apparent as all that.

"You suttainly must be played out, chile. You just set yourself down, and I'll give you a good hot cup of tea and some of these anise cookies the children are going to have."

"No, no, thank you. Am I to go now?"

"You suttainly are, and I'm telling you that you saved all our lives by comin' to help out thisaway. All those extra children piling up on us, when the First Lady gets one of her blessed fits of kindness at the last minnit, is a large order. You don't mind, honey, if I saves out this little angel that got its wing crushed? My little grandchild will love it."

"I'll make you a perfect one."

"You just drink this tea down and run yourself along home, honey. I've been watching you. Seemed to me you looked right dizzy there once or twice, but you suttainly turned out your job. I hope you haven't been too hard on yourself?"

Red surged across Elsa's face. Then she *had* noticed!

Above the din of the kitchens and the bustle of its staff a stronger overtone, as of the droning of bees, became increasingly pronounced.

"Are the children all here?"

"Here! Why, honey-chile, this house has been swarming with them since three o'clock. But wait until they sit down to the table. You ain't heard nothing yet!"

"My husband—it was always his dream—before he died—to see the White House on the inside. He never did."

"Now that's too bad. That's mighty too bad. I always say, maybe it ain't the grandest, like kings and queens have, but it's the most sweet house—the sweetest house in all the world. Lak the First Lady herself once told me when I was redding up her sitting room, a great big diplomat from Europe said when he came here and we was having a good old-fashioned fried chicken and corn-pone supper: 'M-m-m-m,' that great big diplomat from Europe said, 'this house smells of liberty!' "

"Even the kitchens are just lovely," said Elsa, her tired glance wandering about the vast, old-fashioned room of new appliances.

"Lord bless my soul, listen to those young ones, will you? But if you think that's noise, wait until they get their tree and ice cream and cake. Well, child, you just tell your man in heaven that the White House is the sweetie-pie house of all the world."

"It's funny you should say that, because I have a crazy habit of talking to him every night about what's happened during the day, just as I used to when he was alive. Maybe he doesn't hear it, but I believe he does."

"Indeed he does, honey. De Lord sees to it that we keep close to those we love."

"I can tell him tonight that I've been to the White House. It may be only the kitchen I've seen, but, after all, the kitchen is White House too."

"Wish I could take you out to where the children is, but us on the kitchen side of the door ain't dressed for that. Tell you what, though! I'm going to do something for you. I know my First Lady wouldn't mind, any more than she did when I took my niece, Leda, when she was visiting me from North Carolina. I'm going to take you upstairs with me while I distribute my towels."

"Upstairs?"

"Yes, right on the floor where the family lives. My first Lady don't mind when I take somebody no further than the halls."

"You'll be doing a wonderful thing for Kurt, Mrs. Worley—my husband."

"You come along with me up these rear stairs. Here, carry along a stack of towels if it will make you feel any better. You can stand outside the very room where Lincoln signed his declaration that freed my people. Only don't move from where I put you, honey. I ain't just exactly breaking rules, never have in all my twenty-three years here, but neither am I exactly keeping them. But the guards all know me and know I wouldn't do nothing wrong against the White House for its weight in gold."

The corridor which divided the living floor into rooms which faced the front lawns and those which faced the rear lawns ran the breadth of the White House and seemed to Elsa to be as wide as a street.

It widened even more at the ends. At one of them it became a breakfast room shut off by a screen, and at the other you walked up a short incline onto a section of corridor that might also have formed another room but was not screened off. It was a used-looking corridor, furnished its entire length in tables with lamps and books on them, chairs for comfortable reading, a secretarial desk or two, models of ships on filled bookshelves, historic portraits, cut flowers in bowls, growing plants in pots. Beside one of the lamplit tables a burly fellow looked up from his magazine.

"Merry Christmas, Mrs. Worley."

"Merry Christmas, Mr. Al. This is a friend, Mr. Al, just lak when I brought my niece. She'll wait right outside the Lincoln room while I do my linen."

"Oke."

"Come along, honey. I'm going to let you stand outside in the hall and get a look right into the room where Lincoln, God rest his noble soul, signed dat declaration I was telling you about. That door right there, honey, is the President's office. I don't know if he's in it this afternoon, but I reckon he is, because Mr. Al is one of his bodyguards."

"Just that door between him and us!"

"You don't have to whisper. Back there where we passed that screen is where the First Lady's sitting room and breakfast room are."

It was quiet in the long corridor; the remote buzz of the children barely audible. Lamps made little pools of light along the way of the closed doors. Even in a democracy, mused Elsa to herself, where the child born with the silver spoon in his mouth, or the woodchopper's ax in his hand shared the right to succeed to this House, it was not usually given to an ordinary person to thus find herself within these historic walls.

Actually, it was not inconceivable that as she stood there one of those doors might open and the President of the United States emerge. Actually! Sensation raced up and down her spine in rapid arpeggios. It would be too much. She would shrivel in her tracks.

George Washington had probably never walked these corridors. The White House was not that old. But Lincoln had, and General Grant. Kurt, who liked history books, used to tell about his big black cigar. Or did Grant ever get to be President?

The short incline that led to the far end of the corridor had a strip of ribbed rubber, to insure against slipperiness. Elsa, whose legs felt weak, was glad. Suddenly at the top of this incline she was between two doors, both of them standing open. To her left a large, high-ceilinged front room, overlooking lawns seen through snow flying between white pillars! To her left, sure enough, the Lincoln room! And beyond its peaceful interior of high, four-poster bed and heavy walnut furniture of another day you could see the Washington Monument, clear, white, and tall enough to stab eternity, its base encircled in snow smoke.

Somewhere, too, out there in the snow smoke of this same vicinity Lincoln sat in the immense shadow of his monument, brooding in white marble over the humanity he had loved and served.

Kurt used to stand before the Lincoln Monument so quiet that sometimes he became strange to Elsa, and she would slide her hand into his a little jealously.

Oh, to have Kurt here now! On a table before the window that overlooked the front lawns, and outlined in the dusk, stood a sculptured bust of the second of the Roosevelts, the boyish upward thrust of head unmistakable and at variance with what she knew must be the lines that would need to be carved into the granite flesh in order properly to convey the burdens that lay across the face of this war President.

Heavy, heavy over his head and over this house hung cyclonic and ballooning clouds. Uneasy that head—uneasy this land. War; pillage; lifeless bodies lying hard as rock on frozen battlefields; wounded babies; shattered churches; defiled nations; youth on the death march; men with red hands; barbed wire; betrayed peoples; flaming ghettos; foundering ships; zoom of bomb divers; purge, and blood bath; gulls riding on dead men's chests off Hatteras.

Through the snow smoke billowing around his monument the deep-hurt heart of Lincoln must be saying to the breathing, sorely burdened man in this White House: "You, my friend, have even a greater task than I had. Slavery must now be removed from the whole of the earth. God give you, and those who follow you, the strength."

Off somewhere, or was it downstairs, shrill voices of children were singing "Holy Night." The dimness and the vastness and the snow smoke filled with song, were a kind of buoyancy upon which she was floating——

Even through the turmoil raging between the two Presidents, the light that had been kindled that Holy Night two thousand years ago was burning; would go on burning—through the darkness of a world as wounded as a soldier with a bloody pit in his side.

But out in the swirling night between the Presidents something bigger than agony, and vast as Holy Night—would survive—life—the beginning of life—it was terrible to feel her legs folding under her—just when she needed this moment to flow on and on—through her——

This much Elsa realized with the utmost clarity, when she opened her eyes on a white cot that had sunshine on it.

She had keeled, in the White House corridor, and been carried down by Mrs. Worley and the guard named Al. They had said, "Easy now," many times, and the clanging din through her semiconsciousness had been the ambulance. She was safely in the hospital now, she even knew the room. It was number 60, the semiprivate one with the bay window, which she had selected weeks before. And she had her baby.

Strange the things of which she had remained aware, down there under the whiffs of the gases. A man's voice, most surely her doctor's, had said to a nurse, most surely that nice Miss Cox: "This woman has no fight in her. Posthumous cases are often that way. Lady, give us a little help, please! We can't do it all for you! Oxygen!"

"Do as the doctor says, dear. One-two-three—deeply—you're going to have a lovely little one if only you'll help us. If you are very good and cooperate, it will be our first Christmas baby. And our first Christmas baby always gets a little gold locket for luck. Now, Mrs. Johnsson, be helpful——"

—slavery must now be removed from the whole of the earth—you can hear so plainly, Kurt, across the snow—even through the singing of children—the night grew so big, it was "Holy Night" they were singing—the night grew so big—slavery must be removed from the whole of the earth—the night grew so big—and the old spine, Kurt, began to ring—like a bell——

And now there was sun on a cot in a bright room that had three beds in it, two of them empty, and the woman's voice that had been with her during the travail was saying: "Good morning, Mrs. John-sson, and Merry Christmas!"

She could feel her dry lips move but not quite succeed in saying anything.

"And here, dear, fresh as a daisy for Mummy, is eight and a half pounds which came into the world at three minutes past twelve this morning. The hospital's prize-winning Christmas baby! Last year it was a girl. This year, who knows, it may be a future President of the United States! You remember, dear, they brought you here from the White House, and see, here are roses from their conservatories! And that isn't all. Here are your eight and a half pounds of—guess what?"

The tired eyes of Elsa rolled toward the nurse's extended armful of blue-eyed beet, its head already covered with a heavy fuzz of what she was to call Kurt-colored hair.

"Well, this much I'll tell you. It's not a girl!"

"It's—it's——"

"Yes! Eight and a half pounds of healthy little future-President-of-the-United-States material."

"Why, that's a fact," said Elsa, the first full declarative sentence coming through the dry lips that continued to want to stick together in spite of ice applications. "Kurt could—be the father—of a Presi-dent—couldn't he? That's the way America is."

"It most certainly is."

"I never thought of—that——"

"Here he is."

"He's real!" said Elsa, a little hoarsely, poking at him and smiling slightly. "He's *real!*"

"Does he sound like a dream? If so, your dream has a good lusty pair of lungs."

"Those two—talking across the snow—they must once have cried like this——"

"What two, dear?"

"Those two. And their mothers didn't know then that they would be Presidents. Sh-h-h-h, little Kurt—my baby—your mother doesn't know it, either, but just the same you could be! Stranger things have happened. . . ."

WASHINGTON IRVING

⋰⋱

The Christmas Dinner

Lo, now is come our joyful'st feast!
    Let every man be jolly,
Eache roome with yvie leaves is drest,
    And every post with holly.
Now all our neighbours' chimneys smoke,
    And Christmas blocks are burning;
Their ovens they with bak't meats choke,
    And all their spits are turning.
        Without the door let sorrow lie,
        And if, for cold, it hap to die,
        Wee 'l bury 't in a Christmas pye,
        And evermore be merry.

WITHERS'S *Juvenilia*

I had finished my toilet, and was loitering with Frank Bracebridge in the library, when we heard a distant thwacking sound, which he informed me was a signal for the serving up of the dinner. The Squire kept up old customs in kitchen as well as hall; and the rolling-pin struck upon the dresser by the cook, summoned the servants to carry in the meats.

Just in this nick the cook knock'd thrice,
And all the waiters in a trice
    His summons did obey;
Each serving man, with dish in hand,
March'd boldly up, like our train band,
    Presented, and away.[1]

[1] Sir John Suckling.

138

The dinner was served up in the great hall, where the Squire always held his Christmas banquet. A blazing, crackling fire of logs had been heaped on to warm the spacious apartment, and the flame went sparkling and wreathing up the wide-mouthed chimney. The great picture of the crusader and his white horse had been profusely decorated with greens for the occasion; and holly and ivy had likewise been wreathed round the helmet and weapons on the opposite wall, which I understood were the arms of the same warrior. I must own, by the by, I had strong doubts about the authenticity of the painting and armor as having belonged to the crusader, they certainly having the stamp of more recent days; but I was told that the painting had been so considered time out of mind; and that, as to the armor, it had been found in a lumber-room, and elevated to its present situation by the Squire, who at once determined it to be the armor of the family hero; and as he was absolute authority on all such subjects in his own household, the matter had passed into current acceptation. A sideboard was set out just under this chivalric trophy, on which was a display of plate that might have vied (at least in variety) with Belshazzar's parade of the vessels of the temple: "flagons, cans, cups, beakers, goblets, basins, and ewers"; the gorgeous utensils of good companionship that had gradually accumulated through many generations of jovial housekeepers. Before these stood the two Yule candles, beaming like two stars of the first magnitude; other lights were distributed in branches, and the whole array glittered like a firmament of silver.

We were ushered into this banqueting scene with the sound of minstrelsy, the old harper being seated on a stool beside the fireplace, and twanging his instrument with a vast deal more power than melody. Never did Christmas board display a more goodly and gracious assemblage of countenances; those who were not handsome were, at least, happy; and happiness is a rare improver of your hard-favored visage. I always consider an old English family as well worth studying as a collection of Holbein's portraits or Albert Dürer's prints. There is much antiquarian lore to be acquired; much knowledge of the physiognomies of former times. Perhaps it may be from having continually before their eyes those rows of old family portraits, with which the mansions of this country are stocked; certain it is, that the quaint features of antiquity are often most faithfully perpetuated in these ancient lines; and I have traced an old family nose through a whole picture gallery, legitimately handed down from generation to generation, almost from the time of the Conquest. Something of the kind was to be observed in the worthy company around me. Many of their faces had evidently originated in a Gothic age, and been merely copied by succeeding generations; and there was one little girl in particular, of staid demeanor, with a high Roman nose, and an antique vinegar aspect, who was a great favorite of the Squire's, being, as he said, a Bracebridge all over, and the very counterpart of one of his ancestors who figured in the court of Henry VIII.

The parson said grace, which was not a short familiar one, such as is commonly addressed to the Deity in these unceremonious days; but a long, courtly, well-worded one of the ancient school. There was now a pause, as if something was expected; when suddenly the butler entered the hall with some degree of bustle: he was attended by a servant on each side with a large wax-light, and bore a silver dish, on which was an enormous pig's head, decorated with rosemary, with a lemon in its mouth, which was placed with great formality at the head of the table. The moment this pageant made its appearance, the harper struck up a flourish; at the conclusion of which the young Oxonian, on receiving a hint from the Squire, gave, with an air of the most comic gravity, an old carol, the first verse of which was as follows:—

> Caput apri defero
> Reddens laudes Domino.
> The boar's head in hand bring I,
> With garlands gay and rosemary.
> I pray you all synge merrily
> Qui estis in convivio.

Though prepared to witness many of these little eccentricities, from being apprised of the peculiar hobby of mine host, yet, I confess, the parade with which so odd a dish was introduced somewhat perplexed me, until I gathered from the conversation of the Squire and the parson, that it was meant to represent the bringing in of the boar's head: a dish formerly served up with much ceremony and the sound of minstrelsy and song, at great tables, on Christmas day.

"I like the old custom," said the Squire, "not merely because it is stately and pleasing in itself, but because it was observed at the college at Oxford at which I was educated. When I hear the old song chanted, it brings to mind the time when I was young and gamesome,—and the noble old college-hall,—and my fellow-students loitering about in their black gowns; many of whom, poor lads, are now in their graves!"

The parson, however, whose mind was not haunted by such associations, and who was always more taken up with the text than the sentiment, objected to the Oxonian's version of the carol; which he affirmed was different from that sung at college. He went on, with the dry perseverance of a commentator, to give the college reading, accompanied by sundry annotations; addressing himself at first to the company at large; but finding their attention gradually diverted to other talk and other objects, he lowered his tone as his number of auditors diminished, until he concluded his remarks in an undervoice, to a fat-headed old gentleman next him, who was silently engaged in the discussion of a huge plateful of turkey.[1]

The table was literally loaded with good cheer, and presented an epitome of country abundance, in this season of overflowing larders. A distinguished post was allotted to "ancient sirloin," as mine host termed it; being, as he added, "the standard of old English hospi-

---

[1] The old ceremony of serving up the boar's head on Christmas day is still observed in the hall of Queen's College, Oxford. I was favored by the parson with a copy of the carol as now sung, and, as it may be acceptable to such of my readers as are curious in these grave and learned matters, I give it entire.

> The boar's head in hand bear I,
> Bedeck'd with bays and rosemary;
> And I pray you, my masters, be merry
>   Quot estis in convivio.
>   Caput apri defero,
>   Reddens laudes domino.
>
> The boar's head, as I understand,
> Is the rarest dish in all this land,
> Which thus bedeck'd with a gay garland
>   Let us servire cantico.
>   Caput apri defero, etc.
>
> Our steward hath provided this
> In honor of the King of Bliss,
> Which on this day to be served is
>   In Reginensi Atrio.
>   Caput apri defero,
>   etc., etc., etc.

tality, and a joint of goodly presence, and full of expectation." There were several dishes quaintly decorated, and which had evidently something traditional in their embellishments; but about which, as I did not like to appear over-curious, I asked no questions.

I could not, however, but notice a pie, magnificently decorated with peacock's feathers, in imitation of the tail of that bird, which overshadowed a considerable tract of the table. This, the Squire confessed, with some little hesitation, was a pheasant-pie, though a peacock-pie was certainly the most authentical; but there had been such a mortality among the peacocks this season, that he could not prevail upon himself to have one killed.[1]

It would be tedious, perhaps, to my wiser readers, who may not have that foolish fondness for odd and obsolete things to which I am a little given, were I to mention the other makeshifts of this worthy old humorist, by which he was endeavoring to follow up, though at humble distance, the quaint customs of antiquity. I was pleased, however, to see the respect shown to his whims by his children and relatives; who, indeed, entered readily into the full spirit of them, and seemed all well versed in their parts; having doubtless been present at many a rehearsal. I was amused, too, at the air of profound gravity with which the butler and other servants executed the duties assigned them, however eccentric. They had an old-fashioned look; having, for the most part, been brought up in the household, and grown into keeping with the antiquated mansion, and the humors of its lord; and most probably looked upon all his whimsical regulations as the established laws of honorable housekeeping.

When the cloth was removed, the butler brought in a huge silver vessel of rare and curious workmanship, which he placed before the

[1] The peacock was anciently in great demand for stately entertainments. Sometimes it was made into a pie, at one end of which the head appeared above the crust in all its plumage, with the beak richly gilt; at the other end the tail was displayed. Such pies were served up at the solemn banquets of chivalry, when knights-errant pledged themselves to undertake any perilous enterprise, whence came the ancient oath, used by Justice Shalloy, "by cock and pie."

The peacock was also an important dish for the Christmas feast; and Massinger, in his "City Madam," gives some idea of the extravagance with which this, as well as other dishes, was prepared for the gorgeous revels of the olden times:

"Men may talk of Country Christmasses,
Their thirty pound butter'd eggs, their pies of carps' tongues;

"Their pheasants drench'd with ambergris; *the carcases of three fat wethers bruised for gravy to make sauce for a single peacock.*"

Squire. Its appearance was hailed with acclamation; being the Wassail Bowl, so renowned in Christmas festivity. The contents had been prepared by the Squire himself; for it was a beverage in the skilful mixture of which he particularly prided himself; alleging that it was too abstruse and complex for the comprehension of an ordinary servant. It was a potation, indeed, that might well make the heart of a toper leap within him; being composed of the richest and raciest wines, highly spiced and sweetened, with roasted apples bobbing about the surface.[1]

The old gentleman's whole countenance beamed with a serene look of indwelling delight, as he stirred this mighty bowl. Having raised it to his lips, with a hearty wish of a merry Christmas to all present, he sent it brimming round the board, for every one to follow his example, according to the primitive style; pronouncing it "the ancient fountain of good feeling, where all hearts met together."[2]

There was much laughing and rallying as the honest emblem of Christmas joviality circulated, and was kissed rather coyly by the ladies. When it reached Master Simon, he raised it in both hands, and with the air of a boon companion struck up an old Wassail chanson.

> The brown bowle,
> The merry brown bowle,
> As it goes round about-a,
> Fill
> Still,
> Let the world say what it will,
> And drink your fill all out-a.

[1] The Wassail Bowl was sometimes composed of ale instead of wine; with nutmeg, sugar, toast, ginger, and roasted crabs: in this way the nut-brown beverage is still prepared in some old families, and round the hearths of substantial farmers at Christmas. It is also called Lamb's Wool, and is celebrated by Herrick in his "Twelfth Night":—

> Next crowne the bowle full
> With gentle Lamb's Wool;
> Add sugar, nutmeg, and ginger,
> With store of ale too;
> And thus ye must doe
> To make the Wassaile a swinger.

[2] The custom of drinking out of the same cup gave place to each having his cup. When the steward came to the doore with the Wassel, he was to cry three times, *Wassel, Wassel, Wassel*, and then the chappell (chaplein) was to answer with a song.—*Archaeologia.*

> The deep canne,
> The merry deep canne,
> As thou dost freely quaff-a,
>   Sing
>   Fling,
> Be as merry as a king,
> And sound a lusty laugh-a.[1]

Much of the conversation during dinner turned upon family topics, to which I was a stranger. There was, however, a great deal of rallying of Master Simon about some gay widow, with whom he was accused of having a flirtation. This attack was commenced by the ladies; but it was continued throughout the dinner by the fat-headed old gentleman next the parson, with the persevering assiduity of a slow hound; being one of those long-winded jokers, who, though rather dull at starting game, are unrivalled for their talents in hunting it down. At every pause in the general conversation, he renewed his bantering in pretty much the same terms; winking hard at me with both eyes, whenever he gave Master Simon what he considered a home thrust. The latter, indeed, seemed fond of being teased on the subject, as old bachelors are apt to be; and he took occasion to inform me, in an undertone, that the lady in question was a prodigiously fine woman, and drove her own curricle.

The dinner-time passed away in this flow of innocent hilarity, and, though the old hall may have resounded in its time with many a scene of broader rout and revel, yet I doubt whether it ever witnessed more honest and genuine enjoyment. How easy it is for one benevolent being to diffuse pleasure around him; and how truly is a kind heart a fountain of gladness, making everything in its vicinity to freshen into smiles! the joyous disposition of the worthy Squire was perfectly contagious; he was happy himself, and disposed to make all the world happy; and the little eccentricities of his humor did but season, in a manner, the sweetness of his philanthropy.

When the ladies had retired, the conversation, as usual, became still more animated; many good things were broached which had been thought of during dinner, but which would not exactly do for a lady's ear; and though I cannot positively affirm that there was much wit uttered, yet I have certainly heard many contests of rare

---

[1] From Poor Robin's Almanac.

wit produce much less laughter. Wit, after all, is a mighty tart, pungent ingredient, and much too acid for some stomachs; but honest good-humor is the oil and wine of a merry meeting, and there is no jovial companionship equal to that where the jokes are rather small, and the laughter abundant.

The Squire told several long stories of early college pranks and adventures, in some of which the parson had been a sharer; though in looking at the latter, it required some effort of imagination to figure such a little dark anatomy of a man into the perpetrator of a madcap gambol. Indeed, the two college chums presented pictures of what men may be made by their different lots in life. The Squire had left the university to live lustily on his paternal domains, in the vigorous enjoyment of prosperity and sunshine, and had flourished on to a hearty and florid old age; whilst the poor parson, on the contrary, had dried and withered away among dusty tomes, in the silence and shadows of his study. Still there seemed to be a spark of almost extinguished fire, feebly glimmering in the bottom of his soul; and as the Squire hinted at a sly story of the parson and a pretty milkmaid, whom they once met on the banks of the Isis, the old gentleman made an "alphabet of faces," which, as far as I could decipher his physiognomy, I verily believe was indicative of laughter;—indeed, I have rarely met with an old gentleman that took absolute offense at the imputed gallantries of his youth.

I found the tide of wine and wassail fast gaining on the dry land of sober judgment. The company grew merrier and louder as their jokes grew duller. Master Simon was in as chirping a humor as a grasshopper filled with dew; his old songs grew of a warmer complexion, and he began to talk maudlin about the widow. He even gave a long song about the wooing of a widow, which he informed me he had gathered from an excellent black-letter work, entitled "Cupid's Solicitor for Love," containing store of good advice for bachelors, and which he promised to lend me. The first verse was to this effect:—

> He that will woo a widow must not dally,
>   He must make hay while the sun doth shine;
> He must not stand with her, shall I, shall I?
>   But boldly say, Widow, thou must be mine.

This song inspired the fat-headed old gentleman, who made several attempts to tell a rather broad story out of Joe Miller, that was pat to the purpose; but he always stuck in the middle, everybody recollecting the latter part excepting himself. The parson, too, began to show the effects of good cheer, having gradually settled down into a doze, and his wig sitting most suspiciously on one side. Just at this juncture we were summoned to the drawing-room, and, I suspect, at the private instigation of mine host, whose joviality seemed always tempered with a proper love of decorum.

After the dinner-table was removed, the hall was given up to the younger members of the family, who, prompted to all kinds of noisy mirth by the Oxonian and Master Simon, made its old walls ring with their merriment, as they played at romping games. I delight in witnessing the gambols of children, and particularly at this happy holiday season, and could not help stealing out of the drawing-room on hearing one of their peals of laughter. I found them at the game of blindman's-buff. Master Simon, who was the leader of their revels, and seemed on all occasions to fulfil the office of that ancient potentate, the Lord of Misrule,[1] was blinded in the midst of the hall. The little beings were as busy about him as the mock fairies about Falstaff; pinching him, plucking at the skirts of his coat, and tickling him with straws. One fine blue-eyed girl of about thirteen, her flaxen hair all in beautiful confusion, her frolic face in a glow, her frock half torn off her shoulders, a complete picture of a romp, was the chief tormentor; and, from the slyness with which Master Simon avoided the smaller game, and hemmed this wild little nymph in corners, and obliged her to jump shrieking over chairs, I suspected the rogue of being not a whit more blinded than was convenient.

When I returned to the drawing-room, I found the company seated round the fire, listening to the parson, who was deeply ensconced in a high-backed oaken chair, the work of some cunning artificer of yore, which had been brought from the library for his particular accommodation. From this venerable piece of furniture, with which his shadowy figure and dark weazen face so admirably accorded, he was dealing out strange accounts of the popular super-

---

[1] At Christmasse there was in the Kinge's house, wheresoever hee was lodged, a lorde of misrule, or mayster of merie disportes, and the like had ye in the house of every nobleman of honor, or good worshippe, were he spirituall or temporall.—STOW.

stitions and legends of the surrounding country, with which he had become acquainted in the course of his antiquarian researches. I am half inclined to think that the old gentleman was himself somewhat tinctured with superstition, as men are very apt to be who live a recluse and studious life in a sequestered part of the country, and pore over black-letter tracts, so often filled with the marvellous and supernatural. He gave us several anecdotes of the fancies of the neighboring peasantry, concerning the effigy of the crusader, which lay on the tomb by the church-altar. As it was the only monument of the kind in that part of the country, it had always been regarded with feelings of superstition by the good wives of the village. It was said to get up from the tomb and walk the rounds of the churchyard in stormy nights, particularly when it thundered; and one old woman, whose cottage bordered on the churchyard, had seen it through the windows of the church, when the moon shone, slowly pacing up and down the aisles. It was the belief that some wrong had been left unredressed by the deceased, or some treasure hidden, which kept the spirit in a state of trouble and restlessness. Some talked of gold and jewels buried in the tomb, over which the spectre kept watch; and there was a story current of a sexton in old times, who endeavored to break his way to the coffin at night, but, just as he reached it, received a violent blow from the marble hand of the effigy, which stretched him senseless on the pavement. These tales were often laughed at by some of the sturdier among the rustics, yet, when night came on, there were many of the stoutest unbelievers that were shy of venturing alone in the footpath that led across the churchyard.

From these and other anecdotes that followed, the crusader appeared to be the favorite hero of ghost-stories throughout the vicinity. His picture, which hung up in the hall, was thought by the servants to have something supernatural about it; for they remarked that, in whatever part of the hall you went, the eyes of the warrior were still fixed on you. The old porter's wife, too, at the lodge, who had been born and brought up in the family, and was a great gossip among the maid-servants, affirmed, that in her young days she had often heard say, that on Midsummer eve, when it was well known all kinds of ghosts, goblins, and fairies become visible and walk abroad, the crusader used to mount his horse, come down from his picture, ride about the house, down the avenue, and so to the church to visit the tomb; on which occasion the church-door most civilly swung open of itself; not that he needed it, for he rode through closed gates and even stone walls, and had been seen by one of the dairymaids to pass between two bars of the great park-gate, making himself as thin as a sheet of paper.

All these superstitions I found had been very much countenanced by the Squire, who, though not superstitious himself, was very fond of seeing others so. He listened to every goblin-tale of the neighboring gossips with infinite gravity, and held the porter's wife in high favor on account of her talent for the marvellous. He was himself a great reader of old legends and romances, and often lamented that he could not believe in them; for a superstitious person, he thought, must live in a kind of fairyland.

Whilst we were all attention to the parson's stories, our ears were suddenly assailed by a burst of heterogeneous sounds from the hall, in which were mingled something like the clang of rude minstrelsy, with the uproar of many small voices and girlish laughter. The door suddenly flew open, and a train came trooping into the room, that might almost have been mistaken for the breaking up of the court of Fairy. That indefatigable spirit, Master Simon, in the faithful discharge of his duties as Lord of Misrule, had conceived the idea of a Christmas mummery or masking; and having called in to his assistance the Oxonian and the young officer, who were equally ripe for anything that should occasion romping and merriment, they had carried it into instant effect. The old housekeeper had been consulted; the antique clothes-presses and wardrobes rummaged, and made to yield up the relics of finery that had not seen the light for several generations; the younger part of the company had been privately convened from the parlor and hall, and the whole had been bedizened out, into a burlesque imitation of an antique mask.[1]

Master Simon led the van, as "Ancient Christmas," quaintly apparelled in a ruff, a short cloak, which had very much the aspect of one of the old housekeeper's petticoats, and a hat that might have served for a village steeple, and must indubitably have figured in the days of the Covenanters. From under this his nose curved boldly

---

[1] Maskings or mummeries were favorite sports at Christmas in old times; and the wardrobes at halls and manor-houses were often laid under contribution to furnish dresses and fantastic disguisings. I strongly suspect Master Simon to have taken the idea of his from Ben Jonson's "Masque of Christmas."

forth, flushed with a frost-bitten bloom, that seemed the very trophy of a December blast. He was accompanied by the blue-eyed romp, dished up as "Dame Mince Pie," in the venerable magnificence of a faded brocade, long stomacher, peaked hat, and high-heeled shoes. The young officer appeared as Robin Hood, in a sporting dress of Kendal green, and a foraging cap with a gold tassel.

The costume, to be sure, did not bear testimony to deep research, and there was an evident eye to the picturesque, natural to a young gallant in the presence of his mistress. The fair Julia hung on his arm in a pretty rustic dress, as "Maid Marian." The rest of the train had been metamorphosed in various ways: the girls trussed up in the finery of the ancient belles of the Bracebridge line, and the striplings bewhiskered with burnt cork, and gravely clad in broad skirts, hanging sleeves, and full-bottomed wigs, to represent the character of Roast Beef, Plum Pudding, and other worthies celebrated in ancient maskings. The whole was under the control of the Oxonian, in the appropriate character of Misrule; and I observed that he exercised rather a mischievous sway with his wand over the smaller personages of the pageant.

The irruption of his motley crew, with beat of drum, according to ancient custom, was the consummation of uproar and merriment. Master Simon covered himself with glory by the stateliness with which, as Ancient Christmas, he walked a minuet with the peerless, though giggling, Dame Mince Pie. It was followed by a dance of all the characters, which, from its medley of costumes, seemed as though the old family portraits had skipped down from their frames to join in the sport. Different centuries were figuring at cross hands and right and left; the dark ages were cutting pirouettes and rigadoons; and the days of Queen Bess jigging merrily down the middle, through a line of succeeding generations.

The worthy Squire contemplated these fantastic sports, and this resurrection of his old wardrobe, with the simple relish of childish delight. He stood chuckling and rubbing his hands, and scarcely hearing a word the parson said, notwithstanding that the latter was discoursing most authentically on the ancient and stately dance at the Paon, or peacock, from which he conceived the minuet to be derived.[1] For my part, I was in a continual excitement from the varied

---

[1] Sir John Hawkins, speaking of the dance called the Pavon, from *pavo*, a peacock, says: "It is a grave and majestic dance; the method of dancing it anciently was by

scenes of whim and innocent gayety passing before me. It was inspiring to see wild-eyed frolic and warm-hearted hospitality breaking out from among the chills and glooms of winter, and old age throwing off his apathy, and catching once more the freshness of youthful enjoyment. I felt also an interest in the scene, from the consideration that these fleeting customs were posting fast into oblivion, and that this was, perhaps, the only family in England in which the whole of them was still punctiliously observed. There was a quaintness, too, mingled with all this revelry, that gave it a peculiar zest; it was suited to the time and place; and as the old manor-house almost reeled with mirth and wassail, it seemed echoing back the joviality of long departed years.[1]

But enough of Christmas and its gambols; it is time for me to pause in this garrulity. Methinks I hear the questions asked by my graver readers, "To what purpose is all this; how is the world to be made wiser by this talk?" Alas! is there not wisdom enough extant for the instruction of the world? And if not, are there not thousands of abler pens laboring for its improvement?—It is so much pleasanter to please than to instruct,—to play the companion rather than the preceptor.

What, after all, is the mite of wisdom that I could throw into the mass of knowledge; or how am I sure that my sagest deductions may be safe guides for the opinions of others? But in writing to amuse, if I fail, the only evil is in my own disappointment. If, however, I can by any lucky chance, in these days of evil, rub out one wrinkle from the brow of care, or beguile the heavy heart of one moment of sorrow; if I can now and then penetrate through the gathering film of misanthropy, prompt a benevolent view of human nature, and make my reader more in good-humor with his fellow-beings and himself, surely, surely, I shall not then have written entirely in vain.

---

gentlemen dressed with caps and swords, by those of the long robe in their gowns, by the peers in their mantles, and by the ladies in gowns with long trains, the motion whereof in dancing resembled that of a peacock."—*History of Music.*

[1] At the time of the first publication of this paper, the picture of an old-fashioned Christmas in the country was pronounced by some as out of date. The author had afterwards an opportunity of witnessing almost all the customs above described, existing in unexpected vigor in the skirts of Derbyshire and Yorkshire, where he passed the Christmas holidays. The reader will find some notice of them in the author's account of his sojourn at Newstead Abbey.

JOSEPH HENRY JACKSON

⁕⸰⸰⁕

The Christmas Flower

FATHER CLEMENTE stood in the door of his church, his worn gray robe tucked up in an extra fold under its cord so that it might not sweep the earthen floor. He lifted his round, good-humored face to the sunlight, feeling the breeze cool on his cheek and breathing the early morning freshness it brought down from the high peaks into his little valley.

From the church steps the road ran straight and dusty between small fields of winter stubble, through a narrow belt of mountain forest, oak and cedar and stunted pine all tangled in weedy undergrowth. For a brief space it became the village street, the brown, thatched adobes clustering along it on both sides, two or three of them stringing out past the village into the hills where the road shrank to dry ruts and wandered irresolutely toward Mexico City somewhere over the ridge.

Standing in the doorway, Father Clemente could see thin blue smoke beginning to leak from the roofs beyond the trees, and he smiled to himself as its pungent, resinous odor reached his nostrils.

This was the day of the year he liked best, the Christmas morning when he held early service especially for the village children.

They would come—his bright blue eyes grew softer as he remembered—bringing their small gifts as he had taught them; and they would sit, hushed and solemn, listening to the story of the Infant Jesus. Father Clemente had told it each Christmas for almost thirty years, ever since he had come to this remote valley in the high country of New Spain and shown the Indians how to build the strange, tall house in which they would find the Truth he had been sent to bring them.

151

Sometimes the priest thought unhappily that he had failed. The children grew up. They continued to come obediently to church; they accepted their penances, sinned and came again; they were docile and in this sense devout, no more frail perhaps than any Christians anywhere. Yet after they were grown it was not the same. Somehow, Father Clemente knew, he had lost them. The little ones watched him so seriously when he told them of the Child, one like themselves but King and Savior too. But then all at once they were men and women, and although the dark, liquid eyes were trusting still, they were without depth; a door had closed behind them.

Father Clemente understood what it was, and now he sighed as he became once more aware of the little belt of forest between the church and the houses of the village. He had learned eventually to ignore the carved stone image that stood there, back from the road under the dark trees. The evilly grinning thing, he knew, was Tlaloc, old Aztec god of the rains. The priest felt suddenly colder in the wind from the mountain as he thought of those days before the Spaniard had brought the true Faith to Mexico, and of the sacrifice that Tlaloc had required—the blood of the littlest ones, the living hearts of the children.

Remembering the ancient, dreadful story, Father Clemente drew in his breath and shivered under his robe.

All that was past and done. The Conquest was nearly a century old, the priest reminded himself; there was no longer any question of living sacrifices. Yet he knew that his people did not forget the squat, hideous stone figure in the half-darkness of the forest. Sometimes, passing the spot, he would see that the earth before the god had been swept smooth, and there would be the cold ashes of a tiny fire in the clearing and the wild, sweet perfume of *copal* in the air. And there was that other, almost daily, reminder that his Indians, even the children following their elders, remembered their god. A hundred, a thousand times Father Clemente had seen it—the slight but unmistakable crook and dip of the knee, as they passed the image, the turned head and quick nod that symbolized what long ago had undoubtedly been an abject prostration before Tlaloc the Powerful.

At first the young priest had fought this vigorously. He had exhorted his Indians, had tried to show them the wickedness of their hearts that spoke with two voices, one to the true God and one to the false and evil Tlaloc. His Indians had listened, but it had never been any use. The day before, the month before, a woman had forgotten her gesture of respect to Tlaloc; the child she carried had been stillborn. Only last year a man had returned weary from the fields and had slept, refusing to go out with the rest on the Night Of The God to sweep the earth smooth and to burn incense; the next morning he did not wake at all. These things were in the minds of his people, the priest knew, unspoken but deeply rooted. And though he spoke to them with all the eloquence he could summon, and though the impassive brown faces watched him seriously, as if it were all clearly understood, the eyes remained flat and dead. The obeisance to the stone image went on, a part of his Indians' inward life, forever shut away from their priest. Father Clemente had been able, not to accept the gesture but to put it out of his mind for most of the time. Now and then he could not avoid seeing the pause, the crook of the knee, the little tip of the head. At such times he averted his eyes, saddened momentarily by what he thought of as his own failure.

Father Clemente was never sad for very long, for he would remember the children.

If the elders clung to their old gods, there would still be a new generation without such memories. All his Indians were children in a manner of speaking, simple and childlike in their scattering of rose-petals and the token drops of strong, aromatic *aguardiente* on the church floor, their acknowledgment, along with Christian observance, of the age-old ritual their priest had never known. But the little ones—Father Clemente's heart would grow lighter as he felt his faith in the children spring up once more.

When he thought of them it did not matter so much that the men went secretly at night to clear the ground and burn incense before the hidden god. Always the priest held fast to the hope that one day he would reach at least a child so surely that the heathen image would be forgotten. There would be one—one was all he asked—who would keep to the Faith. One boy would grow strong in the Truth as he grew older; his open look would never change; he would sponge utterly from his heart all memory of the evil of Tlaloc. In some way, the priest had often thought, he must show, clearly and in terms that such a boy and all of the children would understand, the folly of their homage to the idol in the forest. He had never been able to find the way, but he thought of it always. Perhaps this would be a miracle. Father Clemente thought now that it could be nothing less. But surely God might grant him such a sign. He had labored long and hard; had he not earned this one small miracle? Then he bent his head humbly, knowing his folly, and the words of the prophet Daniel came to him: "Those that walk in pride He is able to abase." Yet the stubborn hope remained. One child brought to God; could it be a sinful thing to wish this?

Father Clemente put the thought from him and lifted his face again to the sun, warmer now, and he thought with pleasure of how it would soon strike through the quatrefoil window high above the door.

In his boyhood there had been such a window in the church in Spain where he had first heard the story of the Christ Child, and he had taken quiet happiness in reproducing the shape here from memory when, as a strong young priest, he had worked with his hands beside his Indians in the raising of God's house. Like the window of his childhood recollection, this one opened toward the morning sun, and Father Clemente had placed it so that the long golden finger of light would fall directly upon the altar. He had always been glad that at Christmastime the illumination was strongest. He turned from the doorway, pleased to see his small altar already growing brighter. Even the first shallow gleam felt warm and good on his back as he moved down the aisle.

The altar was in order as he had known it would be. Below it, a little in front of the first row of wooden benches, was the small table Father Clemente set out each year to receive the children's gifts to the Child on His day. He smiled as he remembered how the sunlight would pour down upon the little heap of gifts. These would be unimportant in themselves, a few tiny mats raggedly woven of reeds or perhaps of threads raveled from some useless scrap at home; maybe a crude, miniature bowl or two, pressed out of clay by inexpert fingers and baked in the sun. But each child would bring something; mothers would see to it that they did not forget.

The priest remembered now that the candles must be lighted, and he brought a flaming pine splinter from the small fire in his sacristy and touched the tall wax tapers into life. Then he walked, more quickly this time, to the front of the church and across to where the bell-rope hung, smiling again as he thought of how the voice of the bell, quickening the bright morning air, would bring his children trooping down the road.

As he bent to the rope, Father Clemente allowed himself once more to slip for a moment into his cherished dream.

His dream, as it always did, centered on one boy for whom he held a special hope.

There had been a long procession of them over the years, good, eager children who had grown older and slipped away from him into the part-Christian, part-Indian worship that was not enough. The disappointment pricked him in the same way each time. Yet some day there would be one who would remain steadfast. One would reject the evil image and accept the Faith entire. This time—at the thought Father Clemente leaned strongly to the rope and the bell above him pealed joyously in response—it might be the shy, sensitive Pablo, small for his nine years but so responsive, so quiet, so earnest and quick to learn.

For months now, Father Clemente had built his hope on Pablo, instructing and guiding the boy with special love. The child was lonely; the others played their games without him, made sport of him excepting when they left him to himself. The priest knew why, though the children did not fully understand. The boy's mother, widowed young and bitter from her loss, had rejected the church. In the meanest adobe of the village, where the road lost itself in the hills, she had given Pablo a succession of "uncles" about whom the other children gibed unpleasantly, repeating what they heard from their elders. Pablo accepted their harshness and his own solitary state, as he did the fact that his mother never came to services. Father Clemente had tried to reason with her but without success.

"Hah!" she had spat once. "Your strong god! Can he bring back my husband whom Tlaloc took away? You tell us of miracles! Show me, then, one small miracle! Your god can do such a thing, no?" She had laughed loudly and turned away. The priest knew he should have gone back and back again, and shame came over him when he thought of how he had not.

But there was Pablo, who came to listen and to learn what the priest could teach, who sat so attentively and answered questions so intelligently, whose wide, dark eyes were so eager and candid, who would grow up—how could it be wrong to hope for this?—firm and unwavering in the Faith. It must happen, Father Clemente told himself. This time it must.

Yet, like the others, Pablo too always made the automatic obeisance to Tlaloc as he passed through the narrow forest strip where the stone god stood. Once, when the priest had asked him why, the boy had said only "One does this, Father, in our village!" and when it was explained that a Christian boy must put aside the savage superstitions of his parents, Pablo had murmured "Yes, Father, surely!" But he had continued to make the gesture. In some way about which he was not quite certain, Father Clemente had begun to think of Pablo as the symbol of his own stubborn hope. If, just once, the boy would pass the stone god without acknowledgment, would not this be a sign? Could it not be, in itself, the miracle for which he had hoped so long? And—the thought surged powerfully in him—might not this be the year it would happen, even the very day?

As he swayed forward with the rope and the last note of the bell sounded sonorously in the tower, Father Clemente shook himself from his dream and stood up, flexing his shoulders, the rope falling from his hands to sway and then hang still and straight. He listened to the last long humming in the tower and patiently put away the thought of miracles and symbols. The children would be coming, and because he loved to watch their straggling, innocent procession he moved quickly to the doorway once more, letting the hem of his robe fall its full length to his ankles and tightening the cord about his waist. His stocky frame in the heavy, shapeless garment, almost filled the space as he stood, his arms spread wide and his hands braced on the doorposts, his eyes warm and happy as he saw the small, distant figures come into the road beyond the trees and turn toward the church.

The early breeze had died, and little puffs of gray dust rose and hung, dispersing slowly in the clear, quiet air behind the children as they emerged into the brief, straight stretch of road that led to the church door. Through the floating haze, the priest's eyes found the figure they sought, walking a little after the rest as always. With a momentary pang, he watched Pablo give the dip and nod toward the image of Tlaloc. Then the first little group was at the steps below him, and Father Clemente turned and moved rapidly down to the altar to watch them lay their gifts on the low table and seat themselves in chirping bird-rows on the long benches.

The children were very quiet on this special morning, tiptoeing down to leave their gifts and back again to sit solemnly, their eyes on their priest. Father Clemente lifted his hands and the children bowed with him. As he began the brief prayer that he knew would draw them into the spirit of the Story he was to tell, he sensed that Pablo had come softly down the aisle, hesitated for a moment at the low table, and walked back to his place on a bench all to himself. Then suddenly the cadence of the prayer which had filled the church was interrupted by a quick confusion of sound among the benches, and Father Clemente looked up, shocked to see the even, hushed rows broken into shifting leaning groups, and to hear the sound of half-suppressed, mocking laughter. The words of the prayer died on his lips and his voice rose.

"Children!" he said. "What is this? You must not! Why do you laugh?"

The whispering quieted, and a child, bolder than the others, spoke shrilly. "It is the stupid Pablo, Father! See what he brings!"

As the priest looked down, following the pointing finger, the light, cruel laughter rose again among the benches, and the mocking words came. "Leaves! Foolish little weed-leaves from the forest! A gift for the Christ Child! Leaves! Only leaves!"

The single young voice shrilled again. "It was last night, Father! All of us saw! It was Pablo beneath the trees, leaving there his small straw basket. We saw, and heard him ask that it be filled in the morning with gold—gold for the Child! And this morning it was not even there any more!" The shrill little voice paused, then finished, sharp-edged with malice, "The god remembered! It was the father of Pablo who would not burn incense last year—his father who slept instead and did not wake afterward!"

Father Clemente raised his hand and the church grew still. He saw on the small table what Pablo had brought, the drooping cluster of dull, dusty leaves, broken in haste and desperation from one of the tall, rank weeds that grew so profusely along the road where the trees gave them shade. Then he was aware of Pablo's small figure sitting apart from the rest on the last bench, not huddled and tear-ful, the priest noted, as in his childhood he would have been in such a case, but only very still, staring straight before him.

The priest's voice was gentle as he said, "Tell us, Pablo, why do you bring leaves?" Pablo looked up at him and Father Clemente saw that the boy's eyes were all Indian now, the eyes that said nothing, an-swered nothing, that had defeated him in a generation of reaching for his people. He said again, "Pablo, the leaves of the forest weed! Why do you bring them to the Child?"

The boy's words came slowly. "There was nothing . . . I could not . . . I had no other gift, Father!"

Father Clemente's face was grave and his voice rang loudly in the small room.

"Children," he said. "Children! You have heard. Pablo has brought what he could, as all of you have done. Would one mock at you . . ." his finger pointed among them, ". . . or you . . . or you . . . be-cause you did not bring a fine silver candlestick but only a small bowl of clay or a mat of reeds?"

His tone softened. "Children," he said, "Pablo brings his gift as you bring yours, in love for the Child!" He lifted his hands. "Pray, then," he said, "to be forgiven, for the Christ Child receives one gift as He receives another, because it is the gift of the heart!"

He bent his head and the children, stilled by the ringing voice, followed his motion. As Father Clemente began to pray, he felt the full warmth of the sun through the window, and his serenity returned. The children were thoughtless, even cruel, though without compre-hension of their cruelty. But they were his children—not Pablo only, but all of them. His spirit grew tranquil as, behind his rolling words and on another level of his mind, he remembered another Light, the Star the shepherds had seen in the dark blue evening sky in Galilee. This was the Story, and he knew he would reach the children with it as he had never done before. As he shaped in his mind the words with which he would close his prayer, he sensed that the sunlight had grown in intensity. His body and mind were bathed in the warm brilliance, and fresh strength flowed through him.

Then, all at once, there was a new sound from the benches. This time it was not laughter, but a swift whisper like a wind sweeping through the church, growing more insistent each moment. Father Clemente said "Amen!" loudly, and raised his head.

Once more the even rows of children were broken into little groups, and once more there were pointing fingers and the high susurration of small voices. But now there was no mockery, only the rising, sighing rush of excited whispering in which at last the priest could distinguish words: "The leaves! Pablo's weed-leaves! See! The leaves!"

Father Clemente looked down at the low table that held the gifts, and his heart leaped. In the full, golden flood of light that streamed from the window lay the miracle, Pablo's pitiful little handful of desperately snatched leaves, their dusty green now a deep glowing emerald, and the topmost cluster a spreading, shining scarlet star.

As Father Clemente looked up, the whispering died. The children sat motionless, upright and silent, their enormous eyes fixed on their priest as his voice sounded triumphantly in the small room, telling them of the miracle they had seen, and of that other miraculous, heavenly Star that had guided men, both simple and wise, to the birthplace of the Child that was to be their King. He knew now, too, that this was the opportunity he had sought so long, and he spoke to them of what they had seen and how it was no greater than the miracle of all God's world, of His Heaven and His earth and His Law. The seed that swelled in the ground and grew into a tall green weed that had become, by God's will, a scarlet flower—this was like the seed of true belief that, once planted in the heart, would grow and flourish and blossom at last into the Flower of Faith which would fill them wholly, leaving no space for the false god, the cold stone image in the forest that old men had made long ago when they did not know the Truth. As he finished, he felt his new peace flow ever more strongly in him, and his heart was warm with gratitude and love for the Power that had shown him the way to reach his children at last.

The service was over, and Father Clemente stood again at the church door, his heart overflowing as he watched the children scatter down the road to the village.

The sun was warm now, the sky was cloudless and endlessly deep, and the priest thought again of the children's eyes, so alive and shining with wonder at the thing they had seen. He knew that they would remain so, would never grow opaque and dead again in the ancient

Indian way. He thought of the miracle, and he understood, as by a revelation, what his sin of pride had been and where it had lain. It had been rooted in his wish, his obstinate and selfish hope that he might reach one child only, Pablo or another, instead of all the children, all his people who were his children too. It had flourished, that sin, like a forest weed in his mind when he foolishly dreamed of the private miracle he had wanted—arrogantly demanded of God, he saw now— as though he had earned a special reward for something accomplished alone. In his new, profound humility, he understood at last that he also had been granted a miracle, and that it was in his own heart, which had been cleansed of pride.

He lifted his head and his eyes followed the small, diminishing figures. Somewhere among them was Pablo, he knew, but the priest could no longer distinguish one from another as they came to the trees.

Then he saw that the band of forest was no longer dark and chill, the shadowy dwelling-place of Tlaloc Of The Rains. For beneath the oak and cedar, springing up under the pines, cutting off the evil image from sight and memory, there glowed a thousand dazzling spearpoints of flaming crimson.

As he watched, he saw the children break into a run in which there was no pause, no nod, no acknowledgment to the old god hidden somewhere behind the multitudinous scarlet glory of the Christmas Flower.

Father Clemente turned and knelt in his doorway, the light from the window above him flooding down upon the altar. Below it, on the crude wooden table, the Flower seemed to grow and spread until its burning radiance filled the little church. He bent to pray, his heart filled with peace, warm and steady in its submission to a newly encompassing love.

As he prayed, he could hear behind him from the village beyond the trees the tiny, far echo of young voices, high and soft, "The Flower!" they cried. "The miracle! The miracle!"

SELMA LAGERLÖF

⁓§⁓

The Legend of the Christmas Rose

ROBBER MOTHER, who lived in Robbers' Cave up in Göinge forest, went down to the village one day on a begging tour. Robber Father, who was an outlawed man, did not dare to leave the forest. She took with her five youngsters, and each youngster bore a sack on his back as long as himself. When Robber Mother stepped inside the door of a cabin, no one dared refuse to give her whatever she demanded; for she was not above coming back the following night and setting fire to the house if she had not been well received. Robber Mother and her brood were worse than a pack of wolves, and many a man felt like running a spear through them; but it was never done, because they all knew that the man stayed up in the forest, and he would have known how to wreak vengeance if anything had happened to the children or the old woman.

Now that Robber Mother went from house to house and begged, she came to Övid, which at that time was a cloister. She rang the bell of the cloister gate and asked for food. The watchman let down a small wicket in the gate and handed her six round bread cakes—one for herself and one for each of the five children.

While the mother was standing quietly at the gate, her youngsters were running about. And now one of them came and pulled at her skirt, as a signal that he had discovered something which she ought to come and see, and Robber Mother followed him promptly.

The entire cloister was surrounded by a high and strong wall, but the youngster had managed to find a little back gate which stood ajar. When Robber Mother got there, she pushed the gate open and walked inside without asking leave, as it was her custom to do.

161

Övid Cloister was managed at that time by Abbot Hans, who knew all about herbs. Just within the cloister wall he had planted a little herb garden, and it was into this that the old woman had forced her way.

At first glance Robber Mother was so astonished that she paused at the gate. It was high summertide, and Abbot Hans' garden was so full of flowers that the eyes were fairly dazzled by the blues, reds, and yellows, as one looked into it. But presently an indulgent smile spread over her features, and she started to walk up a narrow path that lay between many flower beds.

In the garden a lay brother walked about, pulling up weeds. It was he who had left the door in the wall open, that he might throw the weeds and tares on the rubbish heap outside.

When he saw Robber Mother coming in, with all five youngsters in tow, he ran toward her at once and ordered them away. But the beggar woman walked right on as before. The lay brother knew of no other remedy than to run into the cloister and call for help.

He returned with two stalwart monks, and Robber Mother saw that now it meant business! She let out a perfect volley of shrieks, and, throwing herself upon the monks, clawed and bit at them; so did all the youngsters. The men soon learned that she could overpower them, and all they could do was to go back into the cloister for reinforcements.

As they ran through the passage-way which led to the cloister, they met Abbot Hans, who came rushing out to learn what all this noise was about.

He upbraided them for using force and forbade their calling for help. He sent both monks back to their work, and although he was an old and fragile man, he took with him only the lay brother.

He came up to the woman and asked in a mild tone if the garden pleased her.

Robber Mother turned defiantly toward Abbot Hans, for she expected only to be trapped and overpowered. But when she noticed his white hair and bent form, she answered peaceably, "First, when I saw this, I thought I had never seen a prettier garden; but now I see that it can't be compared with one I know of. If you could see the garden of which I am thinking you would uproot all the flowers planted here and cast them away like weeds."

The Abbot's assistant was hardly less proud of the flowers than the Abbot himself, and after hearing her remarks he laughed derisively.

Robber Mother grew crimson with rage to think that her word was doubted, and she cried out: "You monks, who are holy men, certainly must know that on every Christmas Eve the great Göinge forest is transformed into a beautiful garden, to commemorate the hour of our Lord's birth. We who live in the forest have seen this happen every year. And in that garden I have seen flowers so lovely that I dared not lift my hand to pluck them."

Ever since his childhood, Abbot Hans had heard it said that on every Christmas Eve the forest was dressed in holiday glory. He had often longed to see it, but he had never had the good fortune. Eagerly he begged and implored Robber Mother that he might come up to the Robbers' Cave on Christmas Eve. If she would only send one of her children to show him the way, he could ride up there alone, and he would never betray them—on the contrary, he would reward them insofar as it lay in his power.

Robber Mother said no at first, for she was thinking of Robber Father and of the peril which might befall him should she permit Abbot Hans to ride up to their cave. At the same time the desire to prove to the monk that the garden which she knew was more beautiful than his got the better of her, and she gave in.

"But more than one follower you cannot take with you," said she, "and you are not to waylay us or trap us, as sure as you are a holy man."

This Abbot Hans promised, and then Robber Mother went her way.

It happened that Archbishop Absalon from Lund came to Övid and remained through the night. The lay brother heard Abbot Hans telling the Bishop about Robber Father and asking him for a letter of ransom for the man, that he might lead an honest life among respectable folk.

But the Archbishop replied that he did not care to let the robber loose among honest folk in the villages. It would be best for all that he remain in the forest.

Then Abbot Hans grew zealous and told the Bishop all about Göinge forest, which, every year at Yuletide, clothed itself in summer bloom around the Robbers' Cave. "If these bandits are not so bad but that God's glories can be made manifest to them, surely we cannot be too wicked to experience the same blessing."

The Archbishop knew how to answer Abbot Hans. "This much I will promise you, Abbot Hans," he said, smiling, "that any day you send me a blossom from the garden in Göinge forest, I will give you letters of ransom for all the outlaws you may choose to plead for."

The following Christmas Eve Abbot Hans was on his way to the forest. One of Robber Mother's wild youngsters ran ahead of him, and close behind him was the lay brother.

It turned out to be a long and hazardous ride. They climbed steep and slippery side paths, crawled over swamp and marsh, and pushed through windfall and bramble. Just as daylight was waning, the robber boy guided them across a forest meadow, skirted by tall, naked leaf trees and green fir trees. Back of the meadow loomed a mountain wall, and in this wall they saw a door of thick boards. Now Abbot Hans understood that they had arrived, and dismounted. The child opened the heavy door for him, and he looked into a poor mountain grotto, with bare stone walls. Robber Mother was seated before a log fire that burned in the middle of the floor. Alongside the walls were beds of virgin pine and moss, and on one of these beds lay Robber Father asleep.

"Come in, you out there!" shouted Robber Mother without rising, "and fetch the horses in with you, so they won't be destroyed by the night cold."

Abbot Hans walked boldly into the cave, and the lay brother followed. Here were wretchedness and poverty! and nothing was done to celebrate Christmas.

Robber Mother spoke in a tone as haughty and dictatorial as any well-to-do peasant woman. "Sit down by the fire and warm yourself, Abbot Hans," said she; "and if you have food with you, eat, for the food which we in the forest prepare you wouldn't care to taste. And if you are tired after the long journey, you can lie down on one of these beds to sleep. You needn't be afraid of oversleeping, for I'm sitting here by the fire keeping watch. I shall awaken you in time to see that which you have come up here to see."

Abbot Hans obeyed Robber Mother and brought forth his food sack; but he was so fatigued after the journey he was hardly able to eat, and as soon as he could stretch himself on the bed, he fell asleep.

The lay brother was also assigned a bed to rest and he dropped into a doze.

When he woke up, he saw that Abbot Hans had left his bed and was sitting by the fire talking with Robber Mother. The outlawed robber sat also by the fire. He was a tall, raw-boned man with a dull, sluggish appearance. His back was turned to Abbot Hans, as though he would have it appear that he was not listening to the conversation.

Abbot Hans was telling Robber Mother all about the Christmas preparations he had seen on the journey, reminding her of Christmas feasts and games which she must have known in her youth, when she lived at peace with mankind.

At first Robber Mother answered in short, gruff sentences, but by degrees she became more subdued and listened more intently. Suddenly Robber Father turned toward Abbot Hans and shook his clenched fist in his face. "You miserable monk! did you come here to coax from me my wife and children? Don't you know that I am an outlaw and may not leave the forest?"

Abbot Hans looked him fearlessly in the eyes. "It is my purpose to get a letter of ransom for you from Archbishop Absalon," said he. He had hardly finished speaking when the robber and his wife burst out laughing. They knew well enough the kind of mercy a forest robber could expect from Bishop Absalon!

"Oh, if I get a letter of ransom from Absalon," said Robber Father, "then I'll promise you that never again will I steal so much as a goose."

Suddenly Robber Mother rose. "You sit here and talk, Abbot Hans," she said, "so that we are forgetting to look at the forest. Now I can hear, even in this cave, how the Christmas bells are ringing."

The words were barely uttered when they all sprang up and rushed out. But in the forest it was still dark night and bleak winter. The only thing they marked was a distant clang borne on a light south wind.

When the bells had been ringing a few moments, a sudden illumination penetrated the forest; the next moment it was dark again, and then light came back. It pushed its way forward between the stark trees, like a shimmering mist. The darkness merged into a faint daybreak. Then Abbot Hans saw that the snow had vanished from the ground, as if someone had removed a carpet, and the earth began to take on a green covering. The moss-tufts thickened and raised themselves, and the spring blossoms shot upward their swelling buds, which already had a touch of color.

Again it grew hazy; but almost immediately there came a new wave of light. Then the leaves of the trees burst into bloom, crossbeaks hopped from branch to branch, and the woodpeckers hammered on the limbs until the splinters fairly flew around them. A flock of starlings from up country lighted in a fir top to rest.

When the next warm wind came along, the blueberries ripened and the baby squirrels began playing on the branches of the trees.

The next light wave that came rushing in brought with it the scent of newly ploughed acres. Pine and spruce trees were so thickly clothed with red cones that they shone like crimson mantles and forest flowers covered the ground till it was all red, blue, and yellow.

Abbot Hans bent down to the earth and broke off a wild strawberry blossom, and, as he straightened up, the berry ripened in his hand.

The mother fox came out of her lair with a big litter of black-legged young. She went up to Robber Mother and scratched at her skirt, and Robber Mother bent down to her and praised her young.

Robber Mother's youngsters let out perfect shrieks of delight. They stuffed themselves with wild strawberries that hung on the bushes. One of them played with a litter of young hares; another ran a race with some young crows, which had hopped from their nest before they were really ready.

Robber Father was standing out on a marsh eating raspberries. When he glanced up, a big black bear stood beside him. Robber Father broke off a twig and struck the bear on the nose. "Keep to your own ground, you!" he said; "this is my turf." The huge bear turned around and lumbered off in another direction.

Then all the flowers whose seeds had been brought from foreign lands began to blossom. The loveliest roses climbed up the mountain wall in a race with the blackberry vines, and from the forest meadow sprang flowers as large as human faces.

Abbot Hans thought of the flower he was to pluck for Bishop Absalon; but each new flower that appeared was more beautiful than the others, and he wanted to choose the most beautiful of all.

Then Abbot Hans marked how all grew still; the birds hushed their songs, the flowers ceased growing, and the young foxes played no more. From far in the distance faint harp tones were heard, and celestial song, like a soft murmur, reached him.

He clasped his hands and dropped to his knees. His face was radiant with bliss.

But beside Abbot Hans stood the lay brother who had accompanied him. In his mind there were dark thoughts. "This cannot be a true miracle," he thought, "since it is revealed to malefactors. This does not come from God, but is sent hither by Satan. It is the Evil One's power that is tempting us and compelling us to see that which has no real existence."

The angel throng was so near now that Abbot Hans saw their bright forms through the forest branches. The lay brother saw them, too; but back of all this wondrous beauty he saw only some dread evil.

All the while the birds had been circling around the head of Abbot Hans, and they let him take them in his hands. But all the animals were afraid of the lay brother; no bird perched on his shoulder, no snake played at his feet. Then there came a little forest dove. When she marked that the angels were nearing, she plucked up courage and flew down on the lay brother's shoulder and laid her head against his cheek.

Then it appeared to him as if sorcery were come right upon him, to tempt and corrupt him. He struck with his hand at the forest dove and cried in such a loud voice that it rang throughout the forest, "Go thou back to hell, whence thou art come!"

Just then the angels were so near that Abbot Hans felt the feathery touch of their great wings, and he bowed down to earth in reverent greeting.

But when the lay brother's words sounded, their song was hushed and the holy guests turned in flight. At the same time the light and the mild warmth vanished in unspeakable terror for the darkness and cold in a human heart. Darkness sank over the earth, like a coverlet; frost came, all the growths shrivelled up; the animals and birds hastened away; the leaves dropped from the trees, rustling like rain.

Abbot Hans felt how his heart, which had but lately swelled with bliss, was now contracting with insufferable agony. "I can never outlive this," thought he, "that the angels from heaven had been so close to me and were driven away; that they wanted to sing Christmas carols for me and were driven to flight."

Then he remembered the flower he had promised Bishop Absalon, and at the last moment he fumbled among the leaves and moss to try and find a blossom. But he sensed how the ground under his fingers froze and how the white snow came gliding over the ground. Then his heart caused him even greater anguish. He could not rise, but fell prostrate on the ground and lay there.

When the robber folk and the lay brother had groped their way back to the cave, they missed Abbot Hans. They took brands with them and went out to search for him. They found him dead upon the coverlet of snow.

When Abbot Hans had been carried down to Övid, those who took charge of the dead saw that he held his right hand locked tight around something which he must have grasped at the moment of death. When they finally got his hand open, they found that the thing which he had held in such an iron grip was a pair of white root bulbs, which he had torn from among the moss and leaves.

When the lay brother who had accompanied Abbot Hans saw the bulbs, he took them and planted them in Abbot Hans' herb garden.

He guarded them the whole year to see if any flower would spring from them. But in vain he waited through the spring, the summer, and the autumn. Finally, when winter had set in and all the leaves and the flowers were dead, he ceased caring for them.

But when Christmas Eve came again, he was so strongly reminded of Abbot Hans that he wandered out into the garden to think of him. And look! as he came to the spot where he had planted the bare root bulbs, he saw that from them had sprung flourishing green stalks, which bore beautiful flowers with silver white leaves.

He called out all the monks at Övid, and when they saw that this plant bloomed on Christmas Eve, when all the other growths were as if dead, they understood that this flower had in truth been plucked by Abbot Hans from the Christmas garden in Göinge forest. Then the lay brother asked the monks if he might take a few blossoms to Bishop Absalon.

When Bishop Absalon beheld the flowers, which had sprung from the earth in darkest winter, he turned as pale as if he had met a ghost. He sat in silence a moment; thereupon he said, "Abbot Hans has faithfully kept his word and I shall also keep mine."

He handed the letter of ransom to the lay brother, who departed at once for the Robbers' Cave. When he stepped in there on Christmas Day, the robber came toward him with axe uplifted. "I'd like to hack you monks into bits, as many as you are!" said he. "It must be your fault that Göinge forest did not last night dress itself in Christmas bloom."

"The fault is mine alone," said the lay brother, "and I will gladly die for it; but first I must deliver a message from Abbot Hans." And he drew forth the Bishop's letter and told the man that he was free.

Robber Father stood there pale and speechless, but Robber Mother said in his name, "Abbot Hans has indeed kept his word, and Robber Father will keep his."

When the robber and his wife left the cave, the lay brother moved in and lived all alone in the forest, in constant meditation and prayer that his hard-heartedness might be forgiven him.

But Göinge forest never again celebrated the hour of our Savior's birth; and of all its glory, there lives today only the plant which Abbot Hans had plucked. It has been named CHRISTMAS ROSE. And each year at Christmastide she sends forth from the earth her green stalks and white blossoms, as if she never could forget that she had once grown in the great Christmas garden at Göinge forest.

STEPHEN LEACOCK

The Errors of Santa Claus

IT WAS Christmas Eve.

The Browns, who lived in the adjoining house, had been dining with the Joneses.

Brown and Jones were sitting over wine and walnuts at the table. The others had gone upstairs.

"What are you giving to your boy for Christmas?" asked Brown.

"A train," said Jones, "new kind of thing—automatic."

"Let's have a look at it," said Brown.

Jones fetched a parcel from the sideboard and began unwrapping it.

"Ingenious thing, isn't it?" he said, "goes on its own rails. Queer how kids love to play with trains, isn't it?"

"Yes," assented Brown, "how are the rails fixed?"

"Wait, I'll show you," said Jones, "just help me to shove these dinner things aside and roll back the cloth. There! See! you lay the rails like that and fasten them at the ends, so—"

"Oh, yes, I catch on, makes a grade, doesn't it? Just the thing to amuse a child, isn't it? I got Willie a toy aeroplane."

"I know, they're great. I got Edwin one on his birthday. But I thought I'd get him a train this time. I told him Santa Claus was going to bring him something altogether new this time. Edwin, of course, believes in Santa Claus absolutely. Say, look at this locomotive, would you? It has a spring coiled up inside the fire box."

"Wind her up," said Brown with great interest, "let's see her go."

"All right," said Jones, "just pile up two or three plates or something to lean the end of the rails on. There, notice the way it buzzes before it starts. Isn't that a great thing for a kid, eh?"

170

"Yes," said Brown, "and say! see this little string to pull the whistle. By Gad, it toots, eh? Just like real?"

"Now then, Brown," Jones went on, "you hitch on those cars and I'll start her. I'll be engineer, eh!"

Half an hour later Brown and Jones were still playing trains on the dining-room table.

But their wives upstairs in the drawing room hardly noticed their absence. They were too much interested.

"Oh, I think it's perfectly sweet," said Mrs. Brown, "just the love-liest doll I've seen in years. I must get one like it for Ulvina. Won't Clarisse be perfectly enchanted?"

"Yes," answered Mrs. Jones, "and then she'll have all the fun of arranging the dresses. Children love that so much. Look! there are three little dresses with the doll, aren't they cute? All cut out and ready to stitch together."

"Oh, how perfectly lovely," exclaimed Mrs. Brown, "I think the mauve one would suit the doll best—don't you?—with such golden hair—only don't you think it would make it much nicer to turn back the collar, so, and to put a little band—so?"

"*What* a good idea!" said Mrs. Jones, "do let's try it. Just wait, I'll get a needle in a minute. I'll tell Clarisse that Santa Claus sewed it himself. The child believes in Santa Claus absolutely."

And half an hour later Mrs. Jones and Mrs. Brown were so busy stitching dolls' clothes that they could not hear the roaring of the little train up and down the dining table, and had no idea what the four children were doing.

Nor did the children miss their mothers.

"Dandy, aren't they?" Edwin Jones was saying to little Willie Brown, as they sat in Edwin's bedroom. "A hundred in a box, with cork tips, and see, an amber mouthpiece that fits into a little case at the side. Good present for dad, eh?"

"Fine!" said Willie, appreciatively. "I'm giving father cigars."

"I know, I thought of cigars too. Men always like cigars and ciga-rettes. You can't go wrong on them. Say, would you like to try one or two of these cigarettes? We can take them from the bottom. You'll like them, they're Russian—away ahead of Egyptian."

"Thanks," answered Willie. "I'd like one immensely. I only started smoking last spring—on my twelfth birthday. I think a feller's a fool to begin smoking cigarettes too soon, don't you? It stunts him. I waited till I was twelve."

"Me too," said Edwin, as they lighted their cigarettes. "In fact, I wouldn't buy them now if it weren't for dad. I simply *had* to give him something from Santa Claus. He believes in Santa Claus absolutely, you know."

And while this was going on, Clarisse was showing little Ulvina the absolutely lovely little bridge set that she got for her mother. "Aren't these markers perfectly charming?" said Ulvina, "and don't you love this little Dutch design—or is it Flemish, darling?"

"Dutch," said Clarisse, "isn't it quaint? And aren't these the dearest little things—for putting the money in when you play. I needn't have got them with it—they'd have sold the rest separately—but I think it's too utterly slow playing without money, don't you?"

"Oh, abominable," shuddered Ulvina, "but your mamma never plays for money, does she?"

"Mamma! Oh, gracious, no. Mamma's far too slow for that. But I shall tell her that Santa Claus insisted on putting in the little money boxes."

"I suppose she believes in Santa Claus, just as my Mamma does."

"Oh, absolutely," said Clarisse, and added, "What if we play a little game! With a double dummy, the French way, or Norwegian Skat, if you like. That only needs two."

"All right," agreed Ulvina, and in a few minutes they were deep in a game of cards with a little pile of pocket money beside them.

About half an hour later, all the members of the two families were down again in the drawing room. But of course nobody said anything about the presents. In any case they were all too busy looking at the beautiful big Bible, with maps in it, that the Joneses had bought to give to Grandfather. They all agreed that with the help of it, Grandfather could hunt up any place in Palestine in a moment, day or night.

But upstairs, away upstairs in a sitting room of his own, Grandfather Jones was looking with an affectionate eye at the presents that stood beside him. There was a beautiful whisky decanter, with silver filigree outside (and whisky inside) for Jones, and for the little boy a big nickel-plated Jew's harp.

Later on, far in the night, the person, or the influence, or whatever it is called Santa Claus, took all the presents and placed them in the people's stockings.

And, being blind as he always has been, he gave the wrong things to the wrong people—in fact, he gave them just as indicated above.

But the next day, in the course of Christmas morning, the situation straightened itself out, just as it always does.

Indeed, by ten o'clock, Brown and Jones were playing with the train, and Mrs. Brown and Mrs. Jones were making dolls' clothes, and the boys were smoking cigarettes, and Clarisse and Ulvina were playing cards for their pocket money.

And upstairs—away up—Grandfather was drinking whisky and playing the Jew's harp.

And so Christmas, just as it always does, turned out all right after all.

ROBERT KEITH LEAVITT

ৢৡৡ৶

The Christmas Miracle

O N THE MORNING before the Christmas that fell when I was six, my father took my brother and me for a walk in the woods of the Old Colony town where we lived. Three times as we walked he stopped, and cut a small balsam tree. There was a very tiny one, hardly more than a seedling; a small one a foot or so high; and a youthful one of perhaps four feet. So we each had a tree to bear, flag-like, back to the house. It didn't occur to us single-minded larvae that this had the least connection with Christmas. Our father was a bota-nist Ph.D., given to plucking all manner of specimens whenever we walked, with the offhand explanation, "A fine *Tsuga canadensis*," or whatever it was. By nightfall we had forgotten all about the walk.

For this was Christmas Eve, and we were suddenly in a panic. Where was The Tree? On experience, we knew that it was usually delivered in the morning, that Father set it up in the afternoon and that Mother trimmed it at night, letting us help with the ornaments before she put us to bed in a fever of anticipation. But this year we had seen no tree arrive; look where we would, we could not find one; and even Mother turned aside our questions. Would there be no Tree? Would there, perhaps, be no Christmas at all for us? How we wished, now, that we had not put the cat in the milk-pail!

But after supper Father and Mother took us into the sitting-room. In a cleared corner over by the big closet stood a jar of earth. "Christ-mas," said Father, "is a day of miracles, to remind us of the great-est Miracle of all. Perhaps we shall see one." Then Mother led us out, closing the door on Father and the jar of earth—and the closet.

"We can help," she said, "by learning this song." And she be-gan, softly but very true, "O Little Town of Bethlehem." We tried hard, in our shrill way. But even Mother had to admit it was only a good try. Yet when the door opened and we went again into the sitting-room, behold! A tiny Tree had appeared in the jar of earth! Hardly more than a seedling, to be sure, and not old enough yet to bear ornaments, but indubitably a Tree. Marveling, we went out again.

This time we did better—on the words, if not the tune. And when we re-entered the sitting-room, the Tree had grown—to perhaps a foot or so in height! A blaze of hope flashed upon us. We went out and tried harder on that song. And sure enough, this time the Tree was taller than either boy. Terrific! We could hardly wait to get outside and sing some more with Mother. For now hope was a rapture of certainty.

To this day I cannot hear "O Little Town of Bethlehem," from however cracked a curbside organ, without hearing through and beyond it the clear, true voice of my mother. Nor hear that long-vanished sweetness without knowing that presently, somewhere, somehow a great door is going to open and disclose unearthly beauty. It is more than sixty years since our sitting-room door swung back for the fourth time, that night in the Old Colony of Massachusetts. But I can still see, sharp as life, the splendor of the Tree that towered to the ceiling in its glossy dark green, sparkling with silver tinsel, glowing with candles and half hiding in its crisp, fragrant needles, the incomparable perfection of spheres that shone like far-off other worlds, red and blue and green and gold . . .

Cynics say that miracles are all man-made—contrived, like a Christmas tree hidden in a closet and flashed upon wondering kids. That even the Christmas spirit is only a spell we work up to bemuse one another—and then fall for, ourselves, like so many simple children. What of it? So much the better! If mankind, by its own devoted labor, can induce in itself—if only for a day—an all-pervading spirit of friendship and cheer and good will and loving kindness, that alone is a very great miracle. It is the kind of miracle that must please above all others Him who knows how miracles are wrought.

❧❦

A Christmas Tale

THIS IS A very strange tale I have got to tell you to-day. It is about a mysterious well—a deep, deep well which lay in the centre of a dark forest. It is also a Christmas tale.

No one knew why that well was there, nor who had dug it, nor how old it was.

The peasants from the villages around stood in great awe of this well, because from its depth a weird sound could be heard, a sort of moan, half sob, half gurgle, and sometimes a sound as though some-one were knocking against its sides, which made you think of a lost soul in distress, perhaps held captive down there and unable to get out.

The village nearest the forest was called Galea. It was a very poor little village, its cottages small and miserable, with tiny gardens in which the flowers always looked sad and anaemic, for the ground was stony and unfruitful.

In the centre of the village stood a little wooden church. It was ancient and rather shaky, its huge roof looked too big for it, but the passing seasons had toned it down to a rich brown with a gray shimmer, which was pleasant to the eye.

Old stunted lilac bushes clustered round it, protecting the humble graves which lay scattered about beneath their shade, like a forlorn flock of sheep.

The peasants were rather ashamed of their tiny dilapidated church, and dreamed of building a fine edifice, all white with a tin roof, that would shine like silver in the sun, and not let the rain nor the snow through in the bad seasons, a church with stout columns in front, all decorated in bright colors, and with God's eye painted over the door.

176

You and I would probably have infinitely preferred the crooked little wooden church with its over-large roof, but then you see, each community has its ambition and its pride, and does not want to stand behind other communities. Bostea, the village on the other side of the forest, had a beautiful new big church of the kind that Galea coveted. But Galea was a much, much poorer village than Bostea, and it sadly felt its inferiority.

But it was about the mysterious well I was going to tell you, was it not?

The villagers for some reason had conceived the idea that the unknown being who was held captive in that well, could become a danger to the country-side if it ever managed to get out, and that the only way to keep it contented was by throwing small offerings down into its depth.

The poor often think that they must make sacrifices to God or to any power greater than themselves; it is a sort of way of keeping off ill-luck from their thresholds. And yet God knows their lives are full enough of sacrifices from beginning to end.

There were certain feast-days on which the villagers had the habit of taking their offerings to the dreaded well, and these were especially St. Maria Mare and St. Dumitru.

The moment Mass was over, before any dancing or drinking could begin, they would collect in groups and start off into the forest with their queer little offerings.

Some brought flowers or colored eggs, others flat breads sprinkled with poppy seeds; some brought bunches of corn tied with bright ribbons. Little children would sacrifice their first ripe plums, cherries, or nuts, also the precious little pebbles picked up in the river-bed, and which became a lovely bright pink when you licked them.

The maidens made sacrifice of beads from their girdles and little painted cards with pictures of the saints or small holy medals, or of trinkets bought at the "moshi."[1] The young men would throw down small coins, buttons from their military tunics, or the bright red carnation they so fondly wore stuck behind their left ear.

Even quite old women would go limping through the sunshine, distaff in hand. Quite exhausted they would sink down on the well's edge and pronounce strange wishes over the water, throwing in wisps

[1] "Moshi," fair.

of wool or flax, whilst they murmured prayers, watching the while with one eye what the young ones were doing, always ready to criticize or to disapprove.

But in winter the well was almost quite forsaken, for no one particularly cared to go through the forest in that season. Right on the outskirts of Galea, lived a widow in a cottage so small and humble that it was really hardly more than a hut. In all the village she was known as poor Maria, and she had but one little boy, Petru, who had large gray eyes set in a pale, anxious small face.

Petru had had two little sisters, but both of them lay under the lilac bushes of the churchyard, and so poor was Maria that she had not even been able to mark the spot with crosses, and this made Petru very sad.

Petru was pious and an ardent believer. He faithfully observed all the precepts of the Church; he was a conscientious faster, though verily at all times Petru had but little to eat.

He would devoutly listen to all that old Popa Toader had to say, though sometimes he did not properly understand what it meant, and certain scraps of his exhortations would remain sticking in his mind, taking undue proportions.

Amongst others, Petru had conceived an uncomfortable belief that because the church of Bostea was larger and newer than their poor little wooden church, it was, therefore, also a holier place.

This idea had come to him because, on Easter Sunday, Popa Toader had spoken about collecting money for building a new church, and had held up as example the Bostea church which God would surely bless, as it had been erected by sacrifices made by every inhabitant, who each year had offered part of his hard-earned economies for the honor of God.

Petru of course had no money, not even the poorest little farthing; certainly if he had, he would have gladly given it for the building of the new church.

Petru had never been to Bostea, and just because of that, he had created in his imagination a wonderful vision of its church, which must have all the beauties and qualities Galea's poor little sanctuary never possessed.

Petru was about seven years old when his mother fell very ill indeed; it was just at the beginning of winter, which that year had set in with unusual severity. Petru loved his mother beyond all things on earth, and his poor little heart was wrung with terrible grief, seeing her thus pining away, and he so utterly helpless before her suffering.

Maria was a very patient woman, she never complained; it was from her that Petru had his big gray eyes and pathetic face.

There was no real bed in Maria's hovel; she lay on a sort of wooden bench over which a few ragged rugs had been spread, and upon this miserable pallet she lay all shaken by fever, her lips blue and cracked. A large earthen oven took up part of the hut; it had all sorts of shapes so as to fit into the crooked little room. Maria lay behind this oven, which Petru tried to keep as warm as he could by going each day to fetch wood on the outskirts of the forest, whence he would wearily return carrying on his back as many dry branches as he could. Petru was small, so that the weight was almost too much for him, and would quite bend him in two until he looked like a giant porcupine crawling home through the snow.

Petru would also try to cook. A few strings of dry onions hung against the wall behind the oven, and in a wooden bowl on the floor was their meagre provision of "malaiu."[1]

Probably Petru was not a very successful cook; anyhow Maria turned away with a weary sigh from the daily mess he so anxiously offered her.

This made Petru terribly unhappy and great round tears would roll down his pinched little face. He would hide away in a corner and say his prayers over and over again, all the prayers Popa Toader had ever taught him, even if they had no connection with his trouble —but they were prayers, therefore of course acceptable to God.

After that the little boy would crawl on to the wooden pallet beside his mother, nestling close up to her, hoping to keep her warm with the embrace of his skinny little arms.

Alas, God did not seem to listen to Petru's prayers, because his mother grew worse and worse instead of better, till Petru began tormenting himself, imagining that he must have displeased God in some way. Yet worry his head as he would, he could not remember a single occasion upon which he had broken the law, for Petru was an almost painfully well-behaved little boy, who never had any time to

[1] "Malaiu," meal, maize.

enjoy life or to be naughty, having had to work and make himself useful, ever since he had been able to stand on his feet. He had always been an anxious little soul, ever ready to carry burdens too heavy for his frail shoulders.

It was Christmas Eve, and still poor Maria lay on her pallet, sick unto death, when an idea came into Petru's head.

Petru had ideas sometimes, but they would not always work out, because no one had ever time to bother about his mind, nor to help it to expand. But this idea had grown and grown till it had become a fixture, and then, when it was quite ripe, Petru set about carrying it out, and this is what it was:

He knew that when one desires something very, very much, one must offer a taper to some blessed image, more especially to that of the Mother of God. Those little lights have a wonderful way of reinforcing prayer. Now Petru had obtained one of these little tapers from the old village chanter, as recompense for small services rendered last Sunday during Mass. It was certainly a very thin, fragile-looking little taper, a thing to be treated with infinite care, but the old man had also given him a smashed old match-box, in which there were still five unused matches, and if he could keep them from the damp, they certainly would light his little taper for him when he placed it before the icon of his choice.

All might have been quite simple, had not Petru been possessed with the idea that he must carry his candle to the Bostea church, for, with the other villagers, he shared the mistaken idea that their own old wooden church was not quite an entirely worthy House of God— poor dear crooked little church.

Now to get to Bostea, you had either to take a very, very long road, or you had to take the short-cut through the dark forest where the mysterious well stood.

Even in summer-time Petru dreaded the groaning, moaning well; how much more, therefore, in winter, when the forest was all black and when wolves might be prowling about. Yet he dare not remain away too long from his mother's bedside, so in spite of his fear he made up his mind that he must face that grim path through the wood.

Petru put on his rough, well-used "suman"[1] and the old "caciula"[2]

---

1 "Suman," cape, overcoat.
2 "Caciula," peasant's fur cap or bonnet.

which had once been his father's, and which gave him the quaint appearance of a wandering fungus, slipped on his fingerless gloves, which were so much darned that there was more darn about them than glove, and having hidden the precious taper and matches in his pocket, he was ready to start.

Before slipping outside, however, he did not forget to pile all the reserve of dried sticks upon the fire, and to place a small mug of water beside his mother, who lay with her face turned to the wall, mumbling all sorts of strange things which had no sense and which filled poor little Petru's soul with dread.

Dusk was already gathering, but Petru had not been able to get off sooner. He felt nervous, but now that his mind was made up he meant to carry out his plan, never matter what the effort might cost him.

Soon he reached the edge of the forest and bravely plunged into its shade, but his heart beat like a heavy hammer in his breast.

"Perhaps I shall be able to avoid the well," thought the boy. "I know there are two paths—one is a little longer, but it does not go past the well. . . ."

The wind was howling through the branches; in the stillness of the forest it sounded like an angry voice. Petru shivered, it was terribly cold. But luckily the snow was not very deep, except in places where it lay in drifts.

Hurry as he would, night seemed to be pursuing him, gaining on him, catching him up. His breath came in hard gasps which hurt him at the bottom of his throat. What a terribly big forest, and how tall the trees were! Never had poor Petru felt so small.

"I hope, oh, I do hope I am on the right road," said the child almost aloud, "I do not want to come past that terrible old well."

And just as he said this, thump, thump, he heard an uncanny sound that made his heart jump into his mouth.

Thump—thump, and then came another sound more like a moan rising from the very bosom of the earth.

Perspiration broke out on poor Petru's forehead in spite of the cold. How dark it was getting, the trees had become walls of darkness shutting him in on all sides. . . .

Thump—thump . . . oh, dear, oh, dear, that certainly was the sound of the well.

As though hypnotized, Petru advanced. He might have turned

away, have slipped through the trees avoiding the place of dread, but he somehow never thought of this but advanced steadily, fascinated by the horror of the thing!

Yes, there stood the well, a dark, sinister object that he could not avoid.

In his anxiety Petru stumbled, tried to recover his footing, but fell with a little gasp at the very edge of the well!

For a moment he lay there, his face buried in the cold snow whilst great dry sobs tore his breast. But what was that? Someone else was weeping? He was not alone in his solitude, someone besides himself was in distress, and—could he be mistaken? It seemed to be a child's voice, weeping, weeping.

Petru picked himself up. He was feeling less afraid now—why should he be afraid of a little child crying in the dark?

But then came again the sound he dreaded—thump, thump. Oh! That dreadful well! His knees shook beneath him, and yet he must look over the edge—some force stronger than himself seemed to oblige him to do so.

Petru had always hated looking down into the well, even in the day-time, when his mother had held his hand; for nights afterwards he could not sleep, always imagining that he was falling down that terrible black shaft. Now he was quite alone, it was almost night, nevertheless he *must* look over the edge.

Who could be down there? What secret could be hidden in that unknown depth?

Thump—thump—was it Petru's heart beating, or did the sound really come from the well?

Then suddenly a shrill child's voice cried, "Oh, let me out, let me out, throw me down your little taper—I am all alone here in the dark, and so cold, so cold."

"My little taper!" gasped Petru, forgetting his astonishment, his fear and everything else in the one desire of guarding that most precious of possessions. "Oh, I cannot throw you down my little taper that I really cannot, cannot do."

"But I am cold down here," cried the child's voice, "I am cold and frightened, it is Christmas Eve, and I am all alone down here, and it is so dark."

"But my mother's ill, she is dying," answered Petru, now quite fearlessly leaning over the shaft. He did not pause to ponder about the extraordinary thing that was happening to him, instinctively his one thought was to cling to that precious taper which was to buy back his mother's health. "I cannot give you my taper"—there was anguish in his voice—"I must go to Bostea to light it in front of the Virgin's image, so that Mother may get well."

"There are many tapers lit before that image on Christmas Eve," answered the voice. "The Blessed One would not miss your poor little light, whilst down here I am cold and lost and forsaken; give me, give me your light."

"But all the other lights burning before the Queen of Heaven would not be my light," sobbed Petru, now entirely overcome by grief. "I'll never be able to get another taper, I am quite a poor little boy, and if Mother dies, I am alone upon earth, and I am too small to know how to live all alone!" and the little fellow sank to his knees, resting his forehead against the well's edge.

"In the name of the Holy Virgin's blessed Child, give me your taper," pleaded the voice. "This is the night of His Birth, can any prayer be refused if asked in His Name to-night?"

Still Petru wavered, soul torn in two—what was his duty? Both ways his religious convictions stood up to confront him; he had put all his hope in the lighting of this taper in the Bostea church.

"In the name of the Holy Child," repeated the voice which was becoming fainter. "On this night of His Birth, and in the name of His Mother—oh, I am so cold, so lonely, and I too am a child, a little child—oh, give me your light."

Petru was sobbing now, his soul seemed to be dissolving in the bitter grief. Grief for the captive child down there, grief for his mother, grief for himself, grief for the whole sad world where everything was sordid and miserable and poor—poor like their hut and like the little old wooden church with the overlarge roof, and as he leaned there, all bent in two by grief, a vision of the Bostea church rose before him, that church he would now never reach. An impossible glory surrounded it, the glory of things one cannot touch, for now Petru knew that he would sacrifice his little taper—had it not been asked for in the name of the Blessed One whose birthday it was to-night?

Somehow Petru never paused to consider how his one poor little taper could save the captive down there. In the confusion of his thoughts that one small candle had taken enormous proportions, had become the one important thing upon earth.

"Here is my little taper," he sobbed; "take it. And here are the five only matches I have—be sure and catch them before the water can damp them," he added with childish anxiety, "because if they get wet they will not light." And leaning over the shaft of the hated well, little Petru made sacrifice of all he possessed.

After that he fell with his forehead against the frozen edge, his face hidden in his hands, weeping as though his heart would break.

Suddenly he raised his head. What was that? Music? Was he dreaming? A sound of harps seemed to be throbbing in the air around him, the sound of many, many harps. And whence did that light come! That wonderful golden light?

Petru stumbled to his feet, his "caciula" falling from his head as he did so. Both the light and the rapturous music were mounting out of the well, out of that dreaded dark shaft. What was it? What was happening? Why had he suddenly the feeling that his heart was filled to overflowing with joy, with infinite joy?

"Oh!" gasped Petru, and as in church, when the Holy Mystery is being fulfilled, the ragged little fellow fell to his knees.

For now a wondrous child had stepped out of the well and stood before him, a child with golden curls and a beautiful face, a child who seemed all made of light.

"Thank you," said the bright vision to Petru. "You had pity on me, delivering me from the dark, you sacrificed to me what seemed your only hope, but see what glory your one little taper can shed around," and the child held up his hand and Petru saw how his one little taper had become as a light which could light the whole world!

"Go home to your mother, she is waiting for you," said the Wondrous One; "I am going to carry your taper to the little old wooden church, for verily it is just as holy as any great church ever built."

With trembling hands Petru picked up his "caciula," but he did not put it on his head, which he could not cover in a presence so holy, and as one walking in a dream he followed the Child of Light whose radiance filled the whole forest.

Petru felt neither cold nor fear, nor fatigue, and it was as though wings had grown on his feet.

When the village was reached, the Child of Light stood still for a moment, and with his hand pointed towards poor Maria's hut.

"She is waiting for you," he repeated; "then after you've seen her, go to the old, old church."

Of course Petru obeyed the Wondrous One's bidding, and with beating heart hurried to his mother's dwelling. Tearing open the door and bursting into the room, "Mother, Mother!" he cried.

And there stood poor Maria with a smile on her face, all trace of illness wiped from her; she seemed suddenly to have become very beautiful, even the rags she wore had become lovely, so young did she look. Her arms were wide open, those arms that were the only soft place Petru had ever known upon earth. And into those arms did Petru take refuge, hiding his face upon her bosom, too overcome for speech.

Maria did not ask what had happened, she only knew that all sickness had gone from her, that it was Christmas Eve, and that Petru, her only child, was lying against her heart.

Later, Petru stole out of the hut towards the old wooden church as the Child of Light had bidden him do.

The stars were all out, but the village was fast asleep, everything was quite silent, the houses were but dark shadows on the white snow.

Generally the church was but a darker shadow amidst shadows, hardly more dignified than the peasants' dwellings, except that it possessed a small belfry. But to-night! oh! to-night, it had suddenly turned into a casket full of light!

Light streamed out through its windows, through the cracks of its beam-walls, through the chinks of the great roof; the much-despised little building had become a thing of radiance, casting long rays of light towards the heavens, and long rays of light over the frozen snow.

Hands folded, with faltering step, Petru approached God's House, like a pilgrim come from afar; with bent head he stepped over the threshold and there fell on his knees, overcome by wonder and joy. The three doors of the altar-screen stood wide open, and on the altar itself burned Petru's little taper; no other candle had been lit in all the church, and yet the light of that one little taper was strong

enough to turn the lowly little sanctuary into a thing of beauty, a
thing of radiance, a thing of peace and joy.

Surely even the church of Bostea could not be more beautiful
than Galea's church was to-night!

Petru understood that a miracle had come to pass: his mother had
been cured, the old well delivered of its curse, and although the
Holy Child was nowhere to be seen, the Holy Child's hand it was
which had placed Petru's humble offering upon the altar of God.

But one thing Petru had not realized: that it was his love which
had brought about the miracle—his love and his faith.

And this strange thing came to pass one Christmas Eve—on the
Birthday of Christ.

F. VAN WYCK MASON

Valley Forge

24 DECEMBER 1777

CORPORAL TIMOTHY MADDOX of Smallwood's Maryland Cavalry, presently detailed to the Commander-in-Chief's bodyguard, stood disgustedly considering the armful of fir boughs he had dropped at the rear of the General's weather-beaten marquee. In evident disappointment Sergeant Hiram Toulmin considered the fruits of his corporal's labors.

"And is that all ye have to show for a half hour's rummagin'?"

"Yer cussed right," the Corporal grunted, retying the length of cotton cord serving him in place of a belt. "I had to get mighty 'cute to find as much. Only two days here and there ain't an evergreen within a mile o' here but's been stripped clean."

The Sergeant blew on grimy, reddish-blue fingers. "I believe ye, Maddox, but I'd been hopin' fer more. That much won't bank above five feet of the marquee. Wish to God we could come across some hay. The wind beats in cruel sharp under them canvas bottoms, and to-night bein' Christmas Eve His Excellency will be expectin' guests, no doubt."

"Even so," Maddox observed, "the General'd never let us use them boughs for banking, Christmas Eve or no Christmas Eve—not with a third o' the Army setting up all night around fires for lack o' beddin'."

Mechanically, Sergeant Toulmin's smoke-reddened eyes sought the campfires of the Blue Hen's Chickens—General Billy Maxwell's Delaware troops. In the fading yellow-gray sunset he could see that the smoke of their campfires veered ever more sharply away to the

187

southwest. A veteran of White Plains and Brandy-wine, he noticed subconsciously that the fires they had built were too big and hot by far. Even now the huddled soldiers began to move away—roasted on one side and half frozen on the other.

Beyond the trampled fields to his right, Conway's and Huntington's ragged battalions were faring better. Quite a few rough huts had been near enough completed for occupancy, and a dogwood grove afforded them a measure of shelter.

Despite the plans of Colonel Duportail, that competent if irascible Frenchman, for a permanent arrangement, there was no order about the way in which the campfires had been kindled; dozens upon dozens of them glowed within easy eyeshot, and farther across the weed-tufted expanse of meadows more fires winked and blinked. These marked the camp's outer line of defenses.

The snowy ground between the General's marquee and the outer defenses had, during the day, become heavily crisscrossed by caisson and forage wagon wheels, splashed with dark groups of horse droppings, and trampled by the feet of nearly nine thousand men.

A gust of wind stirred sere brown leaves clinging doggedly to the branches of some oaks growing between the temporary headquarters and an old schoolhouse standing at the intersection of Gulph and Baptist roads.

The Corporal sniffed a clear drop back into his nose. "Lay you two to one, Sergeant, if that blasted wind holds out o' the northeast we'll get a three-day blizzard. As if we ain't been nipped raw already."

"Don't want an easy bet, do ye?" Though his effort was hardly more than a gesture, Sergeant Toulmin knelt, commenced carefully to arrange the fir boughs along the base of the marquee's windward side. So few branches would not go very far towards dispelling the frost-laden wind now beginning to dislodge remnants of old snow from the tops of tall oaks.

Plague take it! Why did the General persist in being so careless of his own comfort? Why, Generals Varnum, Wayne, Patterson, and even tough old Teufel Piet Muhlenberg had long since ensconced themselves, more or less comfortably, in various sturdy stone or wood farmhouses of the neighborhood. Lord, how the General's aide, Major Alexander Hamilton, had cursed—out of his superior's earshot

—when the General had refused courteously but firmly to occupy Mrs. Deborah Hewes's well-constructed mansion. Under no conditions, the General had declared, would he occupy a comfortable billet while his rank and file chattered their teeth in this uncommonly bitter December air.

The Corporal's attention became attracted by a flight of belated crows flapping along in ragged formation. Above them heavy whitish-gray clouds were commencing to scud furiously across the darkening sky. A regimental clerk appeared at the marquee's flap. He was rubbing ink-stained fingers in an effort to warm them and ended by tucking them under his armpits.

"Maddox! Why in Tunket you loafin' out here? Yer wanted—take a message to Weedon's command."

The Corporal's sharp young features contracted. Weedon? Weedon's brigade was camped about as far at it was possible to go within the new encampment—a generous two miles away. Well, maybe he could warm himself there, the Virginians had been putting the finishing touches on the huts they had built so quickly and according to specification. Old soldiers, they were mighty handy at contriving shelters, didn't stand helplessly about like the city men of Lachlan McIntosh or Knox's Artillery.

The Corporal began making his way towards a side entrance of the marquee. A faint and querulous outcry drew his attention to an attenuated V of Canada geese fleeing on rhythmically beating wings before what must certainly be an oncoming storm.

At this familiar discordant music from the sky Tim Maddox's eyes filled, so poignant was the reminder of his home at the mouth of the Patuxent. Why, only a year ago this very Christmas Eve he, Brother John and Billy Stumpp had conducted a mighty successful hunt for just such mighty honkers.

Even inside the marquee, and out of the rising wind, it remained perishingly cold. The chief clerk was still writing, so Maddox seized the opportunity to blow his nose on the dull blue cuff of his stained gray uniform. Those pewter buttons which once had decorated its revers long since had been lost and so did not scratch his nose. Mechanically, the Corporal's stiff red fingers tugged his tunic into a few less wrinkles. He then kicked his feet together, but gently, because the sole of his right shoe was held in precarious security by

only two or three oaken pegs and the good Lord knew he didn't
want to get his feet full of snow. Of course they had been wet and
aching for time out of mind, but still the stout wool of his socks lent
a considerable protection.

From beyond a canvas partition separating the orderly room from
the rest of the tent rose a deep voice which, somehow, always started
a tremor tumbling the length of Tim Maddox's spine.

"You must try to be patient, Wayne. For the moment nothing
more can be done than has been done. All this week I have written to
every imaginable authority, begging and imploring assistance."

"Then, sir, can we expect no supplies for certain?" Major-General
Anthony Wayne's voice was hoarse as the rasping of a grindstone
against a sword blade.

"Nothing, I fear, within five days."

"Five days!" The Pennsylvanian exploded. "God in heaven! The
army will long since have mutinied and dispersed."

Maddox heard the Commander-in-Chief fetch a slow sigh, indescribably descriptive of fatigue. "You are convinced there is danger
of mutiny?"

"As surely as I stand on this spot!" came the immediate reply.
"What else can be in the minds of men so betrayed, so victimized
by the petty jealousies and greeds of Congress?"

At the far end of the marquee beyond the General's quarters rose
angry voices. Maddox recognized them as belonging to various commanding officers. They were lodging complaints and making requisi-
tions which were bound to prove fruitless. The voices grew more
strident. One rose above the rest. " 'Fore God we've had no meat in
five days, no flour for two! Half of my third platoon wear women's
clothes! You don't believe that?" The speaker's accents were shaking
with fury. "Then I'll show you. Send in Private Hacker."

Tim Maddox couldn't help peeking around the canvas door in time
to behold the shambling entrance of a sunken-eyed, unshaven fellow.
He came to an uneasy halt in the midst of a semicircle of red-faced
officers. He wore but a single boot; his other foot being clumsily
swathed in what looked like a length of lace-edged window curtain.
The wrapping was foul, stained with mud and horse manure. Just
above his ankle glowed a damp red spot. Private Hacker's breeches
hung in tatters, and beneath filthy crossbelts supporting his cartridge

box and bayonet was wound a woman's bright red woolen petticoat.

Because he had no sleeves the soldier's arms remained hidden and useless beneath the folds of the petticoat. About his gaunt neck had been twisted an indescribably ragged and worn gray woolen stocking. A woman's dark green calash hat was set on the back of the soldier's head.

"And this, gentlemen," the fierce-eyed Colonel was snapping, "is one of the more warmly dressed of my third platoon." The Colonel, his ear bleeding from an old frostbite, made a derisive gesture. "I give you Private Hacker, sirs, as a Christmas present from our beloved and patriotic Congressmen!"

"What purpose to continue?" A heavy-set major in a patched and bloodstained gray watch cloak turned bitterly aside. "Have we not done all we can? During two long years we have fought the good fight and there remains no strength in us. Tomorrow I resign——"

"And I, too, will send in my commission." The speaker wore the remains of a blue Delaware uniform. "My men are dying of the cold. There is nothing, no straw, no hay, not even fir boughs for them to lie on, let alone blankets."

A hard-pressed commissary officer spread plump hands in despair. "Gentlemen, gentlemen! Would to God I were a magician and could conjure you blankets, uniforms, and provisions out of grass and leaves, but I assure you I am not."

The officers departed sullenly silent or in harsh and bitter complaint. Sulphurous were the curses they laid on Congress and the hopeless inefficiency of the Transport Corps. Mightily depressed, Corporal Maddox returned his attention to the chief clerk. He was barely in time, for that harassed individual was holding out a square of paper sealed with a pale blue wafer.

"For Brigadier-General George Weedon." He coughed. "Urgent; shake your butt getting there, Corporal."

Outside, the wind tore at a man like a harpy's claws, so Maddox halted long enough to tie a battered tricorn onto his head with the bight of a three-yard-long muffler. Right now he wouldn't have taken ten pounds gold for that length of warm green wool.

The sun had almost disappeared but still managed to gild the tops of some hardwood trees towering above the General's marquee. Here and there it sketched bright streaks along the barrels of the guns in a park of artillery arranged along the edge of that great field which would, at a later date, become known as the Grand Parade.

Every few rods Maddox encountered little groups of soldiers stumping along, their heads tilted against the rising wind. Most were lugging armfuls of fagots, but quite a few were engaged in hauling hewn and notched lengths of log towards a row of huts rising among the stark black dogwood trees back of Woodford's Virginia Continentals. Because during the day the snow had become trampled and hard packed their progress was not too painful.

All the same Tim Maddox proceeded gingerly because of his bad shoe. In all directions he discerned knots of soldiers in every manner of garb, sitting on logs, crouched shoulder to shoulder about smoky green wood campfires attempting to cook whatever scraps of food they had been able to discover.

High in the darkening heavens a faint, sibilant singing sound had made itself noticeable. Corporal Maddox recognized the phenomenon at once. Frost—snow, and lots of it, would soon start falling.

The snow beneath his feet commenced to creak—another bad sign. And to think that once, long, comfortable years ago, he, his brothers and sisters had prayed for snow on Christmas Eve!

The wind continued to increase, lashing pitilessly at rows of ribby nags tethered, forlorn and miserable, to the artillery picket lines. Gradually, the beasts were shifting to present their rumps to the impending blizzard. The darker it grew, the more effectively did fires tint the snow a pretty rose red and cast into silhouette the miserable artillerists.

While plodding on across a field tenanted by empty and abandoned baggage wagons the courier came upon three scarecrow figures. They were from Stirling's New York levies. Their capes fluttering like a bird's broken wings, two of them bent over a third who lay motionless and inert across the ruts of mud created by the passage of some heavy caisson.

"Come on, Hans," one of them was pleading. " 'Tain't much further to them fires—not above two hundred yard. Ye can do it, Hans. Then ye'll be nice and warm and maybe, because it's Christmas Eve, they'll give us somethin' to eat."

The other shook the prostrate man's shoulder. "Hans," he cried, "rouse up. You can't lie here like this, ye'll freeze, sure fire. Hans, ain't you and me come all the way from Staten Island? We come all that distance, we can make another—Oh, blazes, it ain't above a hundred yards." But the man lying face downwards in the snow only groaned.

Maddox saw why the soldier, Hans, was unable to rise. The soles of his naked feet had degenerated into a pulpy mass of mud, torn flesh, and sticky blood.

"You'll never get him up," he predicted. "Suppose you fellers take his shoulders and I'll lug his feet."

The New Yorkers looked up, hollow eyes ringed in numb surprise.

"What for you helpin' us? You ain't New York. What outfit are you from anyway?"

"Smallwood's Maryland Cavalry," Maddox announced in conscious pride.

"Shucks! thought all you fancy Nancys had traipsed off south." The larger of the New Yorkers blew his nose with his fingers.

"They were ordered away. I'm a courier at Headquarters."

The smaller New Yorker's lip curled. "Oh, one of them fat cats? Good to know somebody gets something t' eat around here, eh, Job?"

A sharp resentment heated in Maddox's features, but he controlled himself. "Come on, if you want me to help you. I've got a message to deliver."

The weight they lifted was slight, for the man Hans was hardly a man, but a boy roughly Maddox's own age—nineteen. Pretty soon they came up to a sagging tent marked Medical Service. Already it was jam packed, but they slid the semi-conscious Hans in on top of a fellow who looked more dead than alive.

"Thanks," was all the two soldiers said, but Maddox didn't expect any more. They were New Yorkers from whom none but a fool would have looked for any politeness.

Pretty soon Corporal Maddox reached the outer cantonments of Anthony Wayne's burly Pennsylvanians and, as he had fully expected, found them in considerably better case. There were enough sturdy German farmers among them to have built huts sufficient to shelter most of their number. In the next company street the courier slowed his pace.

Despite the wind and the penetrating chill, a group of Germans was engaged in dressing a small fir tree with whatever had come to hand. Brass buttons, bits of tarnished gold lace, lengths of soiled pink ribbon were being employed. A big-handed sergeant was, with great care, unraveling a worn-out red stocking. Another was laboriously cutting six pointed stars out of bits of foolscap.

Yes, the Pennsylvanians were mighty lucky; they'd a stone jug warming beside their roaring campfire.

Corporal Maddox would have liked to linger at least until the lice, chilled and dormant in the seams of his clothing, felt impelled to start feeding, but Weedon's troops lay encamped a good mile farther on.

*   *   *

Hands clenched behind him, Major-General Anthony Wayne tramped angrily back and forth over broken leaves, dead grass, and melting snow marking the grimy canvas flooring of the Commander-in-Chief's compartment.

"Your Excellency," he was growling, "there is no longer any purpose in continuing this campaign. Is it not now entirely plain that the Congress has traduced and abandoned us? To disperse at once is our only recourse. Even so hundreds will perish—to delay will cost still more lives. I assure you, sir, our rank and file are utterly dispirited and the officers disgusted. Yesterday alone four regimental surgeons packed up and rode off—no attempt at a by-your-leave. Possibly in the spring, sir, a new army can be assembled, but at present our situation is hopeless—quite hopeless."

The big Pennsylvanian seated himself momentarily on a corner of a map chest. The once-brilliant red revers of his uniform lapels and cuffs looked more than ever faded, worn, and weather-beaten.

General Washington for some instants remained silent, his wide mouth immobile, its lips compressed. At length he said, "All that you say is only too true, old friend, and you never were a faint-heart. To you I will confess that I, too, find myself at my wit's end. How can our people elect such contemptible, self-seeking poltroons and scoundrels to the Congress?"

The Commander-in-Chief's steel-gray eyes lowered themselves until they came to rest on a litter of papers crowding his field desk.

"I have said my say, Your Excellency." Wayne got stiffly to his feet, fixed a look of deep affection upon his chief. "Whatever is your decision I shall abide by it—to the full limit of my ability." Wayne pulled his triple cape tighter about him. "And now a more immediate matter. Pray indulge me if I protest against your refusal to move into Mrs. Hewes' residence. You, sir, constitute the very soul of this army. Without you it would have dispersed long since. Promise at least to sup with me—'tis the eve of Christmas, after all."

The Commander-in-Chief hesitated, half smiled. He felt sorely tempted. Throughout the Continental Service Anthony Wayne had been long renowned for setting an excellent mess even in the midst of the most miserable campaigns.

"I will attempt to indulge you—and myself, Anthony. You may rely upon it. If possible, I will appear by eight of this evening, otherwise, pray do not wait upon my arrival."

Wayne drew himself up, bowed. "May I wish you a Merry Christmas, sir? Would to God there were some hope of fulfillment!"

"There will be other Christmases," the General reminded, but the words fell heavily from his lips as, with a tired gesture, he turned back to that mound of documents awaiting his attention.

He heard Wayne lift the canvas barrier, heard the rythmic *slap—slap!* of the guard's hands on his piece as he presented arms. As seldom before, the General felt very alone. Light penetrating the canvas was feeble indeed—nearly as dim as the prospects of this half-born Republic.

Mechanically, the General's chilled knuckles rubbed at eyes grown hot and weary from sleeplessness. Practically speaking, what hope remained to an army in a like situation? Even lion-hearts like Nat Greene and Tony Wayne were convinced that the end had come. The weight of massive bullion epaulettes dragged at George Washington's shoulders and his big body sagged on a camp stool until the silvery clamor of wild geese in the sky attracted his attention.

The Potomac must be full of them by now. Christmas Eve! Slaves in the quarters behind his long white mansion would be making merry, crying "Christmas gift!" war or no war. He slumped still more on his stool, absently watched the gray mist of his breath go drifting across the tent. How long since he had ridden his beloved acres? Years. Years. Years.

Christmas at Mount Vernon was a wonderful season—it meant the presence of family friends and neighbors; good wines, fires, candles and lovely women in dazzling silks and brocades.

Grimly, the General surveyed his surroundings. Yonder, only half seen in the gloom, stood a battered chest containing a few clothes, his field desk, and a mud-splashed gray riding cape flung across his folding camp bed. Why must this go on and on? Secretly loving America at the bottom of his heart, Lord Howe undoubtedly would grant the most lenient of terms.

Suddenly the Commander-in-Chief sat erect, selected a sheet of foolscap, and commenced to write.

> *In Camp at Valley Forge*
> *December ye 24, 1777.*

To the President of Congress
Sir:

> *Conscious of the Fruitlessness of further Contest with the Enemy and aware that my Army has been Abandoned to starvation and neglect by the various State Authorities and by the Congress itself, I have, sir, the Honour herewith to tender my resigna—*

The quill ceased its busy scratching. A distant clamor was making itself heard. The General stiffened, listening intently. So Wayne *had* been well informed—already a mutiny was breaking out.

Hastily closing the clasps on his long gray watch cloak, General Washington donned a rabbit's fur cap he favored in cold weather and strode into the anteroom.

"The Sergeant of the Guard and two soldiers will accompany me; no more."

Gray cloak billowing to his long stride, the General strode across the anteroom and, fearful of what awaited in the wind-filled twilight, set off in that direction from which the uproar was arising so rapidly that the three enlisted men at his heels were forced to adopt a sort of dog-trot to keep up.

A keen northeast wind smote him, groped beneath his cloak and uniform like a cold hand equipped with chill fingers. Soon it would be wholly dark, but very pale yellow streaks in the west still marked the last of the daylight. Christmas Eve had indeed commenced.

The tumult had died away; it sounded however as if it had originated somewhere among Major-General Henry Knox's artillery regiments. The Commander-in-Chief halted a moment, listening. As he did so he felt the first gentle impact of falling snowflakes.

"God help us," he muttered. "More snow." More snow, and already this year of 1777 had proved to be the bitterest, snowiest fall and winter within living memory!

Probably children in the streets of Philadelphia were laughing to see the myriad soft white flakes come fluttering, tumbling down to spell good coasting for new Christmas sleds. But to the Valley Forge encampment snow meant blocked roads, ever increasing misery around the campfires, more sick in the hospitals and less hope of supplies.

"Aye, Mark, when it starts dry and fine like this 'tis going to snow hard." The Sergeant of the Guard began cursing softly, and turned up his greasy collar against the chill blasts.

Head bowed against the snowy wind, General Washington made his way towards the nearest ring of campfires and noted that some of the batteries had rigged tarpaulins horizontally between gun carriages and caissons, thus improvising tents under which they huddled. A card game was in progress in one with the players employing bits of biscuit for stakes. A gust of laughter arose when a player's chilled fingers accidentally faced a card and so lost him a big piece of crust.

This, then, was the clamor he had feared. Smiling thinly, the General continued his tour. If mutiny impended, he meant to prepare against it, and at once.

Nearing the outer line of defenses, the tall, erect figure heard, of all things, someone singing, singing an old English Christmas carol. The caroler proved to be a surprisingly aged soldier wearing the tatters of a faded brown uniform; accompanying him was a corporal in a very unsoldierly Quaker hat and some gentleman's long-abandoned dress coat. The garment was of vivid canary-yellow brocade and glowed as if burnished by the campfire's light.

This squad must have something special cooking in the pot, for, unobservant of their visitors, they all kept an eye on it. Vaguely, the General wondered what their prize could be. A moment later he passed, abandoned on the fresh fallen snow, the skins and heads of a pair of striped house cats.

Someone recognized him, immediately sang out, "Here's the General! Three cheers for the Commander-in-Chief. Huzzah! Huzzah!"

The first light layer of snowflakes fell from their clothes as they struggled into a line and stood to attention.

A sergeant, his rag-clad feet flopping and spraying the snow up to his knees, strode forward, saluted awkwardly. "Sorry, sir, I—I can't turn out my platoon no better. Comes another year, sir, we'll turn out fit to make the Royal Tyrant's own guards look like rag-pickers."

"Bravely spoken, Sergeant, and I am sure you will. I am profoundly regretful," Washington said in his big clear Southern voice, "that on this holy eve, you and your platoon enjoy so few of the necessities." He tried to sound encouraging. "You may pass the word that I have made the firmest of representations to the Congress."

"Don't concern yourself over us, Gen'ral," a weak voice hailed from the farther corner of the campfire. "We made out before, sir, and by God we'll make out this time, too. Won't we, lads?"

From the bed of a rickety farm wagon appeared two or three tousled heads. Feebly, they joined in the cheering.

"The sick?" General Washington inquired.

"No, sir," the sergeant said uncomfortably. "It's only they ain't got no coats nor shirts so they're layin' together to keep warm." The Sergeant swayed a little.

"When did you last taste meat?" demanded the Commander-in-Chief; his brows, jutting in the falling snow, were catching a few fine flakes.

"Oh, not so long ago, sir."

"Answer me exactly, Sergeant."

"Why, sir, 'twere five, no, six days ago."

The snow fell thicker, and the wind commenced to rattle and toss the bare limbs of a hickory grove behind the caissons.

The General moved on. Sometimes he found the troops crouched like misshapen gnomes about the fires; they never even raised their heads. Their hats and backs gradually were becoming whitened. They looked, on occasion, like stumps in a burnt-over field.

A miserable company of Poor's command had built a roaring bonfire because their huts stood barely commenced.

Unrecognized here, General Washington circulated quietly. He noticed to one side a young man, a corporal by the green worsted knot on his shoulder holding a cowhide knapsack on his knees and, of all things, attempting to write by the dancing firelight.

"May I obtrude on your privacy enough to inquire what prompts you to write on this cold and miserable evening?"

The boy, recognizing an officer, but not his identity, got up, his face pallid and worried-looking. "Why, why, sir, this being the eve of Christmas, I was thinking of home—and my parents."

"Your name and grade?"

"Corporal Richard Wheeler, sir, of Poor's New York Brigade."

"Your letter. I wish to inspect it."

The Corporal blinked eyes red and swollen from long exposure to acrid wood smoke. "Why, why, sir! I swear 'tis only a letter to my mother."

In response to the silent demand presented by the General's outstretched hand Corporal Wheeler surrendered his rumpled bit of paper.

The General turned his back towards the flames in order to read:

December 24, 1777.

Respected Madam,

This is to convey my Christmas love and duty to all at Home. I would not have you Credit certain unpatriotick Rumors concerning the true Situation of this Army. You need have no concern for we are very Comfortable, we are indeed living on the Fat of the Land——

The General swallowed hard and stared into the flying snow a moment before returning the letter. Then, to Corporal Wheeler's amazement this strange officer very gravely saluted him before stalking off into the wind-filled dark.

The next troops in position along the outer perimeter of defenses proved to be Glover's Massachusetts brigade, a curious organization composed largely of fishermen and sailors which had proved itself useful under a hundred difficult circumstances. This particular half company was enjoying the music of a fiddle and the antics of a pair of gap-toothed and unshaven soldiers ridiculously attired in female garments. To a clapped accompaniment they were kicking up their heels in an old country dance. Subconsciously, the General wondered why this half company seemed extra gay. He beckoned a private, who by the half light also failed to recognize him.

"Why all this merriment? You would appear to have small cause for gaiety."

"Why, sir, have your forgot? This is Christmas Eve." The speaker winked, stepped closer. "Besides, us boys have stumbled on a bit of luck—monstrous good luck."

"Good luck?"

The bearded soldier slid an arm from under the woman's green shawl protecting his shoulders. "D'you mark yonder alder copse— and what's in it?"

The General shielded his eyes against hard-driven snowflakes, barely made out a large dark blur and a small one. "A horse, is it not, and a man on guard?"

"Aye, that's what they are, my friend. Just that."

"What is afoot?"

"Yonder stands a snot-nosed artillery-ist with a fixed bayonet."

The General raised his coat collar against the fine particles beginning to sift in.

"But why is he there, soldier?"

"Like us, he's waiting for yonder old crowbait to fall." The speaker gave a great booming laugh and waved his arms. "So long as the nag stands, he belongs to dear General Knox's artillery, but once he falls and can't rise, he's ours, and then, my friend, we eat, by God! Ain't that cause for cheer?

"Hah! Did you mark how he swayed just then? Your pardon!" The speaker dashed off through the whirling snow.

Like winter wolves ringing a crippled moose, an irregular circle of hollow-eyed infantrymen moved to surround that little alder thicket in which stood the poor furry beast. So gaunt that every rib showed, the horse held its snow-powdered head so low that its loose nether lip almost brushed the ground. It began swaying more noticeably and heaving long, shuddering sighs.

Cursing, hurling obscenities at the gathering crowd, the lone artilleryman kept tramping back and forth, trying to keep warm. Why in hell wouldn't the miserable creature collapse? Satan alone knew where this wretched beast had found strength enough to wander thus far from its picket line. By this time what little there was to eat at his unit must have been consumed, which meant for him another long night on an empty belly.

On second thought, the sentry told himself he wouldn't go right back to his battery. He'd linger here and maybe share in the meat, for all it was certain to prove as tough and stringy as an old boot.

Once more the tall figure and his three followers moved on. The wind now was really roaring, and snow flying in fine particles like spume over the bow of a ship laboring through a storm. The Sergeant lengthened his stride, saluted anxiously.

"Begging the General's pardon, what with this storm worsening we're like to lose our way."

"Very well, but I will have a look at Learned's command on our route back to Headquarters."

The Rhode Islanders recognized their commander at once and ran to form a ragged double line in his honor, yelling all the while, "Long live Liberty!" "Long live the United States!" "Three cheers for the Commander-in-Chief!"

A lieutenant commanding the nearest platoon hurried up and saluted stiffly with his sword.

"Your Excellency, we—er—possess a trifle of Medford rum. We would deem ourselves mighty honored an you would give us your opinion of its worth. After all, sir, 'tis Christmas tomorrow." He beckoned forward a soldier who offered a steaming earthenware cup.

There was only a gallon jug among above two hundred rag-clad and blanket-wrapped Rhode Islanders. If each were lucky he might get a teaspoonful of the fiery spirit.

"Your health—fellow soldiers!" The General barely wet his lips, but made a great pretense of swallowing.

"Next Christmas," called a stumpy little soldier, " 'twill *us* be eatin' roast goose in Philadelphia and the Lobster-backs settin' on their butts out in the cold."

"Perhaps. But have you not suffered enough?" the Commander inquired.

"It's been no bed of roses, sir," the lieutenant said, "but having come this far we may as well go the rest of the distance. With you to lead us, we *can't* lose!"

The General was repassing Glover's position when there arose a wild yell, followed by delighted shouts of "Merry Christmas! Merry Christmas!"

"That poor skate must have fallen at last," grunted one of the bodyguard. "Ain't they the lucky dogs?"

*   *   *

During the General's absence some holly branches and a larger amount of mistletoe had appeared and were being tied in place by Sergeant Toulmin. Fires had been built up at either end of the Headquarters marquee, and about them a motley assortment of junior officers, some of them French, stood warming their hands. Every now and then they shook themselves, dog-like, to rid their coats and cloaks of the whirling snow.

General Washington paused briefly, a thin smile curving his wide mouth.

"A good evening to you, Gentlemen. Pray seek your quarters and find what cheer you can. May God relieve your sufferings, if the Congress will not. A Merry Christmas to you all!"

Snow-powdered cape asway, the big Virginian turned, re-entered his compartment. His aide, darkly handsome young Major Alexander Hamilton, was working in obvious impatience between a pair of stump candles that drew brief flashes from his always well-polished buttons.

"Sir," he said, "General Wayne's compliments. He is dispatching a mount for your convenience at half after seven. He counts on you for supper."

Washington removed his cape and hung it carefully on its peg. "You will go in my place, Major," he announced. "I shall be too occupied with correspondence to take advantage of General Wayne's hospitality—much as I should enjoy it."

The young West Indian hesitated, his bold black eyes half closed. What was up? In arranging documents on the Commander-in-Chief's desk he had come across that incompleted letter to the President of Congress. General Washington's features, however, were enigmatic—and weary, oh, so weary.

"Do you wish to finish this—er communication, sir?"

"Thank you. I will attend to it."

"There is nothing more, sir?"

"No, no, Major. Go and amuse yourself. You have earned the right."

Major Hamilton saluted and stepped outside, but lingered undecided until he was aware of a sudden flare of light beating through the canvas, a glow such as might be caused by a burning document.

GIAN-CARLO MENOTTI

❧

Amahl and the Night Visitors

Cast of characters:
  AMAHL—*a lame shepherd boy*
  HIS MOTHER
  KASPAR—*king bringing incense*
  BALTHAZAR—*king bringing myrrh*
  MELCHIOR—*king bringing gold*
  PAGE—*the kings' attendant*
  SHEPHERD AND SHEPHERDESS

(*The curtain rises. It is night. The crystal-clear winter sky is dotted with stars, the Eastern Star flaming amongst them. Outside the cottage Amahl is playing his shepherd's pipe. Within, the Mother calls.*)

MOTHER: Amahl! Amahl! Time to go to bed.

AMAHL: Coming! (*Amahl does not stir.*)

MOTHER: Amahl! How long must I shout to make you obey?

AMAHL: Oh, very well. (*Amahl takes up his crutch and hobbles into the house.*)

MOTHER: What was keeping you outside?

AMAHL: Oh, Mother, you should go out and see! There's never been such a sky! Hanging over our roof there is a star as large as a window, and the star has a tail and it moves across the sky like a chariot on fire.

MOTHER: Oh! Amahl, when will you stop telling lies? All day long you wander about in a dream. Here we are with nothing to eat, not a stick of wood on the fire, not a drop of oil in the jug, and all you do is to worry your mother with fairy tales.

AMAHL: Mother, I'm not lying. Please do believe me. Come and see for yourself.

203

MOTHER: Why should I believe you? You come with a new one every day!

AMAHL: But there is a star and it has a long tail.

MOTHER: Amahl!

AMAHL: Cross my heart and hope to die.

MOTHER: Poor Amahl! Hunger has gone to your head. Unless we go begging how shall we live through tomorrow? My little son, a beggar! (*She weeps.*)

AMAHL: (*Amahl goes to her.*) Don't cry, Mother, don't worry for me. If we must go begging, a good beggar I'll be. I know sweet tunes to set people dancing. We'll walk and walk from village to town, you dressed as a gypsy and I as a clown. At noon we shall eat roast goose and sweet almonds, at night we shall sleep with the sheep and the stars. I'll play my pipes, you'll sing and you'll shout. The windows will open and people will lean out. The King will ride by and hear your loud voice and throw us some gold to stop all the noise.

MOTHER: My dreamer, good night! You're wasting the light. Kiss me good night.

AMAHL: Good night. (*Amahl goes to his pallet of straw at one side of the fireplace. The Mother secures the door, then lies down to sleep. The lights die from the room except for a faint glow through the window.*)

KASPAR, MELCHIOR, BALTHAZAR: (*The voices of the Three Kings are heard very far away.*) From far away we come and farther we must go. How far, how far, my crystal star? (*Amahl listens with astonishment to the distant singing.*) Frozen the incense in our frozen hands, heavy the gold. How far, how far, my crystal star?

(*Leaning on his crutch, Amahl hobbles over to the window. Outside appear the Three Kings: first Melchior bearing the coffer of gold, then Balthazar bearing the chalice of myrrh, and finally Kaspar bearing the urn of incense. All are preceded by the Page, carrying a rich Oriental rug, and an elaborate jeweled box.*)

KASPAR, MELCHIOR, BALTHAZAR: How far, how far, my crystal star? (*The travelers approach the door of the cottage and King Melchior knocks upon the door.*)

MOTHER: Amahl! Go and see who's knocking at the door.

AMAHL: (*Amahl goes to the door.*) Mother, Mother, Mother, come with me. Outside the door there is a King with a crown.

MOTHER: What shall I do with this boy? If you don't learn to tell the truth, I'll have to spank you!

AMAHL: Mother, Mother, Mother. Come with me. If I tell you the truth, I know you won't believe me.

MOTHER: Try it for a change!

AMAHL: But you won't believe me.

MOTHER: I'll believe you if you tell me the truth.

AMAHL: The Kings are three and one of them is black.

MOTHER: Oh! What shall I do with this boy? I'm going to the door myself and then, young man, you'll have to reckon with me! (*The Mother moves to the door. As it swings open, she beholds the Three Kings. In utter amazement, she bows to them.*)

KASPAR, MELCHIOR, BALTHAZAR: Good evening! Good evening!

BALTHAZAR: May we rest a while in your house and warm ourselves by your fire?

MOTHER: I am a poor widow. A cold fireplace and a bed of straw are all I have to offer you. To these you are welcome.

KASPAR: Oh, thank you!

MOTHER: Come in! Come in!

(*The Mother makes way for the Kings to enter first. The Page enters first. Almost immediately King Kaspar proceeds at a stately march to one side of the fireplace. Balthazar enters and proceeds to a place beside him. Melchior is the last to take his place. Amahl watches the procession with growing wonder and excitement.*)

MELCHIOR: It is nice here.

MOTHER: I shall go and gather wood for the fire. (*The Mother goes to the door.*)

MELCHIOR: We can only stay a little while. We must not lose sight of our star.

MOTHER: Your star?

MELCHIOR: We still have a long way to go.

MOTHER: I shall be right back.

AMAHL: (*The moment his mother is gone, Amahl goes to Balthazar.*) Are you a real King?

BALTHAZAR: Yes.

AMAHL: Where is your home?

BALTHAZAR: I live in a black marble palace full of black panthers and white doves. And you, little boy, what do you do?

AMAHL: I was a shepherd; I had a flock of sheep. But my mother sold them. I had a black goat who gave me warm sweet milk. But she died of old age. But Mother says that now we shall both go begging from door to door. Won't it be fun?

BALTHAZAR: It has its points.

AMAHL: (*Pointing at the jeweled box*) And what is this?

KASPAR: This is my box. I never travel without it. In the first drawer, I keep my magic stones. One carnelian against all evil and envy. One moonstone to make you sleep. One red coral to heal your wounds. One lapis lazuli against quartern fever. One small jasper to help you find water. One small topaz to soothe your eyes. One red ruby to protect you from lightning. In the second drawer I keep my beads. Oh, how I love to play with all kinds of beads. In the third drawer, I keep licorice—black, sweet licorice. Have some. (*Amahl reaches for the candy as his mother enters, bearing a few sticks.*)

MOTHER: Amahl, I told you not to be a nuisance.

AMAHL: But it isn't my fault! They kept asking me questions.

MOTHER: I want you to go and call the other shepherds. Tell them about our visitors and ask them to bring whatever they have in the house, as we have nothing to offer them. Hurry on!

AMAHL: Yes, Mother. (*Amahl hurries out as fast as his crutch will carry him.*)

MOTHER: (*The Mother crosses to the fireplace. Suddenly she sees the coffer of gold and the rich chalices of incense and myrrh.*) Oh, these beautiful things, and all that gold!

MELCHIOR: These are the gifts to the Child.

MOTHER: The child? Which child?

MELCHIOR: We don't know. But the Star will guide us to Him.

MOTHER: But perhaps I know him.

MELCHIOR: Have you seen a child the color of wheat, the color of dawn? His eyes are mild, His hands are those of a King, as King He was born. Incense, myrrh and gold we bring to His side, and the Eastern Star is our guide.

MOTHER: Yes, I know a child the color of wheat, the color of dawn. His eyes are mild, his hands are those of a King, as King he was born. But no one will bring him incense or gold, though sick and poor and hungry and cold. He's my child, my son, my darling, my own.

MELCHIOR, BALTHAZAR: Have you seen a Child the color of earth, the color of thorn? His eyes are sad, His hands are those of the poor, as poor He was born.

MOTHER: Yes, I know a child the color of earth, the color of thorn. His eyes are sad, his hands are those of the poor, as poor he was born. He's my child, my son, my darling, my own.

MELCHIOR: The Child we seek holds the seas and the winds on His palm.

KASPAR: The Child we seek has the moon and the stars at His feet.

BALTHAZAR: Before Him the eagle is gentle, the lion is meek.

KASPAR, MELCHIOR, BALTHAZAR: Choirs of angels hover over His roof and sing Him to sleep. He's fed by a Mother who is both Virgin and Queen. Incense, myrrh and gold we bring to His side, and the Eastern Star is our guide.

MOTHER: The child I know on his palm holds my heart. The child I know at his feet has my life. He's my child, my son, my darling, my own, and his name is Amahl!

MOTHER: (*The call of the shepherds falls sharp and clear on the air.*) The shepherds are coming!

SHEPHERDS: All the flocks are asleep. We are going with Amahl, bringing gifts to the Kings. (*The shepherds stop in the door, struck dumb by the sight of the Kings. Amahl, however, slips in to take his place beside his mother.*)

SHEPHERDS: Oh, look! Oh, look!

MOTHER: Come in, come in! What are you afraid of? Show what you brought them.

SHEPHERD: (*The shepherd boldly marches forward and lays his gift before the Kings, then, bowing shyly, he retreats to his place.*) Olives and quinces, apples and raisins, nutmeg and myrtle, medlars and chestnuts, this is all we shepherds can offer you.

KASPAR, MELCHIOR, BALTHAZAR: Thank you kindly.

SHEPHERD: Citrons and lemons, musk and pomegranates, goat cheese and walnuts, figs and cucumbers, this is all we shepherds can offer you.

KASPAR, MELCHIOR, BALTHAZAR: Thank you kindly.

SHEPHERDS: Take them, eat them, you are welcome.

BALTHAZAR: (*Balthazar rises.*) Thank you, good friends. But now we must bid you good night. We have little time for sleep and a long journey ahead.

SHEPHERDS: (*The shepherds pass before the Kings, bowing as they depart.*) Good night, my good Kings, good night and farewell. The pale stars foretell that dawn is in sight. The night winds foretell the day will be bright. (*Having closed the door, Amahl and his mother bid the Kings good night. While the Mother prepares herself a pallet of sheepskins on the floor, Amahl seizes his opportunity to speak to King Kaspar.*)

AMAHL: Excuse me, sir. Amongst your magic stones is there . . . is there one that could cure a crippled boy? (*Kaspar does not answer. Amahl goes sadly to his pallet.*) Never mind. Good night . . . (*The Mother and Amahl have lain down. The Kings are still sitting on the rude bench. They settle themselves to sleep leaning against each other. The Page lies at their feet, beside the rich gifts.*)

MOTHER: (*The Mother cannot take her eyes from the treasure guarded by the Page.*) All that gold! I wonder if rich people know what to do with their gold! Do they know that a house can be kept warm all day with burning logs? All that gold! Oh, what I could do for my child with that gold! Why should it all go to a child they don't even know? They are asleep. Do I dare? If I take some they will never miss it. They won't miss it. (*Slowly she creeps across the floor.*) For my child . . . for my child. (*As the Mother touches the gold, the Page is aroused. He seizes her arm, crying out.*)

PAGE: Thief! Thief!

MELCHIOR: What is it?

PAGE: I've seen her steal some of the gold. She's a thief! Don't let her go. She's stolen the gold!

KASPAR, MELCHIOR, BALTHAZAR: Shame!

PAGE: Give it back or I'll tear it from you!

KASPAR, MELCHIOR, BALTHAZAR: Give it back! Give it back!

AMAHL: (*Amahl awakens. When he sees his mother in the hands of the Page, he helps himself up with his crutch and awkwardly hurls himself upon the Page.*) Don't you dare! Don't you dare, ugly man, hurt my mother! I'll smash in your face! I'll knock out your teeth! (*Rushing to King Kaspar*) Oh, Mister King, don't let him hurt my mother! My mother is good. She cannot do anything wrong. I'm the one who lies, I'm the one who steals! (*At a sign from Kaspar, the Page releases the Mother. Amahl staggers toward her, sobbing.*)

MELCHIOR: Oh, woman, you may keep the gold. The Child we seek doesn't need our gold. On love, on love alone, He will build His Kingdom. His pierced hand will hold no scepter. His haloed head will wear no crown. His might will not be built on your toil. Swifter than lightning He will soon walk among us. He will bring us new life and receive our death, and the keys of His city belong to the poor. (*Turning to the other Kings*) Let us leave, my friends.

MOTHER: (*Freeing herself from Amahl's embrace, the Mother rushes after the Kings.*) Oh, no, wait. Take back your gold! For such a King I've waited all my life. And if I weren't so poor I would send a gift of my own to such a child.

AMAHL: But, Mother, let me send him my crutch. Who knows, he may need one and this I made myself. (*The Mother moves to stop him as he starts to raise the crutch. Amahl lifts the crutch. He takes one step toward the Kings, then realizes he has moved without the help of his crutch.*)

MOTHER: But you can't, you can't!

AMAHL: I walk, Mother. I walk, Mother!

BALTHAZAR, MELCHIOR, KASPAR: He walks!

MOTHER: He walks, he walks, he walks!

KASPAR, MELCHIOR, BALTHAZAR: He walks! It is a sign from the Holy Child. We must give praise to the newborn King. We must praise Him. This is a sign from God. (*Having placed the crutch in the outstretched hands of the King Kaspar, Amahl moves uncertainly. With growing confidence, Amahl begins to jump and caper about the room*).

AMAHL: Look, Mother, I can dance, I can jump, I can run! (*Amahl stumbles.*)

MOTHER: (*She lifts Amahl from the floor.*) Please, my darling, be careful now. You must take care not to hurt yourself.

MELCHIOR, BALTHAZAR: Oh, good woman, you must not be afraid. For he is loved by the Son of God. Oh, blessed child, may I touch you? (*One by one, the Kings pass before Amahl and lay their hands upon him. Then each with his gift to the Child begins to depart.*)

AMAHL: Oh, Mother, let me go with the Kings! I want to take the crutch to the Child myself.

KASPAR, MELCHIOR, BALTHAZAR: Yes, good woman, let him come with us! We'll take good care of him, we'll bring him back on a camel's back.

MOTHER: Do you really want to go?

AMAHL: Yes, Mother.

MOTHER: Yes, I think you should go, and bring thanks to the Child yourself. What can you do with your crutch?

AMAHL: You can tie it to my back.

MOTHER: So, my darling, goodbye! I shall miss you very much. Wash your ears!

AMAHL: Yes, I promise.

MOTHER: Don't tell lies!

AMAHL: No, I promise.

MOTHER: I shall miss you very much.

AMAHL: I shall miss you very much.

MELCHIOR: Are you ready?

AMAHL: Yes, I'm ready.

MELCHIOR: Let's go then.

SHEPHERDS: Come, oh, come outside. All the stars have left the sky. Oh, sweet dawn, oh, dawn of peace. (*Lead by the Page, the Three Kings start their stately procession out of the cottage. Amahl rushes to his mother, bidding her goodbye, then hurries to catch up with the Kings. Amahl begins to play his pipes as he goes. Outside dawn is brightening the sky. The Mother stands alone in the doorway of the cottage, waving to Amahl. The curtain falls very slowly.*)

CHRISTOPHER MORLEY

❧

The Tree That Didn't Get Trimmed

I F YOU walk through a grove of balsam trees you will notice that the young trees are silent; they are listening. But the old tall ones—especially the firs—are whispering. They are telling the story of The Tree That Didn't Get Trimmed. It sounds like a painful story, and the murmur of the old trees as they tell it is rather solemn; but it is an encouraging story for young saplings to hear. On warm autumn days when your trunk is tickled by ants and insects climbing, and the resin is hot and gummy in your knots, and the whole glade smells sweet, drowsy, and sad, and the hardwood trees are boasting of the gay colours they are beginning to show, many a young evergreen has been cheered by it.

All young fir trees, as you know by that story of Hans Andersen's if you've forgotten it, why not read it again?—dream of being a Christmas Tree some day. They dream about it as young girls dream of being a bride, or young poets of having a volume of verse published. With the vision of that brightness and gayety before them they patiently endure the sharp sting of the ax, the long hours pressed together on a freight car. But every December there are more trees cut down than are needed for Christmas. And that is the story that no one—not even Hans Andersen—has thought to put down.

The tree in this story should never have been cut. He wouldn't have been, but it was getting dark in the Vermont woods, and the man with the ax said to himself, "Just one more." Cutting young trees with a sharp, beautifully balanced ax is fascinating; you go on and on; there's a sort of cruel pleasure in it. The blade goes through the soft wood with one whistling stroke and the boughs sink down with a soft swish.

He was a fine, well-grown youngster, but too tall for his age; his branches were rather scraggly. If he'd been left there he would have been an unusually big tree some day; but now he was in the awkward age and didn't have the tapering shape and the thick, even foliage that people like on Christmas trees. Worse still, instead of running up to a straight, clean spire, his top was a bit lop-sided, with a fork in it.

But he didn't know this as he stood with many others, leaning against the side wall of the greengrocer's shop. In those cold December days he was very happy, thinking of the pleasures to come. He had heard of the delights of Christmas Eve: the stealthy setting-up of the tree, the tinsel balls and coloured toys and stars, the peppermint canes and birds with spun-glass tails. Even that old anxiety of Christmas trees—burning candles—did not worry him, for he had been told that nowadays people use strings of tiny electric bulbs which cannot set one on fire. So he looked forward to the festival with a confident heart.

"I shall be very grand," he said. "I hope there will be children to admire me. It must be a great moment when the children hang their stockings on you!" He even felt sorry for the first trees that were chosen and taken away. It would be best, he considered, not to be bought until Christmas Eve. Then, in the shining darkness someone would pick him out, put him carefully along the running board of a car, and away they would go. The tire-chains would clack and jingle merrily on the snowy road. He imagined a big house with fire glowing on a hearth; the hushed rustle of wrapping paper and parcels being unpacked. Someone would say, "Oh, what a beautiful tree!" How erect and stiff he would brace himself in his iron tripod stand.

But day after day went by, one by one the other trees were taken, and he began to grow troubled. For everyone who looked at him seemed to have an unkind word. "Too tall," said one lady. "No, this one wouldn't do, the branches are too skimpy," said another. "If I chop off the top," said the greengrocer, "it wouldn't be so bad?" The tree shuddered, but the customer had already passed on to look at others. Some of his branches ached where the grocer had bent them upward to make his shape more attractive.

Across the street was a Ten Cent Store. Its bright windows were full of scarlet odds and ends; when the doors opened he could see people crowded along the aisles, cheerfully jostling one another with bumpy packages. A buzz of talk, a shuffle of feet, a constant ringing of cash drawers came noisily out of that doorway. He could see flashes of marvellous colour, ornaments for luckier trees. Every evening, as the time drew nearer, the pavements were more thronged. The handsomer trees, not so tall as he but more bushy and shapely, were ranked in front of him; as they were taken away he could see the gayety only too well. Then he was shown to a lady who wanted a tree very cheap. "You can have this one for a dollar," said the grocer. This was only one third of what the grocer had asked for him at first, but even so the lady refused him and went across the street to buy a little artificial tree at the toy store. The man pushed him back carelessly, and he toppled over and fell alongside the wall. No one bothered to pick him up. He was almost glad, for now his pride would be spared.

Now it was Christmas Eve. It was a foggy evening with a drizzling rain; the alley alongside the store was thick with trampled slush. As he lay there among broken boxes and fallen scraps of holly strange thoughts came to him. In the still northern forest already his wounded stump was buried in forgetful snow. He remembered the wintry sparkle of the woods, the big trees with crusts and clumps of silver on their broad boughs, the keen singing of the lonely wind. He remembered the strong, warm feeling of his roots reaching down into the safe earth. That is a good feeling; it means to a tree just what it means to you to stretch your toes down toward the bottom of a well-tucked bed. And he had given up all this to lie here, disdained and forgotten, in a littered alley. The splash of feet, the chime of bells, the cry of cars went past him. He trembled a little with self-pity and vexation. "No toys and stockings for me," he thought sadly, and shed some of his needles.

Late that night, after all the shopping was over, the grocer came out to clear away what was left. The boxes, the broken wreaths, the empty barrels, and our tree with one or two others that hadn't been sold, all were thrown through the side door into the cellar. The door was locked and he lay there in the dark. One of his branches, doubled under him in the fall, ached so he thought it must be broken. "So this is Christmas," he said to himself.

All that day it was very still in the cellar. There was an occasional creak as one of the bruised trees tried to stretch itself. Feet went along the pavement overhead, and there was a booming of church bells, but everything had a slow, disappointed sound. Christmas is always a little sad, after such busy preparations. The unwanted trees lay on the stone floor, watching the furnace light flicker on a hatchet that had been left there.

The day after Christmas a man came in who wanted some green boughs to decorate a cemetery. The grocer took the hatchet, and seized the trees without ceremony. They were too disheartened to care. Chop, chop, chop, went the blade, and the sweet-smelling branches were carried away. The naked trunks were thrown into a corner.

And now our tree, what was left of him, had plenty of time to think. He no longer could feel anything, for trees feel with their branches, but they think with their trunks. What did he think about as he grew dry and stiff? He thought that it had been silly of him to imagine such a fine, gay career for himself, and he was sorry for other young trees, still growing in the fresh hilly country, who were enjoying the same fantastic dreams.

Now perhaps you don't know what happens to the trunks of left-over Christmas trees. You could never guess. Farmers come in from the suburbs and buy them at five cents each for bean-poles and grape arbours. So perhaps (here begins the encouraging part of this story) they are really happier, in the end, than the trees that get trimmed for Santa Claus. They go back into the fresh, moist earth of spring, and when the sun grows hot the quick tendrils of the vines climb up them and presently they are decorated with the red blossoms of the bean or the little blue globes of the grape, just as pretty as any Christmas trinkets.

So one day the naked, dusty fir-poles were taken out of the cellar, and thrown into a truck with many others, and made a rattling journey out into the land. The farmer unloaded them in his yard and was stacking them up by the barn when his wife came out to watch him.

"There!" she said. "That's just what I want, a nice long pole with a fork in it. Jim, put that one over there to hold up the clothesline." It was the first time that anyone had praised our tree, and his dried-up heart swelled with a tingle of forgotten sap. They put him near one end of the clothesline, with his stump close to a flower bed. The fork that had been despised for a Christmas star was just the thing to hold up a clothesline. It was washday, and soon the farmer's wife began bringing out wet garments to swing and freshen in the clean, bright air. And the very first thing that hung near the top of the Christmas pole was a cluster of children's stockings.

That isn't quite the end of the story, as the old fir trees whisper it in the breeze. The Tree That Didn't Get Trimmed was so cheerful watching the stockings, and other gay little clothes that plumped out in the wind just as though waiting to be spanked, that he didn't notice what was going on—or going up—below him. A vine had caught hold of his trunk and was steadily twisting upward. And one morning, when the farmer's wife came out intending to shift him, she stopped and exclaimed. "Why, I mustn't move this pole," she said. "The morning glory has run right up it." So it had, and our bare pole was blue and crimson with colour.

Something nice, the old firs believe, always happens to the trees that don't get trimmed. They even believe that some day one of the Christmas-tree bean-poles will be the starting point for another Magic Beanstalk, as in the fairy tale of the boy who climbed up the bean-tree and killed the giant. When that happens, fairy tales will begin all over again.

ELIZABETH MORROW

❦

A Pint of Judgment

THE Tucker family made out lists of what they wanted for Christmas. They did not trust to Santa Claus' taste or the wisdom of aunts and uncles in such an important matter. By the first week in December everybody had written out what he or she hoped to receive.

Sally, who was seven, when she could only print had sent little slips of paper up the chimney with her desires plainly set forth. She had wondered sometimes if neatly written requests like Ellen's were not more effective than the printed ones. Ellen was eight. She had asked last year for a muff and Santa had sent it.

Mother always explained that one should not expect to get all the things on the list; "Only what you want most, dear, and sometimes you have to wait till you are older for those."

For several years Sally had asked for a lamb and she had almost given up hope of finding one tied to her stocking on Christmas morning. She had also asked for a white cat and a dove and they had not come either. Instead a bowl of goldfish had been received. Now she wrote so plainly that there was no excuse for misunderstandings like this.

Derek still printed his list—he was only six and yet he had received an Indian suit the very first time he asked for it. It was puzzling.

Caroline, called "Lovey" for short, just stood on the hearth rug and shouted "Dolly! Bow wow!" but anybody with Santa Claus' experience would know that rag dolls and woolly dogs were the proper presents for a four-year-old.

The lists were useful too in helping one to decide what to make for Father and Mother and the others for Christmas. The little

216

Tuckers had been brought up by their grandmother in the belief that a present you made yourself was far superior to one bought in a store. Mother always asked for a great many things the children could make. She was always wanting knitted washcloths, pincushion covers, blotters, and penwipers. Father needed pipe cleaners, calendars and decorated match boxes.

This year Sally longed to do something quite different for her mother. She was very envious of Ellen, who had started a small towel as her present, and was pulling threads for a fringed end.

"Oh! Ellen! How lovely that is!" she sighed. "It is a real grown-up present, just as if Aunt Elsie had made it."

"And it isn't half done yet," Ellen answered proudly. "Grandma is helping me with cross-stitch letters in blue and red for one end."

"If I could only make something nice like that! Can't you think of something for me?"

"A hemmed handkerchief?" suggested Ellen.

"Oh, no! Mother has lots of handkerchiefs."

"Yes, but when I gave her one for her birthday she said she had never had enough handkerchiefs. They were like asparagus."

"They don't look like asparagus," Sally replied, loath to criticise her mother but evidently confused. "Anyway, I don't want to give her a handkerchief."

"A penwiper?"

"No, I'm giving Father that."

"A new pincushion cover?"

"Oh! no, Ellen. I'm sick of those presents. I want it to be a big—lovely—Something—a great surprise."

Ellen thought a minute. She was usually resourceful and she did not like to fail her little sister. They had both been earning money all through November and perhaps this was a time to *buy* a present for Mother—even if Grandma disapproved.

"I know that Mother has made out a new list," she said. "She and Father were laughing about it last night in the library. Let's go and see if it is there."

They found two papers on the desk, unmistakably lists. They were typewritten. Father's was very short: "Anything wrapped up in tissue paper with a red ribbon around it."

"Isn't Father funny?" giggled Ellen. "I'd like to fool him and do up a dead mouse for his stocking."

Mother had filled a full page with her wants. Ellen read out slowly:

> Pair of Old English silver peppers
> Fur coat
> ("Father will give her that.")
> Umbrella
> Robert Frost's Poems
> Silk stockings
> Muffin tins
> Small watering pot for house plants
> Handkerchiefs
> Guest towels
> ("Aren't you glad she asked for that?" Sally broke in.)
> Knitted wash cloths
> A red pencil
> A blue pencil
> Ink eraser
> Pen holders
> Rubber bands
> Hot water bag cover
> *A quart of judgment*

This last item was scribbled in pencil at the bottom of the sheet.

As Ellen finished reading, she said with what Sally called her "little-mother air," "You needn't worry at all about Mother's present. There are lots of things here you could make for her. Couldn't you do a hot water bag cover if Grandma cut it out for you? I'm sure you could. You take a nice soft piece of old flannel . . ."

"No! No! Nothing made out of old flannel!" cried Sally. "That's such a baby thing. I want it to be different—and a great surprise. I wish I could give her the silver peppers . . . That's the first thing on her list; but I've only got two dollars and three cents in my bank and I'm afraid that's not enough."

"Oh! It isn't the peppers she wants most!" cried Ellen. "It's the *last* thing she wrote down—that 'quart of judgment.' I know for I heard her tell Father, 'I need that more than anything else . . . even a pint would help.' And then they both laughed."

"What is judgment?" asked Sally.

"It's what the judge gives—a judgment," her sister answered. "It must be something to do with the law."

"Then I know it would cost more than two dollars and three cents," said Sally. "Father said the other day that nothing was so expensive as the law."

"But she only asked for a pint," Ellen objected. "A pint of anything couldn't be very expensive, unless it was diamonds and rubies."

"She wanted a *quart*," Sally corrected. "And she just said that afterwards about a pint helping because she knew a whole quart would be too much for us to buy."

"A hot water bag cover would be lots easier," cautioned Ellen.

"I don't want it to be easy!" cried Sally. I want it to be what she wants!"

"Well, perhaps you could get it cheap from Uncle John," Ellen suggested. "He's a lawyer—and he's coming to dinner tonight, so you could ask him."

Sally was not afraid to ask Uncle John anything. He never laughed at her or teased her as Uncle Tom sometimes did and he always talked to her as if she were grown up. On any vexed question he always sided with her and Ellen. He had even been known to say before Mother that coconut cake was good for children and that seven-thirty for big girls of seven and eight was a disgracefully early bedtime. He thought arctics unnecessary in winter and when a picnic was planned, he always knew it would be a fine day.

Sally drew him into the little library that evening and shut the door carefully.

"Is it something very important?" he asked as they seated themselves on the sofa.

"Yes," she answered. "Awfully important. It's a secret. You won't tell, will you?"

"No, cross my heart and swear. What is it?"

"It's—it's . . . Oh—Uncle John—what *is* judgment? I must get some."

"Judgment? That *is* an important question, my dear." Uncle John seemed puzzled for a moment. "And it is hard to answer. Why do you bother about that now? You have your whole life to get it . . . Come to me again when you're eighteen."

"But I can't wait so long. I must get it right away. Mother wants it for a Christmas present. She put on her list, 'A quart of judgment.' She said even a pint would help."

Uncle John laughed. He threw back his head and shouted. Sally had never seen him laugh so hard. He shook the sofa with his mirth and tears rolled down his cheeks. He didn't stop until he saw that Sally was hurt—and even then a whirlwind of chuckles seized him occasionally.

"I'm not laughing at you, Sally darling," he explained at last, patting her shoulder affectionately, "but at your mother. She doesn't need judgment. She has it. She always has had it. She's a mighty fine woman—your mother. She must have put that on her list as a joke."

"Oh no! Excuse me, Uncle John," Sally protested. "She told Father she wanted it more than anything else. Wouldn't it be a good Christmas present?"

"Perfectly swell," her uncle answered. "The most useful. If you have any left over, give me some."

"Why, I was going to ask you to sell me some," Sally explained. "Ellen said you would surely have it."

Just then Mother called "Ellen! Sally! Bedtime. Hurry, dears. It's twenty minutes to eight already."

"Brother!" exclaimed Sally. "I'm always having to go to bed. But please tell me where I can get it. At Macy's? Delia is taking us to town tomorrow."

"No, my dear," he answered. "Macy sells almost everything but not that. It doesn't come by the yard."

"Girls!" Mother's voice again.

"Oh! Quick, Uncle John," whispered Sally. "Mother's coming. I'll have to go. Just tell me. What *is* judgment?"

"It is *sense*, Sally," he answered, quite solemn and serious now. "Common sense. But it takes a lot . . ." He could not finish the sentence for at this point Mother opened the door and carried Sally off to bed.

The little girl snuggled down under the sheets very happily. Uncle John had cleared her mind of all doubt. She had only time for an ecstatic whisper to Ellen before Delia put out the light: "It's all right about Mother's present. Uncle John said it would be 'swell.'" Then she began to calculate: "If it is just cents, common cents, I have ever so many in my bank and I can earn some more. Perhaps I have enough already."

With this delicious hope she fell asleep.

*   *   *

The first thing after breakfast the next morning she opened her bank. It was in the shape of a fat man sitting in a chair. When you put a penny in his hand he nodded his head in gratitude as the money slipped into his safetybox. Sally unscrewed the bottom of this and two dollars and three cents rolled out. It was not all in pennies. There were several nickels, three dimes, two quarters and a fifty-cent piece. It made a rich-looking pile. Sally ran to the kitchen for a pint cup and then up to the nursery to pour her wealth into it. No one was there in the room to hear her cry of disappointment. The coins did not reach to the "Half" marked on the measure.

But there was still hope. The half dollar and quarters when they were changed would lift the level of course. She put all the silver into her pocket and consulted Ellen.

Her sister had passed the penny-bank stage and kept her money in a blue leather purse which was a proud possession. Aunt Elsie had given it to her last Christmas. It had two compartments and a small looking-glass—but there was very little money in it now. Ellen had already bought a good many presents. She was only able to change one quarter and one dime.

"Let's ask Derek," she said. "He loves to open his bank because he can use the screwdriver of his tool set."

Derek was delighted to show his savings—forty-five cents—but he was reluctant to give them all up for one quarter and two dimes. It would mean only three pieces to drop into the chimney of the little red house which was his bank.

"They don't clink at all," he complained, experimenting with the coins Sally held out. "You'll take all my money. I won't have hardly anything."

"You'll have *just* as much money to spend," explained Ellen.

"Yes," Derek admitted, "but not to jingle. I like the jingle. It sounds so much more."

He finally decided to change one nickel and one dime.

Then Grandma changed a dime and Sally had sixty pennies all

together to put into the pint cup. They brought the pile up about an inch.

When father came home that night she asked him to change the fifty-cent piece, the quarter and the three nickels, but he did not have ninety cents in pennies and he said that he could not get them until Monday and now it was only Saturday.

"You understand, Sally," he explained looking down into his little daughter's anxious face, "you don't have any more money after this is changed. It only looks more."

"I know, but I want it that way," she answered.

On Monday night he brought her the change and it made a full inch more of money in the cup. Still it was less than half a pint. Sally confided her discouragement to Ellen.

"Are you sure," asked her sister, "that it was this kind of present Mother wanted? She never asked for money before."

"I'm sure," Sally replied. "Uncle John said it was *cents* and that it would take a lot. Besides she prayed for it in church yesterday—so she must want it awfully."

"Prayed for it!" exclaimed Ellen in surprise.

"Yes, I heard her. It's that prayer we all say together. She asked God for 'two cents of all thy mercies.' "

"But if she wants a whole pint why did she only ask for 'two cents'?" demanded the practical Ellen.

"I don't know," Sally answered. "Perhaps she thought it would be greedy. Mother is never greedy."

For several days things were at a standstill. Ellen caught a cold and passed it on to Sally and Derek. They were all put to bed and could do very little Christmas work. While Mother read aloud to them Sally finished her penwiper for Father and decorated a blotter for Uncle John—but sewing on Grandma's pincushion cover was difficult because the pillow at Sally's back kept slipping and she couldn't keep the needle straight. There seemed no way of adding anything to the pint cup.

"Mother, how could I earn some money quickly before Christmas?" Sally asked the first day that she was up.

"You have already earned a good deal, dear," Mother said. "Do you really need more?"

"Yes, Mother, lots more."

"How about getting 100 in your number work? Father gives you a dime every time you do that."

"Yes," sighed Sally, "but it's very hard to get all the examples right. Don't you think when I get all right but one he might give me nine cents?"

"No," said Mother laughing. "Your father believes that nothing is good in arithmetic but 100."

She did earn one dime that way and then school closed, leaving no hope for anything more before Christmas.

On the twentieth of December there was a windfall. Aunt Elsie, who usually spent the holidays with them, was in the South and she sent Mother four dollars—one for each child for a Christmas present. "She told me to buy something for you," Mother explained, "But I thought perhaps you might like to spend the money yourselves—later on—during vacation."

"Oh! I'd like my dollar right away!" cried Sally delightedly. "And," she added rather shamefacedly, "Lovey is so little . . . do you think she needs all her money? Couldn't she give me half hers?"

"Why Sally, I'm surprised at you!" her mother answered. "I can't take your little sister's share for you. It wouldn't be fair. I am buying a new *Benjamin Bunny* for Lovey."

Aunt Elsie's gift brought the pennies in the pint cup a little above the half mark.

On the twenty-first Sally earned five cents by sweeping off the back porch. This had been a regular source of revenue in the fall, but when the dead leaves gave place to snow Mother forbade the sweeping. On the twenty-first there was no snow and Sally was allowed to go out with her little broom.

On the twenty-second Ellen and Sally went to a birthday party and Sally found a shiny bright dime in her piece of birthday cake. This helped a little. She and Ellen spent all their spare moments in shaking up the pennies in the pint measure—but they could not bring the level much above "One Half." Ellen was as excited over the plan now as Sally and she generously added her last four cents to the pile.

On the twenty-third Sally made a final desperate effort. "Mother," she said, "Uncle John is coming to dinner again tonight. Do you think he would be willing to give me my birthday dollar now?"

Mother smiled as she answered slowly—"But your birthday isn't till

June. Isn't it rather strange to ask for your present so long ahead? Where is all this money going to?"

"It's a secret! My special secret!" cried the little girl, taking her mother's reply for consent.

Uncle John gave her the dollar. She hugged and kissed him with delight and he said, "Let me always be your banker, Sally. I'm sorry you are so hard up, but don't take any wooden nickels."

" 'Wooden nickels,' " she repeated slowly. "What are they? Perhaps they would fill up the bottom—"

"Of your purse?" Uncle John finished the sentence for her. "No, no, my dear. They are a very poor bottom for anything—and they are worse on top."

"It wasn't my purse," said Sally. "It was—but it's a secret."

When Father changed the birthday dollar into pennies he said, "You are getting to be a regular little miser, my dear. I don't understand it. Where is all this money going to?"

"That's just what Mother asked," Sally answered. "It's a secret. You'll know on Christmas. Oh, Father, I think I have enough now!"

But she hadn't. The pennies seemed to melt away as they fell into the measure. She and Ellen took them all out three times and put them back again shaking them sideways and forwards, but it was no use. They looked a mountain on the nursery floor but they shrank in size the moment they were put inside that big cup. The mark stood obstinately below "Three Quarters."

"Oh! Ellen!" sobbed Sally after the third attempt. "Not even a pint! It's a horrid mean little present! All my presents are horrid. I never can give nice things like you! Oh dear, what shall I do!"

"Don't cry, Sally—please don't," said Ellen trying to comfort her little sister. "It's not a horrid present. It will look lovely when you put tissue paper around it and lots of red ribbon and a card. It *sounds* so much more than it looks," Ellen went on, giving the cup a vigorous jerk. "Why don't you print on your card 'Shake well before opening,' like our cough mixture?"

"I might," assented Sally, only partly reassured.

She had believed up to the last moment that she would be able to carry out her plan. It was vaguely associated in her mind with a miracle. Anything might happen at Christmas time but this year she had hoped for too much. It was so late now however that there was nothing to do but make the outside of her gift look as attractive as possible. She and Ellen spent most of the afternoon before Christmas wrapping up their presents. The pint cup was a little awkward in shape but they had it well covered and the red satin ribbon gathered tight at the top before Grandma made the final bow. It was a real rosette, for Sally had asked for something special.

Christmas Eve was almost more fun than Christmas. The Tuckers made a ceremony of hanging up their stockings. The whole family formed a line in the upper hall with Father at the head, the youngest child on his back, and then they marched downstairs keeping step to a Christmas chant. It was a home-made nonsense verse with a chorus of "Doodley-doodley, doodley-doo!" which everybody shouted. By the time they reached the living-room the line was in wild spirits.

The stockings were always hung in the same places. Father had the big armchair to the right of the fireplace and Mother the large ma-hogany chair opposite it, Lovey had a small white chair borrowed from the nursery. Derek tied his sock to the hook which usually held the fire tongs above the wood basket (it was a very inconvenient place but he liked it) and Ellen and Sally divided the sofa.

After the stockings were put up, one of the children recited the Bible verses, "And there were in the same country shepherds abiding in the field, keeping watch over their flock by night, 'through' and Mary kept all these things and pondered them in her heart." Sally had said the verses last Christmas—Ellen the year before—and now it was Derek's turn. He only forgot once and Ellen prompted him softly.

Then they all sang Holy Night—and Father read "Twas the Night Before Christmas." Last of all, the children distributed their gifts for the family—with a great many stern directions: "Mother, you won't look at this till tomorrow, will you? Father, you promise not to peek?" Then they went up to bed and by morning Father and Mother and Santa Claus had the stockings stuffed full of things.

It went off as usual this year but through all the singing and the shouting Sally had twinges of disappointment thinking of Mother's unfinished present. She had squeezed it into Mother's stocking with some difficulty. Then came Ellen's lovely towel and on top of that Derek's calendar which he had made in school.

There was a family rule at the Tuckers' that stockings were not opened until after breakfast. Mother said that presents on an empty stomach were bad for temper and digestion and though it was hard to swallow your cereal Christmas morning, the children knew it was no use protesting.

The first sight of the living-room was wonderful. The place had completely changed over night. Of course the stockings were knobby with unknown delights, and there were packages everywhere, on the tables and chairs, and on the floor big express boxes that had come from distant places, marked "Do Not Open Until Christmas."

Some presents are of such unmistakable shape that they cannot be hidden. Last year Derek had jumped right onto his rocking horse shouting, "It's mine! I know it's mine!" This morning he caught sight of a drum and looked no further. Lovey fell upon a white plush bunny. A lovely pink parasol was sticking out of the top of Sally's stocking and Ellen had a blue one. They just unfurled them over their heads and then watched Father and Mother unwrapping their presents.

The girls felt Derek and Lovey were very young because they emptied their stockings without a look towards the two big armchairs. That was the most thrilling moment, when your own offering came to view and Mother said, "Just what I wanted!" or Father, "How did you know I needed a penwiper?"

Mother always opened the children's presents first. She was untying the red ribbon on Ellen's towel now and reading the card which said "Every stitch a stitch of love." As she pulled off the tissue paper she exclaimed, "What beautiful work! What exquisite little stitches! Ellen—I am proud of you. This is a charming guest towel. Thank you, dear, so much."

"Grandma marked the cross-stitch for me," explained Ellen, "but I did all the rest myself."

Sally shivered with excitement as Mother's hand went down into her stocking again and tugged at the tin cup.

"Here is something very heavy," she said. "I can't guess what it is, and the card says 'Merry Christmas to Mother from Sally. Shake well before opening.' Is it medicine or cologne?"

Nobody remembered just what happened after that. Perhaps Grandma's bow was not tied tightly enough, perhaps Mother tilted the cup as she shook it, but in a moment all the pennies were on the floor. They rolled everywhere, past the chairs, into the grate, under the sofa and on to the remotest corners of the room. There was a terrific scramble. Father and Mother and Ellen and Sally and Derek, even Grandma and Lovey got down on their hands and knees to pick them up. They bumped elbows and knocked heads together and this onrush sent the coins flying everywhere. The harder they were chased the more perversely they hid themselves. Out of the hubbub Mother cried, "Sally dear, what is this? I don't understand. All your Christmas money for me? Darling, I can't take it."

Sally flung herself into her mother's arms with a sob. "Oh! you must!" she begged. "I'm sorry it's not a whole pint. I tried so hard. You said—you said—you wanted it most of all."

"Most of all?"

"Yes, judgment, cents. Uncle John said it was cents. You said even a pint would help. Won't half a pint be some good?"

Father and Mother and Grandma all laughed then. Father laughed almost as hard as Uncle John did when he first heard of Mother's list, and he declared that he was going to take Sally into the bank as a partner. But Mother lifted the little girl into her lap and whispered, "It's the most wonderful present I ever had. There's nothing so wonderful as sense—except love."

WALTER H. PAGE

❧

Christmas Letter to His Grandson

Introductory Note
by Burton J. Hendrick

I T WAS one of Walter H. Page's most charming customs, manifest from his early childhood, to write letters to his relatives and intimate friends at Christmas time. Even in the most discouraging moments of his Ambassadorship he never failed to greet his chosen spirits in this fashion. Had he been inclined to ignore any Christmas season, it would have been that of 1915, for there were few reminders of Christmas on that occasion. The date, indeed, was probably the darkest in modern history. In the great war all the principles and causes that Mr. Page held most sacred were at stake—democracy, individual development and independence, peace, and the British-American ideal of civilized progress. On this Christmas day of 1915 all these guiding principles seemed about to plunge into irretrievable ruin. Germany was winning the war on all fronts. Her armies were victorious in all parts of Europe and her submarines were sinking Allied shipping almost at will. British and Australian soldiers were dying by thousands in the Dardanelles, insurrections were threatening in India, and almost every day a new Balkan state joined its fortunes with the Central Empires. The Germans were attacking American ships with practical impunity. The great dispute aroused by the *Lusitania* sinking was still unsettled. The determination of Great Britain to keep American foodstuffs out of Germany had produced a diplomatic situation between Great Britain and the United States almost as tense as that of 1812. Indeed—strange as it seems now—one of the horrors that haunted Mr. Page's mind this Christmas was the

228

possibility of war between the United States and Great Britain. Conditions in London were fairly in keeping with the European crisis. The winter was especially disagreeable and foggy, even for the British capital. All social life had come to an end and the atmosphere in official circles was one of deep anxiety and discouragement. Zeppelins were constantly dropping bombs upon London, and the fragments of shattered buildings not infrequently landed on the American Embassy.

Under these conditions the American Ambassador, clad in his dressing gown, sat late on Christmas night before his little desk in his study at No. 6 Grosvenor Square, pouring out Christmas greetings to friends and relatives across the Atlantic—to his daughter, to his three sons, to Colonel House, to Mr. Frank N. Doubleday and his old working associates. It was characteristic of Mr. Page that he should not overlook the latest recruit to his family circle—his year-old grandson and namesake Walter Hines Page, 2nd. Here was one who suggested no thoughts of war. The baby brought to Mr. Page's mind only the philosophy of contentment and of repose. What things in common has a man of sixty and a child of one? A great poet once wrote of "crabbed age and youth" and found that they could "not live together," but to this genial statesman-philosopher, sitting there in London amid the ruins of mankind, the two extremes of life apparently had many ties of sympathy.

Walter H. Page's
Christmas Letter to His Grandson

London, Christmas, 1915.

SIR:

For your first Christmas, I have the honour to send you my most affectionate greetings; and in wishing you all good health, I take the liberty humbly to indicate some of the favours of fortune that I am pleased to think I enjoy in common with you.

First—I hear with pleasure that you are quite well content with yourself—not because of a reasoned conviction of your own worth, which would be mere vanity and unworthy of you, but by reason of a philosophic disposition. It is too early for you to bother over problems of self-improvement—as for me it is too late; wherefore we are alike in the calm of our self-content. What others may think or say about us is a subject of the smallest concern to us. Therefore they generally speak well of us; for there is little satisfaction in speaking ill of men who care nothing for your opinion of them. Then, too, we are content to be where we happen to be—a fact that we did not order in the beginning and need not now concern ourselves about. Consider the eternal coming and going of folk. On every road many are travelling one way and an equal number are travelling the other way. It is obvious that, if they were all content to remain at the places whence they set forth, the distribution of the population would be the same. Why therefore move hither and yon at the cost of much time and labour and money, since nothing is accomplished thereby? We spare ourselves by being content to remain where we are. We thereby have the more time for reflection. Nor can we help observing with a smile that all persons who have good reasons to see us themselves make the necessary journey after they discover that we remain fixed.

Again, people about us are continually doing this service and that for some other people—running errands, mending fences, bearing messages, building, and tearing down; and they all demand equal service in return. Thus a large part of mankind keeps itself in constant motion like bubbles of water racing around a pool at the foot of a water-fall—or like rabbits hurrying into their warrens and immediately hurrying out again. Whereas, while these antics amuse and sadden us, we for the most part remain where we are. Hence our wants are few; they are generally most courteously supplied without our asking; or, if we happen to be momentarily forgotten, we can quickly secure anything in the neighbourhood by a little judicious squalling. Why, then, should we whirl as bubbles or scurry as rabbits? Our conquering self-possession gives a masterful charm to life that the victims of perpetual locomotion never seem to attain.

You have discovered, and my experience confirms yours, that a perpetual self-consciousness brings most of the misery of this world. Men see others who are richer than they; or more famous, or more fortunate—so they think; and they become envious. You have not reached the period of such empty vanity, and I have long passed it. Let us, therefore, make our mutual vows not to be disturbed by the good luck or the good graces of others, but to continue, instead, to contemplate the contented cat on the rug and the unenvious sky that hangs over all alike.

This mood will continue to keep our lives simple. Consider our diet. Could anything be simpler or better? We are not even tempted by the poisonous victuals wherewith mankind destroys itself. The very first sound law of life is to look to the belly; for it is what goes into a man that ruins him. By avoiding murderous food, we may hope to become centenarians. And why not? The golden streets will not be torn up and we need be in no indecent haste to travel even on them. The satisfactions of this life are just beginning for us; and we shall be wise to endure this world for as long a period as possible.

And sleep is good—long sleep and often; and your age and mine permit us to indulge in it without the sneers of the lark or the cock or the dawn.

I pray you, sir, therefore, accept my homage as the philosopher that you are and my assurance of that high esteem indicated by my faithful imitation of your virtues. I am,

With the most distinguished consideration,
With the sincerest esteem, and
With the most affectionate good wishes,

Sir,
Your proud,
Humble,
Obedient
GRANDDADDY.

To Master Walter Hines Page,
On Christmas, 1915.

JACOB A. RIIS

⌘

Is There a Santa Claus?

Dear Mr. Riis:
"A little chap of six on the Western frontier writes to us:
" 'Will you please tell me if there is a Santa Claus? Papa says not.'
"Won't you answer him?"

That was the message that came to me from an editor last December just as I was going on a journey. Why he sent it to me I don't know. Perhaps it was because, when I was a little chap, my home was way up toward that white north where even the little boys ride in sleds behind reindeer, as they are the only horses they have. Perhaps it was because when I was a young lad I knew Hans Christian Andersen, who surely ought to know, and spoke his tongue. Perhaps it was both. I will ask the editor when I see him. Meanwhile, here was his letter, with Christmas right at the door, and, as I said, I was going on a journey.

I buttoned it up in my greatcoat along with a lot of other letters I didn't have time to read, and I thought as I went to the depot what a pity it was that my little friend's papa should have forgotten about Santa Claus. We big people do forget the strangest way, and then we haven't got a bit of a good time any more.

No Santa Claus! If you had asked that car full of people I would have liked to hear the answers they would have given you. No Santa Claus! Why, there was scarce a man in the lot who didn't carry a bundle that looked as if it had just tumbled out of his sleigh. I felt of one slyly, and it was a boy's sled—a "flexible flyer," I know, because he left one at our house the Christmas before; and I distinctly heard the rattling of a pair of skates in that box in the next seat. They were all good-natured, every one, though the train was behind time—that is a sure sign of Christmas. The brakeman wore a piece of mistletoe in his cap and a broad grin on his face, and he said "Merry Christmas" in a way to make a man feel good all the rest of the day. No Santa Claus, is there? You just ask him!

And then the train rolled into the city under the big gray dome to which George Washington gave his name, and by-and-by I went through a doorway which all American boys would rather see than go to school a whole week, though they love their teacher dearly. It is true that last winter my own little lad told the kind man whose house it is that he would rather ride up and down in the elevator at the hotel, but that was because he was so very little at the time and didn't know things rightly, and, besides, it was his first experience with an elevator.

As I was saying, I went through the door into a beautiful white hall with lofty pillars, between which there were regular banks of holly with the red berries shining through, just as if it were out in the woods! And from behind one of them there came the merriest laugh you could ever think of. Do you think, now, it was that letter in my pocket that gave that guilty little throb against my heart when I heard it, or what could it have been? I hadn't even time to ask myself the question, for there stood my host all framed in holly, and with the heartiest handclasp.

"Come in," he said, and drew me after. "The coffee is waiting." And he beamed upon the table with the veriest Christmas face as he poured it out himself, one cup for his dear wife and one for me. The children—ah! you should have asked *them* if there was a Santa Claus!

And so we sat and talked, and I told my kind friends that my own dear old mother, whom I have not seen for years, was very, very sick in far-away Denmark and longing for her boy, and a mist came into my hostess's gentle eyes and she said, "Let us cable over and tell her how much we think of her," though she had never seen her. And it was no sooner said than done. In came a man with a writing-pad, and while we drank our coffee this message sped under the great stormy sea to the faraway country where the day was shading into evening already, though the sun was scarce two hours high in Washington:

THE WHITE HOUSE.

Mrs. Riis, Ribe, Denmark:

Your son is breakfasting with us. We send you our love and sympathy.

THEODORE AND EDITH ROOSEVELT.

For, you see, the house with the holly in the hall was the White House, and my host was the President of the United States. I have to tell it to you, or you might easily fall into the same error I came near falling into. I had to pinch myself to make sure the President was not Santa Claus himself. I felt that he had in that moment given me the very greatest Christmas gift any man ever received: my little mother's life. For really what ailed her was that she was very old, and I know that when she got the President's dispatch she must have become immediately ten years younger and got right out of bed. Don't you know mothers are that way when any one makes much of their boys? I think Santa Claus must have brought them all in the beginning—the mothers, I mean.

I would just give anything to see what happened in that old town that is full of blessed memories to me, when the telegraph ticked off that message. I will warrant the town hurried out, burgomaster, bishop, beadle and all, to do honor to my gentle old mother. No Santa Claus, eh? What was that, then, that spanned two oceans with a breath of love and cheer, I should like to know. Tell me that!

After the coffee we sat together in the President's office for a little while while he signed commissions, each and every one of which was just Santa Claus's gift to a grown-up boy who had been good in the year that was going; and before we parted the President had lifted with so many strokes of his pen clouds of sorrow and want that weighed heavily on homes I knew of to which Santa Claus had had hard work finding his way that Christmas.

It seemed to me as I went out of the door, where the big policeman touched his hat and wished me a Merry Christmas, that the sun never shone so brightly in May as it did then. I quite expected to see the crocuses and the jonquils, that make the White House garden so pretty, out in full bloom. They were not, I suppose, only because they are official flowers and have a proper respect for the calendar that runs Congress and the Executive Departments, too.

I stopped on the way down the avenue at Uncle Sam's paymaster's to see what he thought of it. And there he was, busy as could be, making ready for the coming of Santa Claus. No need of my asking any questions here. Men stood in line with bank-notes in their hands asking for gold, new gold-pieces, they said, most every one. The paymaster, who had a sprig of Christmas green fixed in his desk just like any other man, laughed and shook his head and said "Santa Claus?" and the men in the line laughed too and nodded and went away with their gold.

One man who went out just ahead of me I saw stoop over a poor woman on the corner and thrust something into her hand, then walk hastily away. It was I who caught the light in the woman's eye and the blessing upon her poor wan lips, and the grass seemed greener in the Treasury dooryard, and the sky bluer than it had been before, even on that bright day. Perhaps—well, never mind! if any one says anything to you about principles and giving alms, you tell him that Santa Claus takes care of the principles at Christmas, and not to be afraid. As for him, if you want to know, just ask the old woman on the Treasury corner.

And so, walking down that Avenue of Good-will, I came to my train again and went home. And when I had time to think it all over I remembered the letters in my pocket which I had not opened. I took them out and read them, and among them were two sent to me in trust for Santa Claus himself which I had to lay away with the editor's message until I got the dew rubbed off my spectacles. One was from a great banker, and it contained a check for a thousand dollars to help buy a home for some poor children of the East Side tenements in New York, where the chimneys are so small and mean that scarce even a letter will go up through them, so that ever so many little ones over there never get on Santa Claus's books at all.

The other letter was from a lonely old widow, almost as old as my dear mother in Denmark, and it contained a two-dollar bill. For years, she wrote, she had saved and saved, hoping some time to have five dollars, and then she would go with me to the homes of the very poor and be Santa Claus herself. "And wherever you decided it was right to leave a trifle, that should be the place where it would be left," read the letter. But now she was so old that she could no longer think of such a trip and so she sent the money she had saved. And I thought of a family in one of those tenements where father and mother are both lying ill, with a boy, who ought to be in school, fighting all alone to keep the wolf from the door, and winning the fight. I guess he has been too busy to send any message up the chimney, if indeed there is one in his house; but you ask him, right now, whether he thinks there is a Santa Claus or not.

No Santa Claus? Yes, my little man, there is a Santa Claus, thank God! Your father had just forgotten. The world would indeed be poor without one. It is true that he does not always wear a white beard and drive a reindeer team—not always, you know—but what does it matter? He is Santa Claus with the big, loving, Christmas heart, for all that; Santa Claus with the kind thoughts for every one that make children and grown-up people beam with happiness all day long. And shall I tell you a secret which I did not learn at the post-office, but it is true all the same—of how you can always be sure your letters go to him straight by the chimney route? It is this: send along with them a friendly thought for the boy you don't like: for Jack who punched you, or Jim who was mean to you. The meaner he was the harder do you resolve to make it up: not to bear him a grudge. That is the stamp for the letter to Santa. Nobody can stop it, not even a cross-draught in the chimney, when it has that on.

Because—don't you know, Santa Claus is the spirit of Christmas: and ever and ever so many years ago when the dear little Baby was born after whom we call Christmas, and was cradled in a manger out in the stable because there was not room in the inn, that Spirit came into the world to soften the hearts of men and make them love one another. Therefore, that is the mark of the Spirit to this day. Don't let anybody or anything rub it out. Then the rest doesn't matter. Let them tear Santa's white beard off at the Sunday-school festival and growl in his bearskin coat. These are only his disguises. The steps of the real Santa Claus you can trace all through the world as you have done here with me, and when you stand in the last of his tracks you will find the Blessed Babe of Bethlehem smiling a welcome to you. For then you will be home.

CORNELIA OTIS SKINNER

 crest

God Rest You Merry

M RS. JONES was awakened at an untoward hour and with a sensation of oppression and pain. The hour was seven-fifteen, the oppression was caused by Adrian, her six-year-old son, who was sitting
for the most part on her chest and the pain arose from the rhythmic
pounding of Adrian's fist on the side of her head.

"Time to get up, Mummy," Adrian was calling in a tone that implied she must be very far away. It would have been nice to have
been far away. Mrs. Jones had stepped out the previous night with
Mr. Jones and some friends from Chicago (or were they friends?)
and she found it difficult to share her child's early morning exuber-
ance. In fact, had she been an introspective person she might have
been horrified to recognize in herself a sudden tendency toward in-
fanticide . . . an abnormality apparently shared by Mr. Jones who,
from the other side of the bed, raised a somewhat ghastly head, muttered, "Why don't you kill that boy?" and sank back into the state
of someone just emerging from a brain operation. Mrs. Jones, collecting what she could find of herself, asked Adrian what his idea was in
waking her.

"You're coming to the play!" Adrian apparently thought his mother
had suddenly gone deaf.

"What play?" It seemed an odd hour for the theatre.

"The Christmas play at school, of course."

Then it all came back to her. Adrian had appeared some days ago
with a mimeographed hand-bill that looked as if his entire class had
walked on it, and that bore the announcement of a Christmas play
to be presented by the primary class and the fond hope that at least
one parent would attend . . . a veiled command to all mothers. At

237

the time Mrs. Jones had thought it would be very nice. Even last night before going out, as she was tucking Adrian into bed, she thought it would be very sweet. Now she knew it was going to be terrible.

"What time is the play?" she croaked weakly.

"Eight-thirty. But I've got to be there at eight to get my halo on. I'm an angel." At which Mr. Jones mumbled, "Oh, yeah?" and Mrs. Jones struggled out of bed. She hadn't been in it long. In fact their home-coming taxi had pulled up at the apartment door alongside of Borden's wagon. That, she told herself, was why she felt so awful. It had nothing to do with any final night-cap at the Stork Club.

Mrs. Jones, of course, was a perfect lady. She dispatched Adrian to his room, put a couple of Alka-Seltzers in a glass to dissolve, and set about the laborious business of dressing. Mr. Jones remained comatose except for an occasional grunt and a moment when he reared up on one elbow, glared at the bubbling Alka-Seltzer and complained that "it made too damn much noise." Mrs. Jones managed to stagger first into her clothes, then into the dining-room, where she found that while she had no appetite, she had an overwhelming capacity for drinking ice-water. Adrian dismayed her by talking incessantly and scattering puffed rice about and she was further unnerved to behold through the glass of the pantry door, the baleful eye of the cook who was a fanatical teetotaler. She choked down some black coffee, sent Adrian back to his room three times to collect forgotten articles of clothing and gathered her own hat and coat. She had even the saintlike forbearance to gaze upon the recumbent form of Mr. Jones and refrain from yelling, "Sissy!" in his somewhat inflamed ear. In a daze she descended in the elevator and in a daze and a taxi rode with Adrian to school.

She felt a little shy on entering the building. Mrs. Jones was a good mother but she wasn't fanatic about it. By that I mean she didn't put in much time at Parent-Teacher's meetings, nor was she one to pay frequent calls on the head master for the sake of discussing Adrian's sense of Group-Consciousness. In fact, except for the opening day, she hadn't set foot in the place. She was determined, however, to make a gracious impression. An elderly gentleman standing just inside the door exchanged greetings with Adrian. Mrs. Jones, thinking he looked distinguished, extended her hand and in a voice that she forced to be bright said: "How do you do? I'm Adrian's mother."

The gentleman hesitated, then silently took her hand while Adrian collapsed with mortification against a statue of Zeus.

"Mother!" he hissed (he never called her Mother unless he was particularly ashamed of her), "that's Bill, the janitor!" Mrs. Jones repressed the impulse to say, "Then what the hell's he doing here?" and with what dignity she could muster followed the rapidly retreating figure of her son.

"Where do I go, Adrian?" she panted, feeling as she did her first day of freshman year. Adrian waved his school-bag in a wild gesture that might have meant anything and vanished through a door. At the end of the corridor a number of women were being ushered into a room by a young master who looked awfully pure and unjaded. Still smarting from the janitor episode she was hesitant to inform him about being Adrian's mother. Judging by the way she must look it would be giving Adrian a break to keep her identity secret. So she merely smiled and the young man smiled back and told her to go in and just take any seat. A classroom had been converted into a theatre with rows of chairs facing an improvised stage. Mrs. Jones selected a position toward the back and near a door. It being an affair of the Primary class, the chairs were those designed for little tots, Mrs. Jones was a tall gal and when she sat down her knees came up somewhere in the vicinity of her chin.

She looked at her watch and sighed. Twenty minutes to wait. Perhaps she should have gone with Adrian to help him with his halo. But who was she to deal with haloes this bleak morning? She must try to get herself into the spirit of Yuletide and little children, however hard. Snatches of music she'd heard at the Stork Club kept running through her head, and her head was in no condition to have anything run through it except a few cool mountain streams. She had a very awful pain at the back of her neck and her eyes felt like freshly dipped Easter eggs. Moreover, her heart was thumping in an alarming way. She told herself this was stage-fright for Adrian.

In misery she gazed at the stage. The curtain, which sagged badly in the middle, gave indications of violent activity on the Thespian side. It fluttered and bulged and kept coming apart until an adult hand reached out and secured it with a safety pin. The room began to fill with mothers, governesses and a few protesting fathers. A young woman in a tweed suit plopped herself down in the adjacent seat. She looked annoyingly clear-eyed and healthy . . . obviously one of those splendid mothers who take courses in vital subjects and go in for exercise as if it were a Cause. She smiled energetically at Mrs. Jones and said, "Your boy in this?" in the cheery voice of a Girl Scout Captain.

Mrs. Jones nodded wanly and at the same time edged slightly away. It hadn't been so long since she'd had that last night-cap and (degrading thought!) she hadn't thought to chew any coffee-beans.

"Both my sons are taking part." The woman talked like a Roman matron. "I have twins."

She would have, Mrs. Jones reflected and thought how fearful it would have been to have been aroused by two Adrians this morning. She managed to cheep, "How lovely," and the woman asked what was her little boy's name. On being informed she said "Oh" in a tone that hinted darkly that she knew him all right. "He's Primary One B, isn't he?" she continued. Mrs. Jones considered it pretty nosey of this woman to know more about Adrian than she herself did but she said she guessed he was and were her twins in the same division? "Oh, dear, no, they're a whole class ahead." Then as an afterthought, "They're a year younger than Adrian." Mrs. Jones started to bridle but it hurt to bridle so she sank back into her state of moral apathy, reflecting moodily that considering his heritage it was only just retribution that her child should be a mental defective. A new arrival took the chair on the other side. Influenced by the community spirit of the mother of the twins, Mrs. Jones essayed a feeble grin and said "How do you do?" The woman returned a stiff salutation in the unmistakable accents of an English governess . . . the superior variety to whom misguided Americans pay a hundred a month to turn their domestic household into living hell. The situation was eased by the entrance of the piano teacher followed by a line of little boys bearing cymbals, tambourines, triangles and other instruments of torture. The entrance of the orchestra coincided with that of a group that looked to be a bevy of green and red elves but turned out to be a portion of the Primary glee club clad as choristers.

The footlights went on and the rest of the room was in darkness. A murmur of fatuous anticipation arose from the rows of beaming

mothers but nothing else happened. The piano teacher rose and in
a loud hiss told some unknown behind the scenes that they'd put out
his light, too, whereat all the lights went on again and the mothers
laughed good-naturedly. After considerable snapping of buttons and
some playful going on and off of side brackets, the desired effect was
obtained and an impressive chord struck on the piano.

The opening selection was "God Rest You Merry, Gentlemen"
sung in sweet treble by the glee club and punctuated by the orchestra
who, on words like *"dismay"* and "Christmas *Day"* came forth with
a goodly wallop of tympany. The mother of the twins looked happy
and said wasn't it darling and Mrs. Jones concurred, although in her
private opinion, it was more like gems from "Hellzapoppin." After
the carol there was a pause and then the curtains were yanked as far
as they'd go with the safety pin still holding them. They were then
yanked back and the fastening removed, all of which convulsed the
choristers. Finally the curtains opened on bare stage and a pause
that turned into an awkward stage wait. There were sounds of scram-
bling and a juvenile voice distinctly said, "Cut it out, will ya?"
At length there entered from the left three rather diminutive Magi,
orientally splendid in glazed muslin, bearing their respective gifts on
sofa-cushions. The scene was in pantomime, the glee club furnishing
the narrative with a rendering of "We Three Kings of Orien-*Tar.*"
There seemed to be some difference of opinion in regard to the lo-
cality of the star. One looked before him, one searched the audience
like a veteran actor counting the house, and one looked directly overhead until his crown started to slip off, whereat he lowered his gaze
to the ground. The Roman matron nudged her and pointed out one
of her Gracchi. He was, of course, the only one acting correctly. The
scene closed with the finish of the carol. At the curtain one or two of
the spectators ventured gentle applause but were shushed by the rest
who regarded it somewhat in the nature of a performance of "Parsi-
fal." During the entr'acte the English governess leaned over and
asked if she'd had her boy bring his own costume. She replied why,
no, that she understood the school furnished them. The governess
made a face like Beatrice Lillie making a face like a governess, and
said yes, but *she* never let *her* charge wear something that had gone
the rounds goodness *how* long, and Mrs. Jones wondered morbidly
if she'd better start watching Adrian for symptoms of Bubonic Plague.

The second scene was reminiscent of the first, it being in this instance a case of shepherds instead of kings and the theme song being "While Shepherds watched their Flocks." On a table disguised as a celestial promontory there appeared a small angel who made beckoning gestures and the finale was considerably enlivened by the angel's little sister who from the audience emitted a joyful "Why, there's Brud!" The second intermission was very long. From backstage came sounds of shuffling feet and of heavy things being dragged forth . . . possibly bodies. The curtains would seem about to part, then would ease up, amid muffled cries of "No, wait!" The choristers threw in a carol or two as a filler. Adrian's big moment was approaching and Mrs. Jones' hands became clammy. Finally all was ready and there was presented a really very charming Nativity tableau. The Manger with its participants was at one side while in the background on and around the same table as that of act two, a closeranked host of angels gave an impression that Heaven was at the moment slightly overcrowded.

"That's my other twin playing Joseph," her neighbor whispered. Mrs. Jones nodded and noted with satisfaction that one side of his beard was noticeably unstuck. For a time she looked vainly for Adrian. After a bit in the back row she spotted a cherub whose diabolical behavior made her recognize her son. Half hidden from view he had a vantage place over his sanctified buddies whom, judging by their wriggling and squirming, he was pinching in their all too mortal rears. She could only hope the All-American mother hadn't noticed, but she had, for she said, "Why, there's Adrian." Then added, "Restless type, isn't he?" Adrian's pastimes were cut short by some unseen authority in the wings and for one carol he remained comparatively tranquil. He looked very sweet, Mrs. Jones thought, except for the fact that his halo was cocked at the angle of a gob's hat. It was apparently loose and he eventually discovered that he could do all sorts of fascinating things with it. As it was about to slide off one ear, a violent jerk would bring it back, while a few vigorous nods would throw it into a sort of spin. To Mrs. Jones it seemed as if all eyes were fixed on her appalling child. Beside him the Principals in the drama paled into insignificance. She prayed fervently for some cataclysm that would wipe out both herself and Adrian at once. It looked as if her prayers were about to be granted, at least in part, for after a few minutes of fiendish head-waggling the angel quite suddenly and unxpectedly fell from view in the tradition of Lucifer.

Mrs. Jones waited to hear those all too familiar bellows but there followed so complete a silence she began to think that perhaps it was a case of concussion. However, in a second, that same adult arm was stretched forth and she could make out the huddled-up form of her son being dragged ignominiously from the boards. This was her cue to make an exit also. The play was nearing its finish and she thought it best to make a quick get-away. As she stumbled out, the choir was again singing "God Rest You Merry, Gentlemen," the audience being asked to join in. She heard herself singing her own version which began, "God help you weary, gentlemen."

In the corridor she was met by Adrian. Far from looking contrite he was all smiles—

"Hi, Mum," he called serenely, "how did you like it?" The words of vituperation died on her lips. She said she liked it very much. Adrian beamed.

"Did you see me?" he asked.

"Yes, dear," she said. "Where do we go to get a cab?"

ROBERT LOUIS STEVENSON

❦

A Christmas Sermon

B Y THE TIME this paper appears, I shall have been talking for twelve months; (footnote—i.e., in the pages of Scribner's Magazine, 1888.) and it is thought I should take my leave in a formal and seasonable manner. Valedictory eloquence is rare, and death-bed sayings have not often hit the mark of the occasion. Charles Second, wit and skeptic, a man whose life had been one long lesson in human incredulity, an easy-going comrade, a manoeuvring king—remembered and embodied all his wit and skepticism along with more than his usual good humor in the famous "I am afraid, gentlemen," I am an unconscionable time a-dying.

I

An unconscionable time a-dying—there is the picture ("I am afraid, gentlemen,") of your life and of mine. The sands run out, and the hours are "numbered and indisputed," and the days go by; and when the last of these finds us, we have been a long time dying, and what else? The very length is something, if we reach that hour of separation undishonoured; and to have lived at all is doubtless (in the soldierly expression) to have served. There is a tale in Tacitus of how the veterans mutinied in the German wilderness; of how, seizing their general's hand, these old, war-worn exiles passed his finger along their toothless gums. *Sunt lacrymae rerum*: this was the most eloquent of the songs of Simeon. And when a man has lived to a fair age, he bears his marks of service. He may have never been remarked

244

upon the breach at the head of the army; at least he shall have lost his teeth on the camp bread.

The idealism of serious people in this age of ours is of a noble character. It never seems to them that they have served enough; they have a fine impatience of their virtues. It were perhaps more modest to be singly thankful that we are no worse. It is not only our enemies, those desperate characters—it is we ourselves who know not what we do;—thence springs the glimmering hope that perhaps we do better than we think: that to scramble through this random business with hands reasonably clean, to have played the part of a man or woman with some reasonable fulness, to have often resisted the diabolic, and at the end to be still resisting it, is for the poor human soldier to have done right well. To ask to see some fruit of our endeavour is but a transcendental way of serving for reward; and what we take to be contempt of self is only greed of hire.

And again if we require so much of ourselves, shall we not require much of others? If we do not genially judge our own deficiencies, is it not to be feared we shall be even stern to the trespasses of others? And he who (looking back upon his own life) can see no more than that he has been unconscionably long a-dying, will he not be tempted to think his neighbor unconscionably long of getting hanged? It is probable that nearly all who think of conduct at all, think of it too much; it is certain we all think too much of sin. We are not damned for doing wrong, but for not doing right; Christ would never hear of negative morality; *thou shalt* was ever his word, with which he superseded *thou shalt not*. To make our idea of morality centre on forbidden acts is to defile the imagination and to introduce into our judgments of our fellow-men a secret element of gusto. If a thing is wrong for us, we should not dwell upon the thought of it; or we shall soon dwell upon it with inverted pleasure. If we cannot drive it from our minds—one thing of two: either our creed is in the wrong and we must more indulgently remodel it; or else, if our morality be in the right, we are criminal lunatics and should place our persons in restraint. A mark of such unwholesomely divided minds is the passion for interference with others: the Fox without the Tail was of this breed, but had (if his biographer is to be trusted) a certain antique civility now out of date. A man may have a flaw, a weakness, that unfits him for the duties of life, that spoils his temper, that threatens his integrity, or that betrays him into cruelty. It has to be conquered; but it must never be suffered to engross his thoughts. The true duties lie all upon the farther side, and must be attended to with a whole mind so soon as this preliminary clearing of the decks has been effected. In order that he may be kind and honest, it may be needful he should become a total abstainer; let him become so then, and the next day let him forget the circumstance. Trying to be kind and honest will require all his thoughts; a mortified appetite is never a wise companion; in so far as he has had to mortify an appetite, he will still be the worse man; and of such an one a great deal of cheerfulness will be required in judging life, and a great deal of humility in judging others.

It may be argued again that dissatisfaction with our life's endeavour springs in some degree from dulness. We require higher tasks, because we do not recognize the height of those we have. Trying to be kind and honest seems an affair too simple and too inconsequential for gentlemen of our heroic mould; we had rather set ourselves to something bold, arduous, and conclusive; we had rather found a schism or suppress a heresy, cut off a hand or mortify an appetite. But the task before us, which is to co-endure with our existence, is rather one of microscopic fineness, and the heroism required is that of patience. There is no cutting of the Gordian knots of life; each must be smilingly unravelled.

To be honest, to be kind—to earn a little and to spend a little less, to make upon the whole a family happier for his presence, to renounce when that shall be necessary and not to be embittered, to keep a few friends but these without capitulation—above all, on the same grim condition, to keep friends with himself—here is a task for all that a man has of fortitude and delicacy. He has an ambitious soul who would ask more; he has a hopeful spirit who should look in such an enterprise to be successful. There is indeed one element in human destiny that not blindness itself can controvert: whatever else we are intended to do, we are not intended to succeed; failure is the fate allotted. It is so in every art and study; it is so above all in the continent art of living well. Here is a pleasant thought for the year's end or for the end of life: Only self-deception will be satisfied, and there need be no despair for the despairer.

II

But Christmas is not only the mile-mark of another year, moving us to thoughts of self-examination: it is a season, from all its associations, whether domestic or religious, suggesting thoughts of joy. A man dissatisfied with his endeavours is a man tempted to sadness. And in the midst of the winter, when his life runs lowest and he is reminded of the empty chairs of his beloved, it is well he should be condemned to this fashion of the smiling face. Noble disappointment, noble self-denial are not to be admired, not even to be pardoned, if they bring bitterness. It is one thing to enter the kingdom of heaven maim; another to maim yourself and stay without. And the kingdom of heaven is of the childlike, of those who are easy to please, who love and give pleasure. Mighty men of their hands, the smiters and the builders and the judges, have lived long and done sternly and yet preserved this lovely character; and among our carpet interests and twopenny concerns, the shame were indelible if *we* should lose it. Gentleness and cheerfulness, these come before all morality; they are the perfect duties. And it is the trouble with moral men that they have neither one nor other. It was the moral man, the Pharisee, whom Christ could not away with. If your morals make you dreary, depend upon it they are wrong. I do not say "give them up," for they may be all you have; but conceal them like a vice, lest they should spoil the lives of better and simpler people.

A strange temptation attends upon man: to keep his eye on pleasures, even when he will not share in them; to aim all his morals against them. This very year a lady (singular iconoclast!) proclaimed a crusade against dolls; and the racy sermon against lust is a feature of the age. I venture to call such moralists insincere. At any excess of perversion of a natural appetite, their lyre sounds of itself with relishing denunciations; but for all displays of the truly diabolic—envy, malice, the mean lie, the mean silence, the calumnious truth, the back-biter, the petty tyrant, the peevish poisoner of family life—their standard is quite different. These are wrong, they will admit, yet somehow not so wrong; there is no zeal in their assault on them, no secret element of gusto warms up the sermon; it is for things not wrong in themselves that they reserve the choicest of their indignation. A man may naturally disclaim all moral kinship with the Reverend Mr. Zola or the hobgoblin old lady of the dolls; for these are gross and naked instances. And yet in each of us some similar element resides. The sight of a pleasure in which we cannot or else will not share moves us to a particular impatience. It may be because we are envious, or because we are sad, or because we dislike noise and romping—being so refined, or because—being so philosophic—we have an overweighing sense of life's gravity: at least, as we go on in years, we are all tempted to frown upon our neighbour's pleasures. People are nowadays so fond of resisting temptations; here is one to be resisted. They are so fond of self-denial; here is a propensity that cannot be too peremptorily denied. There is an idea abroad among moral people that they should make their neighbours good. One person I have to make good: myself. But my duty to my neighbour is much more nearly expressed by saying that I have to make him happy —if I may.

<h2 style="text-align:center">III</h2>

Happiness and goodness, according to canting moralists, stand in the relation of effect and cause. There was never anything less proved or less probable: our happiness is never in our own hands; we inherit our constitution; we stand buffet among friends and enemies; we may be so built as to feel a sneer or an aspersion with unusual keenness, and so circumstanced as to be unusually exposed to them; we may have nerves very sensitive to pain and be afflicted with a disease very painful. Virtue will not help us and it is not meant to help us. It is not even its own reward, except for the self-centered and—I had almost said—the unamiable. No man can pacify his conscience; if quiet be what he want, he shall do better to let that organ perish from disuse. And to avoid the penalties of the law, and the minor *capitis diminutio* of social ostracism, is an affair of wisdom—of cunning, if you will—and not of virtue.

In his own life, then, a man is not to expect happiness, only to profit by it gladly when it shall arise; he is on duty here; he knows not how or why, and does not need to know; he knows not for what hire, and must not ask. Somehow or other, though he does not know what goodness is, he must try to be good; somehow or other, though he cannot tell what will do it, he must try to give happiness to others.

And no doubt there comes in here a frequent clash of duties. How far is he to make his neighbour happy? How far must he respect that smiling face, so easy to cloud, so hard to brighten again? And how far, on the other side, is he bound to be his brother's keeper and the prophet of his own morality? How far must he resent evil?

The difficulty is that we have little guidance; Christ's sayings on the point being hard to reconcile with each other, and (the most of them) hard to accept. But the truth of his teaching would seem to be this: in our own person and fortune, we should be ready to accept and to pardon all; it is *our* cheek we are to turn, *our* coat that we are to give away to the man who has taken *our* cloak. But when another's face is buffeted, perhaps a little of the lion will become us best. That we are to suffer others to be injured and stand by, is not conceivable and surely not desirable. Revenge, says Bacon, is a kind of wild justice; its judgments at least are delivered by an insane judge; and in our own quarrel we can see nothing truly and do nothing wisely. But in the quarrel of our neighbour, let us be more bold. One person's happiness is as sacred as another's; when we cannot defend both, let us defend one with a stout heart. It is only in so far as we are doing this, that we have any right to interfere: the defence of B is our only ground of action against A. A has as good a right to go to the devil, as we to go to glory; and neither knows what he does.

The truth is that all these interventions and denunciations and militant mongerings of moral half-truths, though they be sometimes needful, though they are often enjoyable, do yet belong to an inferior grade of duties. Ill-temper and envy and revenge find here an arsenal of pious disguises; this is the playground of inverted lusts. With a little more patience and a little less temper, a gentler and wiser method might be found in almost every case; and the knot that we cut by some fine heady quarrel-scene in private life, or, in public affairs, by some denunciatory act against what we are pleased to call our neighbour's vices, might yet have been unwoven by the hand of sympathy.

IV

To look back upon the past year, and see how little we have striven and to what small purpose; and how often we have been cowardly and hung back, or temerarious and rushed unwisely in; and how

every day and all day long we have transgressed the law of kindness;
—it may seem a paradox, but in the bitterness of these discoveries, a
certain consolation resides. Life is not designed to minister to a man's
vanity. He goes upon his long business most of the time with a hanging head, and all the time like a blind child. Full of rewards and
pleasures at it is—so that to see the day break or the moon rise, or
to meet a friend, or to hear the dinner-call when he is hungry, fills
him with surprising joys—this world is yet for him no abiding city.
Friendships fall through, health fails, weariness assails him; year after
year, he must thumb the hardly varying record of his own weakness
and folly. It is a friendly process of detachment. When the time
comes that he should go, there need be few illusions left about himself. *Here lies one who meant well, tried a little, failed much*: surely
that may be his epitaph, of which he need not be ashamed. Nor will
he complain at the summons which calls a defeated soldier from the
field; defeated, ay, if he were Paul or Marcus Aurelius!—but if there
is still one inch of fight in his old spirit, undishonoured. The faith
which sustained him in his life-long blindness and life-long disappointment will scarce even be required in this last formality of laying
down his arms. Give him a march with his old bones; there, out of
the glorious sun-coloured earth, out of the day and the dust and the
ecstasy—there goes another Faithful Failure!

From a recent book of verse,* where there is more than one such
beautiful and manly poem, I take this memorial piece: it says better
than I can, what I love to think; let it be our parting word.

> "A late lark twitters from the quiet skies;
> And from the west,
> Where the sun, his day's work ended,
> Lingers as in content,
> There falls on the old, gray city
> An influence, luminous and serene,
> A shining peace.
>
> "The smoke ascends
> In a rosy-and-golden haze. The spires
> Shine, and are changed. In the valley
> Shadows rise. The lark sings on. The sun,
> Closing his benediction,

* Note: From "A Book of Verses" by William Ernest Henley. D. Nutt, 1888.

Sinks, and the darkening air
Thrills with a sense of the triumphing night—
Night, with her train of stars
And her great gift of sleep.

"So be my passing!
My task accomplished and the long day done,
My wages taken, and in my heart
Some late lark singing,
Let me be gathered to the quiet west,
The sundown splendid and serene,
Death."

HAROLD S. STEWART

❧ ❧

A Christmas Fable

I T WAS so cold the snow squeaked as Professor Stone walked up the hill from the university to his home. He was late for supper, having spent longer in the library than he expected. Turning the corner to his home, he noticed lights and many cars parked around the house. *Then,* he remembered! His wife was having a Christmas party. He should have been home hours ago.

Professor Stone entered the basement door, kicked off his rubbers, hung his overcoat on a nail, slipped up the stairs into the kitchen, and tried to appear as if he had been at the party all along. Almost immediately someone cried, "Here he is!" "*Open it! open it!*" And others tugged and pulled the professor into the dining room—into the dining room and up to the table, on which sat a rather large and somewhat odd-looking package.

The dean said, "Careful, Stone. I want those Japanese stamps."

The professor looked at the package. In the corner were many beautiful stamps—Japanese stamps. Cutting them out with his pen knife, he handed them to the dean. "You know," said the professor, "I think this is from that Japanese student we had last year. I seem to remember he was going to send me something."

"*Open it, open it!*" the guests cried.

Inside the heavy brown paper was a white package, tied with a broad white ribbon. "What a beautiful silk ribbon!" someone said. "May I have it?"

And the professor's wife said, "Be careful unwrapping that, dear, I want the rice paper."

As the professor handed the ribbon to the person who wanted it, he said, "That Japanese student said his father worked for the Emperor and could send me . . ." The sentence went unfinished, for under the rice paper there was a beautiful lacquered box painted with many gay scenes.

"What a splendid example of Japanese art!" someone said. "Perhaps you will lend it to the museum?" And the professor said, "Sure. It wasn't a box the boy was going to send. I think it was . . ."

"*Open it! Open it!*" they cried.

Opening the lacquered box, the professor drew out a large roll of beautifully patterned silk. "Oh my," his wife said, "how lovely! There's enough here for draperies!"

"It wasn't silk," the professor said. "It was something of the Emperor's. It was . . ."

"Careful how you unroll that," someone said. "There's a box in it."

So there was! A carved ebony box. The professor stood up on a chair. Holding the box high in the air, he announced, "I am going to keep this box, for, though it isn't the gift, I know what's in it. It's tea! Our Japanese student said his father, who works for the Emperor of Japan, would send me some of the Emperor's own tea." Opening the box, the professor showed his guests the inside—which seemed full of tea.

"It's just time for tea!" said the professor's wife. "I'll make you some Emperor's tea." She did this, and when each guest had a cup, they all tasted together. It was—awful! Each, to be polite, asked for more.

The professor's wife dipped into the ebony box. But what was this? There was something buried in the box—something hard. Digging in, she found a small, exquisite ivory box, and in the ivory box—*tea!* This tea smelled wonderful, and this tea tasted—well, no one had ever tasted such good tea.

Far off in Japan, when the student's father told him of the kind professor, the Emperor agreed that a gift should be sent, and he ordered his chamberlain to deliver tea to the student's father.

The chamberlain thought, "What an exquisite gift. I must put it in an appropriate box." So he took a beautiful ivory box from his own home and in it put the tea.

The student's father took the ivory box and, saying to himself, "Such a gift must be protected with great care," he placed the ivory box in his favorite ebony box and filled up all the empty space with dried mulberry leaves.

The student's wife wrapped the ebony box in yards and yards of patterned silk, thinking, "Even this is not good enough for a gift of the Emperor's tea!"

And the student put the bundle of silk in his finest lacquered box. Handing it to his servant he said, "This is a package of the Emperor's tea. Send it with great care to Professor Stone."

Knowing how precious the gift was, the servant wrapped the lacquered box in rice paper and tied it with his own white silk ribbon.

At the post office he said to the postman, "Think of it! This is a gift of the Emperor's tea for a professor in America!"

The postman picked the most beautiful stamps for the package— a valuable package, full of many charming things.

But the essence of the gift was the Emperor's tea.

And so it is with the gay, lovely wrappings that the minds of men have put around the precious gem of Christmas. Each of us must unwrap the gift for himself, careful not to mistake the one for the other.

DYLAN THOMAS

≈§≈

Conversation about Christmas

SMALL BOY: Years and years ago, when you were a boy . . .

SELF: When there were wolves in Wales, and birds the colour of red-flannel petticoats whisked past the harp-shaped hills, when we sang and wallowed all night and day in caves that smelt like Sunday afternoons in damp front farmhouse parlours, and chased, with the jawbones of deacons, the English and the bears . . .

SMALL BOY: You are not so old as Mr. Beynon Number Twenty-Two who can remember when there were no motors. Years and years ago, when you were a boy . . .

SELF: Oh, before the motor even, before the wheel, before the duchess-faced horse, when we rode the daft and happy hills bareback . . .

SMALL BOY: You're not so daft as Mrs. Griffiths up the street, who says she puts her ear under the water in the reservoir and listens to the fish talk Welsh. When you were a boy, what was Christmas like?

SELF: It snowed.

SMALL BOY: It snowed last year, too. I made a snowman and my brother knocked it down and I knocked my brother down and then we had tea.

SELF: But that was not the same snow. Our snow was not only shaken in whitewash buckets down the sky, I think it came shawling out of the ground and swam and drifted out of the arms and hands and bodies of the trees; snow grew overnight on the roofs of the houses like a pure and grandfather moss, minutely ivied the walls, and settled on the postman, opening the gate, like a dumb, numb thunderstorm of white, torn Christmas cards.

SMALL BOY: Were there postmen, then, too?

SELF: With sprinkling eyes and wind-cherried noses, on spread, frozen feet they crunched up to the doors and mittened on them manfully. But all that the children could hear was a ringing of bells.

SMALL BOY: You mean that the postman went rat-a-tat-tat and the doors rang?

SELF: The bells that the children could hear were inside them.

SMALL BOY: I only hear thunder sometimes, never bells.

SELF: There were church bells, too.

SMALL BOY: Inside them?

SELF: No, no, no, in the bat-black, snow-white belfries, tugged by bishops and storks. And they rang their tidings over the bandaged town, over the frozen foam of the powder and ice-cream hills, over the crackling sea. It seemed that all the churches boomed, for joy, under my window; and the weathercocks crew for Christmas, on our fence.

SMALL BOY: Get back to the postmen.

SELF: They were just ordinary postmen, fond of walking, and dogs, and Christmas, and the snow. They knocked on the doors with blue knuckles . . .

SMALL BOY: Ours has got a black knocker . . .

SELF: And then they stood on the white welcome mat in the little, drifted porches, and clapped their hands together, and huffed and puffed, making ghosts with their breath, and jogged from foot to foot like small boys wanting to go out.

SMALL BOY: And then the Presents?

SELF: And then the Presents, after the Christmas box. And the cold postman, with a rose on his button-nose, tingled down the teatray-slithered run of the chilly glinting hill. He went in his icebound boots like a man on fishmonger's slabs. He wagged his bag like a frozen camel's hump, dizzily turned the corner on one foot, and, by God, he was gone.

SMALL BOY: Get back to the Presents.

SELF: There were the Useful Presents: engulfing mufflers of the old coach days, and mittens made for giant sloths; zebra scarves of a substance like silky gum that could be tug-o'-warred down to the goloshes; blinding tam-o'-shanters like patchwork tea-cosies, and bunny-scutted busbies and balaclavas for victims of head-shrinking tribes; from aunts who always wore wool next to the skin, there were moustached and rasping vests that made you wonder why the aunties had any skin left at all; and once I had a little crocheted nosebag from an aunt now, alas, no longer whinnying with us. And pictureless books in which small boys, though warned, with quotations, not to, *would* skate on Farmer Garge's pond, and did, and drowned; and books that told me everything about the wasp, except why.

SMALL BOY: Get on to the Useless Presents.

SELF: On Christmas Eve I hung at the foot of my bed Bessie Bunter's black stocking, and always, I said, I would stay awake all the moonlit, snowlit night to hear the roof-alighting reindeer and see the hollied boot descend through soot. But soon the sand of the snow drifted into my eyes, and though I stared towards the fireplace and around the flickering room where the black sack-like stocking hung, I was asleep before the chimney trembled and the room was red and white with Christmas. But in the morning, though no snow melted on the bedroom floor, the stocking bulged and brimmed: press it, it squeaked like a mouse-in-a-box; it smelt of tangerine; a furry arm lolled over, like the arm of a kangaroo out of its mothers belly; squeeze it hard in the middle, and something squelched; squeeze it again—squelch again. Look out of the frost-scribbled window: on the great loneliness of the small hill, a blackbird was silent in the snow.

SMALL BOY: Were there any sweets?

SELF: Of course there were sweets. It was the marshmallows that squelched. Hardboileds, toffee, fudge and allsorts, crunches, cracknels, humbugs, glaciers, and marzipan and butterwelsh for the Welsh. And troops of bright tin soldiers who, if they would not fight, could always run. And Snakes-and-Families and Happy Ladders. And Easy Hobbi-Games for Little Engineers, complete with Instructions. Oh, easy for Leonardo! And a whistle to make the dogs bark to wake up the old man next door to make him beat on the wall with his stick to shake our picture off the wall. And a packet of cigarettes: you put one in your mouth and you stood at the corner of the street and you waited for hours, in vain, for an old lady to scold you for smoking a cigarette and then, with a smirk, you ate it. And, last of all, in the toe of the stocking, sixpence like a silver corn. And then downstairs for breakfast under the balloons!

SMALL BOY: Were there Uncles, like in our house?

SELF: There are always Uncles at Christmas. The same Uncles. And on Christmas mornings, with dog-disturbing whistle and sugar fags, I would scour the swathed town for the news of the little world, and find always a dead bird by the white Bank or by the deserted swings: perhaps a robin, all but one of his fires out, and that fire still burning on his breast. Men and women wading and scooping back from church or chapel, with taproom noses and wind-smacked cheeks, all albinos, huddled their stiff black jarring feathers against the irreligious snow. Mistletoe hung from the gas in all the front parlours; there was sherry and walnuts and bottled beer and crackers by the dessertspoons; and cats in their fur-abouts watched the fires; and the high-heaped fires crackled and spat, all ready for the chestnuts and the mulling pokers. Some few large men sat in the front parlours, without their collars, Uncles almost certainly, trying their new cigars, holding them out judiciously at arm's-length, returning them to their mouths, coughing, then holding them out again as though waiting for the explosion; and some few small aunts, not wanted in the kitchen, nor anywhere else for that matter, sat on the very edges of their chairs, poised and brittle, afraid to break, like faded cups and saucers. Not many those mornings trod the piling streets: an old man always, fawn-bowlered, yellow-gloved, and, at this time of year, with spats of snow, would take his constitutional to the white bowling-green, and back, as he would take it wet or fine on Christmas Day or Doomsday; sometimes two hale young men, with big pipes blazing, no overcoats, and windblown scarves, would trudge, unspeaking, down to the forlorn sea, to work up an appetite, to blow away the fumes, who knows, to walk into the waves until nothing of them was left but the two curling smoke clouds of their inextinguishable briars.

SMALL BOY: Why didn't you go home for Christmas dinner?

SELF: Oh, but I did, I always did. I would be slap-dashing home, the gravy smell of the dinners of others, the bird smell, the brandy, the pudding and mince, weaving up my nostrils, when out of a snow-clogged side-lane would come a boy the spit of myself, with a pink-tipped cigarette and the violet past of a black eye, cocky as a bull-finch, leering all to himself. I hated him on sight and sound, and would be about to put my dog-whistle to my lips and blow him off the face of Christmas when suddenly he, with a violent wink, put *his* whistle to *his* lips and blew so stridently, so high, so exquisitely loud, that gobbling faces, their cheeks bulged with goose, would press against their tinselled windows, the whole length of the white echoing street.

SMALL BOY: What did you have for Dinner?

SELF: Turkey, and blazing pudding.

SMALL BOY: Was it nice?

SELF: It was not made on earth.

SMALL BOY: What did you do after dinner?

SELF: The Uncles sat in front of the fire, took off their collars, loosened all buttons, put their large moist hands over their watch-chains, groaned a little, and slept. Mothers, aunts, and sisters scuttled to and fro, bearing tureens. The dog was sick. Auntie Beattie had to have three aspirins, but Auntie Hannah, who liked port, stood in the middle of the snowbound backyard, singing like a big-bosomed thrush. I would blow up balloons to see how big they would blow up to; and, when they burst, which they all did, the Uncles jumped and rumbled. In the rich and heavy afternoon, the Uncles breathing like dolphins and the snow descending, I would sit in the front room, among festoons and Chinese lanterns, and nibble at dates, and try to make a model man-o'-war, following the Instructions for Little Engineers, and produce what might be mistaken for a sea-going tram. And then, at Christmas tea, the recovered Uncles would be jolly over their mince-pies; and the great iced cake loomed in the centre of the table like a marble grave. Auntie Hannah laced her tea with rum, because it was only once a year. And in the evening, there was Music. An uncle played the fiddle, a cousin sang Cherry Ripe, and another uncle sang Drake's Drum. It was very warm in the little house. Auntie Hannah, who had got on to the parsnip wine, sang a song about Rejected Love, and Bleeding Hearts, and Death, and then another in which she said that her Heart was like a Bird's Nest; and then everybody laughed again, and then I went to bed. Looking through my bedroom window, out into the moonlight and the flying, unending, smoke-coloured snow, I could see the lights in the windows of all the other houses on our hill, and hear the music rising from them up the long, steadily falling night. I turned the gas down, I got into bed. I said some words to the close and holy darkness, and then I slept.

SMALL BOY: But it all sounds like an ordinary Christmas.

SELF: It was.

SMALL BOY: But Christmas when you were a boy wasn't any different to Christmas now.

SELF: It was, it was.

SMALL BOY: Why was Christmas different then?

SELF: I mustn't tell you.

SMALL BOY: Why mustn't you tell me? Why is Christmas different for me?

SELF: I mustn't tell you.

SMALL BOY: Why can't Christmas be the same for me as it was for you when you were a boy?

SELF: I mustn't tell you. I mustn't tell you because it is Christmas now.

HENRY VAN DYKE

❧ ❦

The Christmas Angel

I T WAS the hour of rest in the Country Beyond the Stars. All the
silver bells that swing with the turning of the great ring of light
which lies around that land were softly chiming; and the sound of
their commotion went down like dew upon the golden ways of the
city, and the long alleys of blossoming trees, and the meadows of
asphodel, and the curving shores of the River of Life.

At the hearing of that chime, all the angels who had been working
turned to play, and all who had been playing gave themselves joy-
fully to work. Those who had been singing, and making melody on
different instruments, fell silent and began to listen. Those who had
been walking alone in meditation met together in companies to talk.
And those who had been far away on errands to the Earth and other
planets came homeward like a flight of swallows to the high cliff
when the day is over.

It was not that they needed to be restored from weariness, for the
inhabitants of that country never say, "I am tired." But there, as
here, the law of change is the secret of happiness, and the joy that
never ends is woven of mingled strands of labor and repose, society
and solitude, music and silence. Sleep comes to them not as it does
to us, with a darkening of the vision and a folding of the wings of the
spirit, but with an opening of the eyes to deeper and fuller light, and
with an effortless outgoing of the soul upon broader currents of life,
as the sun-loving bird poises and circles upward, without a wing-
beat, on the upholding air.

It was in one of the quiet corners of the green valley called Peacefield, where the little brook of Brighthopes runs smoothly down to
join the River of Life, that I saw a company of angels, returned from

various labors on Earth, sitting in friendly converse on the hill-side, where cyclamens and arbutus and violets and fringed orchids and pale lady's-tresses, and all the sweet-smelling flowers which are separated in the lower world by the seasons, were thrown together in a harmony of fragrance. There were three of the company who seemed to be leaders, distinguished not only by more radiant and powerful looks, but by a tone of authority in their speech and by the willing attention with which the others listened to them, as they talked of their earthly tasks, of the tangles and troubles, the wars and miseries that they had seen among men, and the best way to get rid of them and bring sorrow to an end.

"The Earth is full of oppression and unrighteousness," said the tallest and most powerful of the angels. His voice was deep and strong, and by his shining armor and the long two-handed sword hanging over his shoulder I knew that he was the archangel Michael, the mightiest one among the warriors of the King, and the executor of the divine judgments upon the unjust. "The Earth is tormented with injustice," he cried, "and the great misery that I have seen among men is that the evil hand is often stronger than the good hand and can beat it down.

"The arm of the cruel is heavier than the arm of the kind. The unjust get the better of the just and tread on them. I have seen tyrant kings crush their helpless folk. I have seen the fields of the innocent trampled into bloody ruin by the feet of conquering armies. I have seen the wicked nation overcome the peoples that loved liberty, and take away their treasure by force of arms. I have seen poverty mocked by arrogant wealth, and purity deflowered by brute violence, and gentleness and fair-dealing bruised in the wine-press of iniquity and pride.

"There is no cure for this evil, but by the giving of greater force to the good hand. The righteous cause must be strengthened with might to resist the wicked, to defend the helpless, to punish all cruelty and unfairness, to uphold the right everywhere, and to enforce justice with unconquerable arms. Oh, that the host of Heaven might be called, arrayed, and sent to mingle in the wars of men, to make the good victorious, to destroy all evil, and to make the will of the King prevail!

"We would shake down the thrones of tyrants, and loose the bands of the oppressed. We would hold the cruel and violent with the bit of fear, and drive the greedy and fierce-minded men with the whip of terror. We would stand guard, with weapons drawn, about the innocent, the gentle, the kind, and keep the peace of God with the sword of the angels!"

As he spoke, his hands were lifted to the hilt of his long blade, and he raised it above him, straight and shining, throwing sparkles of light around it, like the spray from the sharp prow of a moving ship. Bright flames of heavenly ardor leaped in the eyes of the listening angels; a martial air passed over their faces as if they longed for the call to war.

But no silver trumpet blared from the battlements of the City of God; no crimson flag was unfurled on those high, secret walls; no thrilling drum-beat echoed over the smooth meadow. Only the sound of the brook of Brighthopes was heard tinkling and murmuring among the roots of the grasses and flowers; and far off a cadence of song drifted down from the inner courts of the Palace of the King.

Then another angel began to speak, and made answer to Michael. He, too, was tall and wore the look of power. But it was power of the mind rather than of the hand. His face was clear and glistening, and his eyes were lit with a steady flame which neither leaped nor fell. Of flame also were his garments, which clung about him as the fire enwraps a torch burning where there is no wind; and his great wings, spiring to a point far above his head, were like a living lamp before the altar of the Most High. By this sign I knew that it was the archangel Uriel, the spirit of the Sun, clearest in vision, deepest in wisdom of all the spirits that surround the throne.

"I hold not the same thought," said he, "as the great archangel Michael; nor, though I desire the same end which he desires, would I seek it by the same way. For I know how often power has been given to the good, and how often it has been turned aside and used for evil. I know that the host of Heaven, and the very stars in their courses, have fought on the side of a favored nation; yet pride has followed triumph and oppression has been the first-born child of victory. I know that the deliverers of the people have become tyrants over those whom they have set free, and the fighters for liberty have been changed into the soldiers of fortune. Power corrupts itself, and might cannot save.

"Does not the Prince Michael remember how the angel of the Lord led the armies of Israel, and gave them the battle against every foe, except the enemy within the camp? And how they robbed and crushed the peoples against whom they had fought for freedom? And how the wickedness of the tribes of Canaan survived their conquest and overcame their conquerors, so that the children of Israel learned to worship the idols of their enemies, Moloch, and Baal, and Ashtoreth?

"Power corrupts itself, and might cannot save. Was not Persia the destroyer of Babylon, and did not the tyranny of Persia cry aloud for destruction? Did not Rome break the yoke of the East, and does not the yoke of Rome lie heavy on the shoulders of the world? Listen!"

There was silence for a moment on the slopes of Peacefield, and then over the encircling hills a cool wind brought the sound of chains clanking in prisons and galleys, the sighing of millions of slaves, the weeping of wretched women and children, the blows of hammers nailing men to their crosses. Then the sound passed by with the wind, and Uriel spoke again:

"Power corrupts itself, and might cannot save. The Earth is full of ignorant strife, and for this evil there is no cure but by the giving of greater knowledge. It is because men do not understand evil that they yield themselves to its power. Wickedness is folly in action, and injustice is the error of the blind. It is because men are ignorant that they destroy one another, and at last themselves.

"If there were more light in the world there would be no sorrow. If the great King who knows all things would enlighten the world with wisdom—wisdom to understand his law and his ways, to read the secrets of the earth and the stars, to discern the workings of the heart of man and the things that make for joy and peace—if he would but send us, his messengers, as a flame of fire to shine upon those who sit in darkness, how gladly would we go to bring in the new day!

"We would speak the word of warning and counsel to the erring, and tell knowledge to the perplexed. We would guide the ignorant in the paths of prudence, and the young would sit at our feet and hear us gladly in the school of life. Then folly would fade away as the morning vapor, and the sun of wisdom would shine on all men, and the peace of God would come with the counsel of the angels."

A murmur of pleasure followed the words of Uriel, and eager looks flashed around the circle of the messengers of light as they heard the praise of wisdom fitly spoken. But there was one among them on whose face a shadow of doubt rested, and though he smiled, it was as if he remembered something that the others had forgotten. He turned to an angel near him.

"Who was it," said he, "to whom you were sent with counsel long ago? Was it not Balaam the son of Beor, as he was riding to meet the King of Moab? And did not even the dumb beast profit more by your instruction than the man who rode him? And who was it," he continued, turning to Uriel, "that was called the wisest of all men, having searched out and understood the many inventions that are found under the sun? Was not Solomon, prince of fools and philosophers, unable by much learning to escape weariness of the flesh and despair of the spirit? Knowledge also is vanity and vexation. This I know well, because I have dwelt among men and held converse with them since the day when I was sent to instruct the first man in Eden."

Then I looked more closely at him who was speaking and recognized the beauty of the archangel Raphael, as it was pictured long ago:

> "A seraph winged; six wings he wore to shade
> His lineaments divine; the pair that clad
> Each shoulder broad came mantling o'er his breast,
> With regal ornament; the middle pair
> Girt like a starry zone his waist, and round
> Skirted his loins and thighs with downy gold
> And colours dipped in Heav'n; the third his feet
> Shadowed from either heel with feathered mail,
> Sky-tinctured grain. Like Maia's son he stood
> And shook his plumes, that Heavenly fragrance filled
> The circuit wide."

"Too well I know," he spoke on, while the smile on his face deepened into a look of pity and tenderness and desire, "too well I know that power corrupts itself and that knowledge cannot save. There is no cure for the evil that is in the world but by the giving of more love to men. The laws that are ordained for earth are strange and unequal, and the ways where men must walk are full of pitfalls and dangers. Pestilence creeps along the ground and flows in the rivers; whirlwind and tempest shake the habitations of men and drive their ships to destruction; fire breaks forth from the mountains and the foundations of the world tremble. Frail is the flesh of man, and many are his pains and troubles. His children can never find peace until they learn to love one another and to help one another.

"Wickedness is begotten by disease and misery. Violence comes from poverty and hunger. The cruelty of oppression is when the strong tread the weak under their feet; the bitterness of pride is when the wise and learned despise the simple; the crown of folly is when the rich think they are gods, and the poor think that God is not.

"Hatred and envy and contempt are the curse of life. And for these there is no remedy save love—the will to give and to bless—the will of the King himself, who gives to all and is loving unto every man. But how shall the hearts of men be won to this will? How shall it enter into them and possess them? Even the gods that men fashion for themselves are cruel and proud and false and unjust. How shall the miracle be wrought in human nature to reveal the meaning of humanity? How shall men be made like God?"

At this question a deep hush fell around the circle, and every listener was still, even as the rustling leaves hang motionless when the light breeze falls away in the hour of sunset. Then through the silence, like the song of a far-away thrush from its hermitage in the forest, a voice came ringing: "I know it, I know it, I know it."

Clear and sweet—clear as a ray of light, sweeter than the smallest silver bell that rang the hour of rest—was that slender voice floating on the odorous and translucent air. Nearer and nearer it came, echoing down the valley, "I know it, I know it, I know it!"

Then from between the rounded hills, among which the brook of Brighthopes is born, appeared a young angel, a little child, with flying hair of gold, and green wreaths twined about his shoulders, and fluttering hands that played upon the air and seemed to lift him so lightly that he had no need of wings. As thistle-down, blown by the wind, dances across the water, so he came along the little stream, singing clear above the murmur of the brook.

All the angels rose and turned to look at him with wondering eyes. Multitudes of others came flying swiftly to the place from which the strange, new song was sounding. Rank within rank, like a garden of living flowers, they stood along the sloping banks of the brook while the child-angel floated into the midst of them, singing:

"I know it, I know it, I know it! Man shall be made like God because the Son of God shall become a man."

At this all the angels looked at one another with amazement, and gathered more closely about the child-angel, as those who hear wonderful news.

"How can this be?" they asked. "How is it possible that the Son of God should be a man?"

"I do not know," said the young angel. "I only know that it is to be."

"But if he becomes a man," said Raphael, "he will be at the mercy of men; the cruel and the wicked will have power upon him; he will suffer."

"I know it," answered the young angel, "and by suffering he will understand the meaning of all sorrow and pain; and he will be able to comfort every one who cries; and his own tears will be for the healing of sad hearts; and those who are healed by him will learn for his sake to be kind to each other."

"But if the Son of God is a true man," said Uriel, "he must first be a child, simple, and lowly, and helpless. It may be that he will never gain the learning of the schools. The masters of earthly wisdom will despise him and speak scorn of him."

"I know it," said the young angel, "but in meekness will he answer them; and to those who become as little children he will give the heavenly wisdom that comes, without seeking, to the pure and gentle of heart."

"But if he becomes a man," said Michael, "evil men will hate and persecute him: they may even take his life, if they are stronger than he."

"I know it," answered the young angel, "they will nail him to a cross. But when he is lifted up, he will draw all men unto him, for he will still be the Son of God, and no heart that is open to love can help loving him, since his love for men is so great that he is willing to die for them."

"But how do you know these things?" cried the other angels. "Who are you?"

"I am the Christmas angel," he said. "At first I was sent as the dream of a little child, a holy child, blessed and wonderful, to dwell in the heart of a pure virgin, Mary of Nazareth. There I was hidden till the word came to call me back to the throne of the King, and tell me my name, and give me my new message. For this is Christmas day on Earth, and to-day the Son of God is born of a woman. So I must fly quickly, before the sun rises, to bring the good news to those happy men who have been chosen to receive them."

As he said this, the young angel rose, with arms outspread, from the green meadow of Peacefield and, passing over the bounds of Heaven, dropped swiftly as a shooting-star toward the night shadow of the Earth. The other angels followed him—a throng of dazzling forms, beautiful as a rain of jewels falling from the dark-blue sky. But the child-angel went more swiftly than the others, because of the certainty of gladness in his heart.

And as the others followed him they wondered who had been favored and chosen to receive the glad tidings.

"It must be the Emperor of the World and his counsellors," they thought. But the flight passed over Rome.

"It may be the philosophers and the masters of learning," they thought. But the flight passed over Athens.

"Can it be the High Priest of the Jews, and the elders and the scribes?" they thought. But the flight passed over Jerusalem.

It floated out over the hill country of Bethlehem; the throng of silent angels holding close together, as if perplexed and doubtful; the child-angel darting on far in advance, as one who knew the way through the darkness.

The villages were all still: the very houses seemed asleep; but in one place there was a low sound of talking in a stable, near to an inn—a sound as of a mother soothing her baby to rest.

All over the pastures on the hillsides a light film of snow had fallen, delicate as the veil of a bride adorned for the marriage; and as the child-angel passed over them, alone in the swiftness of his flight, the pure fields sparkled round him, giving back his radiance.

And there were in that country shepherds abiding in the fields, keeping watch over their flocks by night. And lo! the angel of the Lord came upon them, and the glory of the Lord shone round about them, and they were sore afraid. And the angel said unto them: "Fear not; for behold I bring you glad tidings of great joy which shall be to all nations. For unto you is born this day, in the city of David, a Saviour, which is Christ the Lord. And this shall be a sign unto you; ye shall find the babe wrapped in swaddling clothes, lying in a manger."

And suddenly there was with the angel a multitude of the heavenly host, praising God and saying: "Glory to God in the highest, and on earth peace, good-will toward men." And the shepherds said one to another: "Let us now go, even to Bethlehem, and see this thing which is come to pass."

So I said within myself that I also would go with the shepherds, even to Bethlehem. And I heard a great and sweet voice, as of a bell, which said, "Come!" And when the bell had sounded twelve times, I awoke; and it was Christmas morn; and I knew that I had been in a dream.

Yet it seemed to me that the things which I had heard were true.

HUGH WALPOLE

≈§§≈

Mr. Huffam

O NCE upon a time (it doesn't matter when it was except that it was long after the Great War), young Tubby Winsloe was in the act of crossing Piccadilly just in front of Hatchard's Bookshop. It was three days before Christmas and there had been a frost, a thaw, and then a frost again. The roads were treacherous, traffic nervous and irresponsible, while against the clifflike indifference of brick and mortar a thin faint snow was falling from a primrose-colored sky. Soon it would be dark and the lights would come out. Then things would be more cheerful.

It would, however, take more than lights to bribe Tubby's cheerfulness. Rubicund of face and alarmingly stout of body for a youth of twenty-three, he had just then the spirit of a damp face towel for, only a week ago, Diana Lane-Fox had refused to consider for a moment the possibility of marrying him. "I like you, Tubby," she had said. "I think you have a kind heart. But marry you! You are useless, ignorant, and greedy. You're disgracefully fat and your mother worships you."

He had not known, until Diana had refused him, how bitterly alone he would find himself. He had money, friends, a fine roof above his head; he had seemed to himself popular wherever he went. "Why, there's old Tubby!" everyone had cried. It was true that he was fat, it was true that his mother adored him. He had not until now known that these were drawbacks. He had seemed to himself until a week ago the Friend of All the World. Now he appeared a pariah.

Diana's refusal of him had been a dreadful shock. He had been quite sure that she would accept him. She had gone with him gladly to dances and the pictures. She had, it seemed, approved highly of his mother, Lady Winsloe, and of his father, Sir Roderick Winsloe, Bart. All, it had seemed to him, that was needed was for him to say the word. He could choose his time. Well, he *had* chosen his time—at the Herries dance last Wednesday evening. This was the result.

He had expected to recover. His was naturally a buoyant nature. He told himself, again and again, that there were many other fish in the matrimonial sea. But it appeared that there were not. He wanted Diana, and only Diana.

He halted at the resting place halfway across the street and sighed so deeply that a lady with a little girl and a fierce-looking Chow dog looked at him severely as though she would say: "Now this is Christmas time—a gloomy period for all concerned. It is an unwarranted impertinence for anyone to make it yet more gloomy."

There was someone else clinging to this small fragment of security. A strange-looking man. His appearance was so unusual that Tubby forgot his own troubles in his instant curiosity. The first unusual thing about this man was that he had a beard. Beards are very seldom worn today. Then his clothes, although they were clean and neat, were most certainly old-fashioned. He was wearing a high sharp-pointed collar, a black stock with a jeweled waistcoat, purple in color and covered with little red flowers. He was carrying a large, heavy-looking brown bag. His face was bronzed and he made Tubby think of a retired sea captain.

But the most remarkable thing of all about him was the impression that he gave of restless driving energy. It was all that he could do to keep quiet. His strong, wiry figure seemed to burn with some secret fire. The traffic rushed madly past, but at every moment when there appeared a brief interval between the cars and the omnibuses this bearded gentleman with the bag made a little dance forward, and once he struck the Chow with his bag and once nearly thrust the small child into the road.

The moment came when, most unwisely, he darted forth. He was almost caught by an imperious, disdainful Rolls Royce. The lady gave a little scream and Tubby caught his arm, held him, drew him back.

"That nearly had you, sir!" Tubby murmured, his hand still on his arm. The stranger smiled—a most charming smile that shone from his eyes, his beard, his very hands.

"I must thank you," he said, bowing with old-fashioned courtesy.

"But damn it, as the little boy said to the grocer, 'there's no end to the dog,' as he saw the sausages coming from the sausage machine."

At this he laughed very heartily and Tubby had to laugh, too, although the remark did not seem to him very amusing.

"The traffic's very thick at Christmas time," Tubby said. "Everyone doing their shopping, you know."

The stranger nodded. "Splendid time, Christmas!" he said. "Best of the year!"

"Oh, do you think so?" said Tubby. "I doubt if you'll find people to agree with you. It isn't the thing to admire Christmas these days!"

"Not the thing!" said the stranger, amazed. "Why, what's the matter?"

This was a poser, because so many things were the matter. Tubby was saved for the moment from answering.

"Now there's a break," he said. "We can cross now."

Cross they did, the stranger swinging his body as though at any instant he might spring right off the ground.

"Which way are you going?" Tubby asked. It astonished him afterwards when he looked back and remembered this question. It was not his way to make friends of strangers, his theory being that everyone was out to "do" everyone.

"To tell you the truth I don't quite know," the stranger said. "I've only just arrived."

"Where have you come from?"

The stranger laughed. "I've been moving about for a long time. I'm always on the move. I'm considered a very restless man by my friends."

They were walking along very swiftly, for it was cold and the snow was falling fast now.

"Tell me," said the stranger. "About it's being a bad time. What's the matter?"

What was the matter? What a question!

Tubby murmured: "Why, everything's the matter. Unemployment, no trade—*you* know."

"No, I don't. I've been away. I think everyone looks very jolly."

"I say, don't you feel cold without an overcoat?" Tubby asked.

"Oh, that's nothing," the stranger answered. "I'll tell you when I *did* feel cold, though. When I was a small boy I worked in a factory putting labels on to jam bottles. It was cold *then*. Never known such cold. Icicles would hang on the end of your nose!"

"No!" said Tubby.

"They did, I assure you, and the jam bottles would be coated with ice!"

By this time they had reached Berkeley Street. The Winsloe mansion was in Hill Street.

"I turn up here," said Tubby.

"Oh, do you?" the stranger smiled and held out his hand.

Then Tubby did another extraordinary thing. He said: "Come in and have a cup of tea. Our place is only five yards up the street."

"Certainly," the stranger said. "Delighted."

As they walked up Berkeley Street he went on confidentially—

"I haven't been in London for a long time. All these vehicles are very confusing. But I like it. I like it immensely. It's so lively, and then the town's so quiet compared with what it was when I lived here."

"Quiet!" said Tubby.

"Certainly. There were cobbles and the cabs and drays screamed and rattled like the damned."

"But that's years ago!"

"Yes. I am older than I look."

"Isn't that bag a terrible weight?" Tubby asked.

"I've carried worse things than this," said the stranger. "I carried a trunk full of broken crockery once all the way from one end of the Marshalsea to the other."

They were outside the house now and Tubby realized for the first time his embarrassment. It wasn't his way to bring anyone into the house unannounced, and his mother could be very haughty with strangers. However, here they were and it was snowing hard. So in they went.

The Winsloe mansion was magnificent, belonging in all its features to an age that is gone. There was a marble staircase, and up this the stranger almost ran, carrying his bag like a feather. Tubby toiled behind him but was, unhappily, not in time to prevent the stranger from entering through the open doors of the drawing room.

Here, seated in magnificent state, was Lady Winsloe, a roaring fire encased with marble on one side of her, a beautiful tea table in front of her and walls hung with magnificent imitations of the Great Masters.

Lady Winsloe was a massive woman with snow-white hair, a bosom like a small skating rink and a little face that wore a look of perpetual astonishment. Her dress of black and white silk fitted her so tightly that one anticipated with excitement the moment when she would be compelled to rise. She moved as little as possible; she said as little as possible; she thought as little as possible. She had a kind heart and was sure that the world was going straight to the devil.

The stranger put his bag on the floor and went over to her with his hand outstretched.

"How are you?" he said. "I'm delighted to meet you!"

By good fortune Tubby arrived in the room at this moment.

"Mother," he began. "This is a gentleman—"

"Oh, of course," said the stranger. "You don't know my name. My name's Huffam," and he caught the small white pudgy hand and shook it. At this moment two Pekinese dogs, one brown and one white, advanced from somewhere, violently barking. Lady Winsloe found the whole situation so astonishing that she could only whisper: "Now, Bobo! Now, Coco!"

"You see, mother," Tubby went on, "Mr. Huffam was nearly killed by a motor car and it began to snow heavily."

"Yes, dear," Lady Winsloe said in her queer husky little voice that was always a surprise coming from so vast a bosom. Then she pulled herself together.

For some reason Tubby had done this amazing thing, and whatever Tubby did was right.

"I do hope you'll have some tea, Mr. . . . .?" she hesitated.

"Huffam, ma'am. Yes, thank you. I *will* have some tea!"

"Milk *and* sugar?"

"All of it!" Mr. Huffam laughed and slapped his knee. "Yes, milk *and* sugar. Very kind of you indeed. A perfect stranger as I am. You have a beautiful place here ma'am. You are to be envied."

"Oh, do you think so?" said Lady Winsloe in her husky whisper. "Not in these days—not in these terrible days. Why, the taxes alone! You've no idea, Mr. . . ."

"Huffam."

"Yes, how stupid of me! Now, Bobo. Now, Coco!"

Then a little silence followed and Lady Winsloe gazed at her strange visitor. Her manners were beautiful. She never looked *directly* at her guests. But there was something about Mr. Huffam that *forced* you to look at him. It was his energy. It was his obvious happiness (for happy people are so very rare). It was his extraordinary waistcoat.

Mr. Huffam did not mind in the least being looked at. He smiled back at Lady Winsloe as though he had known her all his life.

"I'm so very fortunate," he said, "to find myself in London at Christmas time. And snow, too! The very thing. Snowballs, mistletoe, holly, the pantomime—nothing so good in life as the pantomime!"

"Oh, do you think so?" said Lady Winsloe, faintly, "I can't, I'm afraid, altogether agree with you. It lasts such a *very* long time and is often exceedingly vulgar!"

"Ah, it's the sausages!" said Mr. Huffam, laughing. "You don't like the sausages! For my part, I dote on 'em. I know it's silly at my age, but there it is—Joey and the sausages—I wouldn't miss them for anything."

At that moment a tall and exceedingly thin gentleman entered. This was Sir Roderick Winsloe. Sir Roderick had been once an Under-Secretary, once a chairman of a company, once famous for his smart and rather vicious repartees. All these were glories of the past. He was now nothing but the husband of Lady Winsloe, the father of Tubby, and the victim of an uncertain and often truculent digestion. He now regarded Mr. Huffam, his bag and his waistcoat with unconcealed astonishment.

"This is my father," said Tubby.

Mr. Huffam rose at once and grasped his hand.

"Delighted to meet you, sir," he said.

Sir Roderick said nothing but "Ah." Then he sat down. Tubby was suffering now from a very serious embarrassment. The odd visitor had drunk his tea and it was time that he should go. Yet it seemed that he had no intention of going. With his legs spread apart, his head thrown back, his friendly eyes taking everyone in as though they were all his dearest friends, he was asking for his second cup.

Tubby waited for his mother. She was a mistress of the art of making a guest disappear. No one knew quite how she did it. There was nothing so vulgarly direct as a glance at the clock or a suggestion as to the imminence of dressing for dinner. A cough, a turn of the wrist, a word about the dogs, and the thing was done. But *this* guest, Tubby knew, was a little more difficult than the ordinary. There was something old-fashioned about him. He took people most naively at their word. Having been asked to tea, he considered that he *was* asked to tea. None of your five minutes' gossip and then hastening on to a cocktail party. However, Tubby reflected, the combination of father, mother, *and* the drawing-room with its marble fireplace and row of copied Old Masters was, as a rule, enough to ensure brief visitors. On this occasion also it would have its effect.

And then—an amazing thing occurred! Tubby perceived that his mother *liked* Mr. Huffam, that she was smiling and even giggling; that her little eyes shone, her tiny mouth was parted in expectation as she listened to her visitor.

Mr. Huffam was telling a story, an anecdote of his youth. About a boy whom he had known in his own childhood, a gay, enterprising, and adventurous boy who had gone as page boy to a rich family. Mr. Huffam described in a marvellous manner his adventures, his *rencontre* with the second footman who was a snob and Evangelical; of how he had handed biscuits through the pantry window to his little sister; of the friendship that he had made with the cook; and as Mr. Huffam told these things, all these people lived before your eyes; the pompous mistress with her ear trumpet, the cook's husband who had a wooden leg, the second footman who was in love with the pastry cook's daughter. The house of this young page boy took on life, and all the furniture in it, the tables and chairs, the beds and looking glasses— everything down to the very red woolen muffler that the footman wore in bed because he was subject to colds in the neck. Then Lady Winsloe began to laugh and Sir Roderick even laughed, and the butler, a big, red-faced man, coming in to remove the tea, could not believe his parboiled eyes but stood there, looking first of all at his mistress, then at his master, then at Mr. Huffam's bag, then at Mr. Huffam himself, until he remembered his manners and with a sudden apologetic cough set sternly (for himself this disgraceful behavior of his employers was no laughing matter) about his proper duties.

The best of all perhaps was the pathos at the end of Mr. Huffam's story. Pathos is a dangerous thing in these days. We so easily call it sentimentality. Mr. Huffam was a master of it. Quite easily and with no exaggeration he described how the sister of the little page boy lost some money entrusted to her by her only-too-bibulous father, of her terror, her temptation to steal from her aged aunt's purse, her final triumphal discovery of the money in a bandbox!

How they all held their breath! How vividly they saw the scene! How real was the sister of the little page boy! At last the story was ended. Mr. Huffam rose.

"Well, ma'am, I must thank you for a very happy hour," he said.

Then the most remarkable thing of all occurred, for Lady Winsloe said:—

"If you have not made any other arrangements, why not stay here for a night or two—while you are looking about you, you know! I'm sure we should be delighted—would we not, Roderick?"

And Sir Roderick said: "Ah . . . Ah . . . Certainly."

II

On looking back, as he so often did afterwards, into the details of this extraordinary adventure, Tubby was never able to arrange the various incidents in their proper order. The whole affair had the inconsequence, the colored fantasy of a dream—one of those rare and delightful dreams that are so much more true and reasonable than anything in one's waking life.

After that astounding invitation of Lady Winsloe's, in what order did the events follow—the cynical luncheon party, the affair of Mallow's young woman (Mallow was the butler), the extraordinary metamorphosis of Miss Allington. All of these were certainly in the first twenty-four hours after Mr. Huffam's arrival. The grand sequence of the Christmas tree, the Mad Party, the London Vision were all part of the tremendous climax.

At once, Tubby realized, the house itself changed. It had never been a satisfactory house; always one of those places rebelliously determined not to live. Even the rooms most often inhabited—the drawing room, the long, dusky dining-room, Sir Roderick's study, Tubby's own bedroom—sulkily refused to play the game. The house was too large, the furniture too heavy, the ceilings too high.

Nevertheless, on the first evening of Mr. Huffam's visit the furniture began to move about. After dinner on that evening there was only the family present. Agatha Allington, an old maid, a relation with money to be left, an unhappy old woman suffering from constant neuralgia, had not yet arrived. There they were in the drawing room and, almost at once, Mr. Huffam had moved some of the chairs away from the wall, had turned the sofa with the gilt spikey back more cosily toward the fire.

He was not impertinent nor officious. Indeed on this first evening he was very quiet, asking them some questions about present-day London, making some rather odd social inquiries about prisons and asylums and the protection of children. He was interested, too, in the literature of the moment and wrote down in a little notebook an odd collection of names, for Lady Winsloe told him that Ethel Dell, Warwick Deeping, and a lady who wrote poetry, called Wilhelmina Stitch, were her favorite writers, while Tubby suggested that he should look into the work of Virginia Woolf, D. H. Lawrence, and Aldous Huxley. They had, in fact, a quiet evening which ended with Mr. Huffam having his first lesson in Bridge. (He had been, he told them, when he had last "tried" cards an enthusiastic whist player.) It was a quiet evening, but as Tubby went up the long, dark staircase to his room, he felt that in some undefined way there was excitement in the air. Before undressing he opened his window and looked out on to the roofs and chimney pots of London. Snow glittered and sparkled under a sky that quivered with stars. Dimly he heard the recurrent waves of traffic as though the sea gently beat at the feet of the black, snow-crowned houses.

"*What* an extraordinary man!" was his last thought before he slept.

Before he had known that he would have Mr. Huffam as his guest, Tubby had invited a few of his clever young friends to luncheon— Diana, Gordon Woolley, Ferris Bland, Mary Polkinghome. Gathered round the Winsloe luncheon table, Tubby regarded them with new eyes. Was it because of the presence of Mr. Huffam? He, gaily flaunting his tremendous waistcoat, was in high spirits. He had, all morning, been recovering some of his old haunts. He was amazed. He could not conceal, he did not attempt to conceal, his amazement. He gave them, as they sat there, languidly picking at their food, a slight notion of what East-End London had once been—the filth, the degradation, the flocks of wild haggard-eyed homeless children. Mary Polkinghome, who had a figure like an umbrella-handle, an Eton crop, and an eye-glass, gazed at him now with an expression of bemused amazement.

"But they say our slums are awful. I haven't been down there myself, but Bunny Carlisle runs a Boys' Club and *he* says . . ."

Mr. Huffam admitted that he had seen some slums that morning but they were nothing, nothing at all to the things he had seen in his youth.

"Who *is* this man?" Ferris Bland whispered to Diana.

"I don't know," she answered. "Someone Tubby picked up. But I like him."

And then this Christmas!

"Oh dear!" young Woolley sighed. "Here's Christmas again! Isn't it awful; I'm going to bed. I shall sleep, and I hope dream, until this dreadful time is over."

Mr. Huffam looked at him with wonder. "Hang up your stocking and see what happens," he said. Everyone screamed with laughter at the idea of young Woolley hanging up his stocking.

Afterwards, in the drawing-room, they discussed literature.

"I've just seen," Ferris Bland explained, "the proofs of Hunter's new novel. It's called 'Pigs in Fever.' It's quite marvellous. The idea is a man has scarlet fever and it's an account of his ravings. Sheer poetry."

There was a book on a little table. He picked it up. It was a first edition of "Martin Chuzzlewit," bound in purple leather.

"Poor old Dickens," he said. "Hunter has a marvellous idea. He's going to rewrite one or two of the Dickens books."

Mr. Huffam was interested.

"Rewrite them?" he asked.

"Yes. Cut them down to about half. There's some quite good stuff in them, hidden away, he says. He'll cut out all the sentimental bits, bring the humor up to date, and put in some stuff of his own. He says it's only fair to Dickens to show people that there's something there."

Mr. Huffam was delighted.

"I'd like to see it," he said. "It will make quite a new thing of it."

"That's what Hunter says," Bland remarked. "People will be surprised."

"I should think they will be," Mr. Huffam remarked.

The guests stayed a long time. Mr. Huffam was something quite new in their experience. Before she went, Diana said to Tubby: "What a delightful man! Where *did* you find him?"

Tubby was modest. She was nicer to him than she had ever been before.

"What's happened to you, Tubby?" she asked. "You've woken up suddenly."

During the afternoon, Miss Agatha Allington arrived with a number of bags and one of her worst colds.

"How are you, Tubby? It's kind of you to ask me. What horrible weather! What a vile thing Christmas is! You won't expect me to give you a present, I hope."

Before the evening, Mr. Huffam made friends with Mallow, the butler. No one knew quite how he did it. No one had ever made friends with Mallow before. But Mr. Huffam went down to the lower domestic regions and invaded the world of Mallow, Mrs. Spence, the housekeeper, Thomas, the footman, Jane and Rose, the housemaids, Maggie, the scullery maid. Mrs. Spence, who was a little round woman like a football, was a Fascist in politics, and said that she was descended from Mary Queen of Scots, permitted no one, except Lady Winsloe, in her sitting room, but she showed Mr. Huffam the photographs of the late Mr. Spence and her son, Darnley, who was a steward in the Cunard line. She laughed immeasurably at the story of the organ-grinder and the lame monkey. But Mallow was Mr. Huffam's great conquest. It seemed (no one had had the least idea of it) that Mallow was hopelessly in love with a young lady who assisted in a flower shop in Dover Street. This young lady, it seemed, admired Mallow very much and he had once taken her to the pictures. But Mallow was shy (no one had conceived it!) wanted to write her a letter, but simply hadn't the courage. Mr. Huffam dictated a letter for him. It was a marvellous letter, full of humor, poetry, and tenderness.

"But I can't live up to this, sir," said Mallow. "She'll find me out in no time."

"That's all right," said Mr. Huffam. "Take her out to tea tomorrow, be a little tender. She won't worry about letters after that."

Mr. Huffam went out after tea and returned, powdered with snow, in a taxicab filled with holly and mistletoe.

"Oh, dear," whispered Lady Winsloe, "we haven't decorated the house for years. I don't know what Roderick will say. He thinks holly so messy."

"I'll talk to him," said Mr. Huffam.

He did, with the result that Sir Roderick came himself and assisted. Through all this Mr. Huffam was in no way dictatorial. Tubby observed that he had even a kind of shyness—not in his opinions, for here he was very clear-minded indeed, seeing exactly what he wanted, but he seemed to be aware, by a sort of ghostly guidance, of the idiosyncrasies of his neighbors. How did he know, for instance, that Sir Roderick was afraid of a ladder! When he, Mallow, Tubby, and Sir Roderick were festooning the hall with holly, he saw Sir Roderick begin, timidly, with trembling shanks to climb some steps. He went to him, put his hand on his arm and led him safely to ground again.

"I know you don't like ladders," he said. "Some people can't stand 'em. I knew an old gentleman once terrified of ladders, and his eldest son, a bright promising lad, *must* become a steeplejack. Only profession he had a liking for."

"Good heavens!" cried Sir Roderick, paling. "What a horrible pursuit! Whatever did the father do?"

"Persuaded him to be a diver instead," said Mr. Huffam. "The lad took to it like a duck to water. Up or down it was all the same to him, he said."

In fact Mr. Huffam looked after Sir Roderick as a father his child and, before the day was out, the noble Baronet was asking Mr. Huffam's opinion upon everything. Tubby, as he listened, could not help wondering where Mr. Huffam had been all these years, in some *very* remote South Sea Island surely! So many things were new to him. But his kindness and energy carried him forward through everything. There was much of the child about him, much of the wise man of the world also, and behind these a hint of melancholy, of loneliness. Tubby was no sentimentalist about his own sex, but he had to confess that he was growing very fond of Mr. Huffam. It was almost as though he had known him before. There were in fact certain phrases, certain tones in the voice that were curiously familiar and reminded Tubby in some dim way of his innocent, departed childhood.

And then, after dinner, there was the conquest of Agatha Allington. Agatha had taken an instant dislike to Mr. Huffam. She prided herself on her plain speech. "My dear," she said to Lady Winsloe, "What a ruffian! He'll steal the spoons."

"I don't think so," said Lady Winsloe with dignity. "We like him very much."

He seemed to perceive that Agatha disliked him. He sat beside her at dinner—he wore a tailcoat of strange old-fashioned cut and carried a large gold fob. He was, as Tubby perceived, quite different with Agatha. He was almost, you might say, an old maid himself—or, rather, a confirmed old bachelor. He discovered that she had a passion for Italy; she visited Rome and Florence every year—and he described to her some of his own Italian journeys taken years ago; confessed to her that he didn't care for frescoes which he described as "dim virgins with mildewed glories"—but Venice! ah! Venice! with its prisoners and dungeons and lovely iridescent waters! All the same, he was always homesick when he was out of London and he described the old London to her, the fogs and the muffin-bell and the "growlers," and enchanted her with a story about a shy little bachelor and how he went out one evening to dine with a vulgar cousin and be kind to a horrible godchild. Then, after dinner, he insisted that they should dance. They made a space in the drawing room, brought up a gramophone and set about it. Then how Mr. Huffam laughed when Tubby showed him a one-step.

"Call that dancing!" he cried. Then, humming a polka, he caught Agatha by the waist and away they polka-d. Then Lady Winsloe, who had adored the polka once, joined in. Then the Barn Dance. Then, few though they were, Sir Roger . . .

"I know!" Mr. Huffam cried. "We must have a party!"

"A party!" almost screamed Lady Winsloe. "What kind of a party?"

"Why, a children's party, of course. On Christmas night."

"But we don't know any children! And children are bored with parties. And they'll all be engaged anyway."

"Not the children I'll ask!" cried Mr. Huffam. "Not the party I'll have! It shall be the best party London has seen for years!"

III

It is well known that good humored, cheerful, and perpetually well-intentioned people are among the most tiresome of their race. Tubby often wondered afterwards why Mr. Huffam was *not* tiresome. It was perhaps because of his childlikeness; it was also, most certainly, be-

cause of his intelligence. Most of all was it because of the special circumstances of the case. In ordinary daily life Mr. Huffam *might* be a
bore—most people are at one time or another. But on this occasion
no one was a bore, not even Agatha.

It was as though the front wall of the Hill Street house had been
taken away and all the details and incidents of those two days—Christmas Eve and Christmas Day became part of it. It seemed that
Berkeley Square was festooned with crystal trees—that candles, red
and green and blue—blazed from every window, that small boys
instead of chanting "King Wenceslas" in the usual excruciating fashion, carolled with divine voices, that processions of Father Christmas,
with snowy beards and red gowns, marched from Selfridge and Har-
rods and Fortnums carrying in their hands small Christmas trees, and
were attended by reindeer, as though brown paper parcels tied with
silver bands and decorated with robins fell in torrents through the
chimneys and gigantic Christmas puddings rolled on their own stout
bellies down Piccadilly, attended by showers of almonds and raisins.
And upon all this first a red-faced sun, then a moon, cherry-colored
and as large as an orange, smiled down, upon a world of crusted glittering snow while the bells pealed and once again the Kings of the
Earth, having surrendered all their tariffs, came to the stable with
gifts in their hands . . .

Of course it was not like that, but most certainly the Winsloe house
was transformed. For one thing there was not the usual present-
giving. At breakfast on Christmas Day everyone gave everyone else
presents that must not cost more than sixpence apiece—Mr. Huffam
had discovered some marvelous things—toy dogs that barked, Father
Christmases glistening with snow, a small chime of silver bells, shiny
pieces of sealing wax.

Then they all went to church at St. James's, Piccadilly. At the midday meal Sir Roderick had turkey and Christmas pudding which he
hadn't touched for many a day.

In the evening came the party. Tubby had been allowed to invite
Diana—for the rest of the guests were to be altogether Mr. Huffam's
. . . No one knew what was in his mind.

At 7:15 exactly came the first ring of the doorbell. When Mallow
opened the portals there on the steps were three very small children,
two girls and a little boy.

"Please, sir, this was the number the gentleman said," whispered the little girl, who was very frightened.

Then up Hill Street the children came, big children, little children, children who could scarcely walk, boys as bold as brass, girls mothering their small relations, some of them shabby, some of them smart, some with shawls, some with mufflers, some with collars, some brave, some frightened, some chatting like monkeys, some silent and anxious —all coming up Hill Street, crowding up the stairs, passing into the great hall.

It was not until they had all been ushered up the stairs by Mallow, were all in their places, that Sir Roderick Winsloe, Bart, Lady Winsloe his wife, Tubby Winsloe their son, were permitted to see their own drawing-room. When they did they gasped with wonder. Under the soft and shining light the great floor had been cleared and, at one end of the room, all the children were gathered. At the other end was the largest, the strongest, the proudest Christmas tree ever beheld, and this tree shone and gleamed with candles, with silver tissue, with blue and gold and crimson balls, and so heavily weighted was it with dolls and horses and trains and parcels it was a miracle that it could support its burden. So there it was, the great room shining with golden light, the children massed together, the gleaming floor like a sea, and only the crackle of the fire, the tick of the marble clock, the wondering whispers of the children for sound.

A pause and from somewhere or another Father Christmas appeared. He stood there, looking across the floor at his guests.

"Good evening, children," he said, and the voice was the voice of Mr. Huffam.

"Good evening, Father Christmas," the children cried in chorus.

"It's all his own money," Lady Winsloe whispered to Agatha. "He wouldn't let me spend a penny."

He summoned them then to help with the presents. The children (who behaved with the manners of the highest of the aristocracy— even *better* than that, to be truthful) advanced across the shining floor. They were told to take turn according to size, the smallest first. There was no pushing, no cries of "I want *that!*" as so often happens at parties. At last the biggest girl and the biggest boy received their gifts. The tree gave a little quiver of relief at its freedom from its burden, and the candles, the silver tissue, the red and blue and golden balls shook with a shimmer of pleasure.

Games followed. Tubby could never afterward remember what the games had been. The room was alive with movements, with cries of joy and shouts of triumph, with songs and kisses and forfeits. Tubby never knew. He only knew that he saw his mother with a paper cap on her head, his father with a false nose, Agatha beating a child's drum—and on every side of him children and children and children, children dancing and singing and running and sitting and laughing.

There came a moment, when Diana, her hair dishevelled, her eyes shining, caught his arm and whispered: "Tubby, you are a dear. Perhaps—one day—if you keep this up—who knows?"

And then there was sudden quiet. Mr. Huffam, no longer Father Christmas, arranged all the children round him. He told them a story, a story about a circus and a small child who, with her old grandfather, wandered in the company of these strange people—of the fat lady and the skeleton man, the jugglers and the beautiful creatures who jumped through the hoops, and the clown with the broken heart and how his heart was mended.

"And so they all lived happily ever after," he ended.

Everyone said goodnight. Everyone went away.

"Oh, dear, I *am* tired!" said Mr. Huffam. "But it *has* been a jolly evening!"

Mallow, in his excitement, forgot to draw the curtains, so the moon looked in through the window and saw the strong dark tree and the long shiny floor covered with silver tissue and brown paper and torn crackers and caps of gold and crimson . . .

"Yes, it *has* been a jolly evening!" said the Tree to the Moon.

"So it appears," said the Moon.

Next morning when Rose, the housemaid, woke Lady Winsloe with her morning cup of tea, she had startling news.

"Oh, dear, my lady, the gentleman's gone!"

"What gentleman?" said Lady Winsloe.

"Mr. Huffam, my lady. His bed's not been slept in and his bag's gone. There isn't a sign of him anywhere."

Alas, it was only too true. Not a sign of him anywhere.

At least one sign only.

The drawing room was as it had always been, every chair in its proper place, the copied Old Masters looking down solemnly from the dignified walls.

One thing was different. The first Edition of "Martin Chuzzlewit," in its handsome blue binding, was propped up against the marble clock.

"How very strange!" said Lady Winsloe.

But opening it, she found that on the first page these words were freshly written:—

"For Lady Winsloe
with gratitude
from her friend
the Author."

And under this, the signature, above a scrawl of thick black lines:—

"Charles Dickens"

LAURA INGALLS WILDER

Mr. Edwards Meets Santa Claus

THE DAYS were short and cold, the wind whistled sharply, but there was no snow. Cold rains were falling. Day after day the rain fell, pattering on the roof and pouring from the eaves.

Mary and Laura stayed close by the fire, sewing their nine-patch quilt blocks, or cutting paper dolls from scraps of wrapping-paper, and hearing the wet sound of the rain. Every night was so cold that they expected to see snow next morning, but in the morning they saw only sad, wet grass.

They pressed their noses against the squares of glass in the windows that Pa had made, and they were glad they could see out. But they wished they could see snow.

Laura was anxious because Christmas was near, and Santa Claus and his reindeer could not travel without snow. Mary was afraid that, even if it snowed, Santa Claus could not find them, so far away in Indian Territory. When they asked Ma about this, she said she didn't know.

"What day is it?" they asked her, anxiously. "How many more days till Christmas?" And they counted off the days on their fingers, till there was only one more day left.

Rain was still falling that morning. There was not one crack in the gray sky. They felt almost sure there would be no Christmas. Still, they kept hoping.

Just before noon the light changed. The clouds broke and drifted apart, shining white in a clear blue sky. The sun shone, birds sang, and thousands of drops of water sparkled on the grasses. But when Ma opened the door to let in the fresh, cold air, they heard the creek roaring.

They had not thought about the creek. Now they knew they would have no Christmas, because Santa Claus could not cross that roaring creek.

Pa came in, bringing a big fat turkey. If it weighed less than twenty pounds, he said, he'd eat it, feathers and all. He asked Laura, "How's that for a Christmas dinner? Think you can manage one of those drumsticks?"

She said, yes, she could. But she was sober. Then Mary asked him if the creek was going down, and he said it was still rising.

Ma said it was too bad. She hated to think of Mr. Edwards eating his bachelor cooking all alone on Christmas day. Mr. Edwards had been asked to eat Christmas dinner with them, but Pa shook his head and said a man would risk his neck, trying to cross that creek now.

"No," he said. "That current's too strong. We'll just have to make up our minds that Edwards won't be here tomorrow."

Of course that meant that Santa Claus could not come, either.

Laura and Mary tried not to mind too much. They watched Ma dress the wild turkey, and it was a very fat turkey. They were lucky little girls, to have a good house to live in, and a warm fire to sit by, and such a turkey for their Christmas dinner. Ma said so, and it was true. Ma said it was too bad that Santa Claus couldn't come this year, but they were such good girls that he hadn't forgotten them; he would surely come next year.

Still, they were not happy.

After supper that night they washed their hands and faces, buttoned their red-flannel night-gowns, tied their night-cap strings, and soberly said their prayers. They lay down in bed and pulled the covers up. It did not seem at all like Christmas time.

Pa and Ma sat silently by the fire. After a while Ma asked why Pa didn't play the fiddle, and he said, "I don't seem to have the heart to, Caroline."

After a longer while, Ma suddenly stood up.

"I'm going to hang up your stockings, girls," she said. "Maybe something will happen."

Laura's heart jumped. But then she thought again of the creek and she knew nothing could happen.

Ma took one of Mary's clean stockings and one of Laura's, and she hung them from the mantel-shelf, on either side of the fireplace. Laura and Mary watched her over the edge of their bedcovers.

"Now go to sleep," Ma said, kissing them goodnight. "Morning will come quicker if you're asleep."

She sat down again by the fire and Laura almost went to sleep. She woke up a little when she heard Pa say, "You've only made it worse, Caroline." And she thought she heard Ma say: "No, Charles. There's the white sugar." But perhaps she was dreaming.

Then she heard Jack growl savagely. The door-latch rattled and some one said, "Ingalls! Ingalls!" Pa was stirring up the fire, and when he opened the door Laura saw that it was morning. The outdoors was gray.

"Great fishhooks, Edwards! Come in, man! What's happened?" Pa exclaimed.

Laura saw the stockings limply dangling, and she scrooged her shut eyes into the pillow. She heard Pa piling wood on the fire, and she heard Mr. Edwards say he had carried his clothes on his head when he swam the creek. His teeth rattled and his voice shivered. He would be all right, he said, as soon as he got warm.

"It was too big a risk, Edwards," Pa said. "We're glad you're here, but that was too big a risk for a Christmas dinner."

"Your little ones had to have a Christmas," Mr. Edwards replied. "No creek could stop me, after I fetched them their gifts from Independence."

Laura sat straight up in bed. "Did you see Santa Claus?" she shouted.

"I sure did," Mr. Edwards said.

"Where? When? What did he look like? What did he say? Did he really give you something for us?" Mary and Laura cried.

"Wait, wait a minute!" Mr. Edwards laughed. And Ma said she would put the presents in the stockings, as Santa Claus intended. She said they mustn't look.

Mr. Edwards came and sat on the floor by their bed, and he answered every question they asked him. They honestly tried not to look at Ma, and they didn't quite see what she was doing.

When he saw the creek rising, Mr. Edwards said, he had known that Santa Claus could not get across it. ("But you crossed it," Laura said. "Yes," Mr. Edwards replied, "but Santa Claus is too old and fat. He couldn't make it, where a long, lean razor-back like me could do so.") And Mr. Edwards reasoned that if Santa Claus couldn't cross the creek, likely he would come no farther south than Independence. Why should he come forty miles across the prairie, only to be turned back? Of course he wouldn't do that!

So Mr. Edwards had walked to Independence. ("In the rain?" Mary asked. Mr. Edwards said he wore his rubber coat.) And there, coming down the street in Independence, he had met Santa Claus. ("In the daytime?" Laura asked. She hadn't thought that anyone could see Santa Claus in the daytime. No, Mr. Edwards said; it was night, but light shone out across the street from the saloons.)

Well, the first thing Santa Claus said was, "Hello, Edwards!" ("Did he know you?" Mary asked, and Laura asked, "How did you know he was really Santa Claus?" Mr. Edwards said that Santa Claus knew everybody. And he had recognized Santa at once by his whiskers. Santa Claus had the longest, thickest, whitest set of whiskers west of the Mississippi.)

So Santa Claus said, "Hello, Edwards! Last time I saw you you were sleeping on a corn-shuck bed in Tennessee." And Mr. Edwards well remembered the little pair of red-yarn mittens that Santa Claus had left for him that time.

Then Santa Claus said: "I understand you're living now down along the Verdigris River. Have you ever met up, down yonder, with two little young girls named Mary and Laura?"

"I surely am acquainted with them," Mr. Edwards replied.

"It rests heavy on my mind," said Santa Claus. "They are both of them sweet, pretty, good little young things, and I know they are expecting me. I surely do hate to disappoint two good little girls like them. Yet with the water up the way it is, I can't ever make it across that creek. I can figure no way whatsoever to get to their cabin this year. Edwards," Santa Claus said. "Would you do me the favor to fetch them their gifts one time?"

"I'll do that, and with pleasure," Mr. Edwards told him.

Then Santa Claus and Mr. Edwards stepped across the street to the hitching-posts where the pack-mule was tied. ("Didn't he have his reindeer?" Laura asked. "You know he couldn't," Mary said. "There isn't any snow." Exactly, said Mr. Edwards. Santa Claus traveled with a pack-mule in the southwest.)

And Santa Claus uncinched the pack and looked through it, and he took out the presents for Mary and Laura.

"Oh, what are they?" Laura cried; but Mary asked, "Then what did he do?"

Then he shook hands with Mr. Edwards, and he swung up on his fine bay horse. Santa Claus rode well, for a man of his weight and build. And he tucked his long, white whiskers under his bandana. "So long, Edwards," he said, and he rode away on the Fort Dodge trail, leading his pack-mule and whistling.

Laura and Mary were silent an instant, thinking of that.

Then Ma said, "You may look now, girls."

Something was shining bright in the top of Laura's stocking. She squealed and jumped out of bed. So did Mary, but Laura beat her to the fireplace. And the shining thing was a glittering new tin cup.

Mary had one exactly like it.

These new tin cups were their very own. Now they each had a cup to drink out of. Laura jumped up and down and shouted and laughed, but Mary stood still and looked with shining eyes at her own tin cup.

Then they plunged their hands into the stockings again. And they pulled out two long, long sticks of candy. It was peppermint candy, striped red and white. They looked and looked at that beautiful candy, and Laura licked her stick, just one lick. But Mary was not so greedy. She didn't take even one lick of her stick.

Those stockings weren't empty yet. Mary and Laura pulled out two small packages. They unwrapped them, and each found a little heart-shaped cake. Over their delicate brown tops was sprinkled white sugar. The sparkling grains lay like tiny drifts of snow.

The cakes were too pretty to eat. Mary and Laura just looked at them. But at last Laura turned hers over, and she nibbled a tiny nibble from underneath, where it wouldn't show. And the inside of that little cake was white!

It had been made of pure white flour, and sweetened with white sugar.

Laura and Mary never would have looked in their stockings again. The cups and the cakes and the candy were almost too much. They were too happy to speak. But Ma asked if they were sure the stockings were empty.

Then they put their arms down inside them, to make sure.

And in the very toe of each stocking was a shining bright, new penny!

They had never even thought of such a thing as having a penny. Think of having a whole penny for your very own. Think of having a cup and a cake and a stick of candy *and* a penny.

There never had been such a Christmas.

Now of course, right away, Laura and Mary should have thanked Mr. Edwards for bringing those lovely presents all the way from Independence. But they had forgotten all about Mr. Edwards. They had even forgotten Santa Claus. In a minute they would have remembered, but before they did, Ma said, gently, "Aren't you going to thank Mr. Edwards?"

"Oh, thank you, Mr. Edwards! Thank you!" they said, and they meant it with all their hearts. Pa shook Mr. Edwards' hand, too, and shook it again. Pa and Ma and Mr. Edwards acted as if they were almost crying, Laura didn't know why. So she gazed again at her beautiful presents.

She looked up again when Ma gasped. And Mr. Edwards was taking sweet potatoes out of his pockets. He said they had helped to balance the package on his head when he swam across the creek. He thought Pa and Ma might like them, with the Christmas turkey.

There were nine sweet potatoes. Mr. Edwards had brought them all the way from town, too. It was just too much. Pa said so. "It's too much, Edwards," he said. They never could thank him enough.

Mary and Laura were too much excited to eat breakfast. They drank the milk from their shining new cups, but they could not swallow the rabbit stew and the cornmeal mush.

"Don't make them, Charles," Ma said. "It will soon be dinner-time."

For Christmas dinner there was the tender, juicy, roasted turkey. There were the sweet potatoes, baked in the ashes and carefully wiped so that you could eat the good skins, too. There was a loaf of salt-rising bread made from the last of the white flour.

And after all that there were stewed dried blackberries and little cakes. But these little cakes were made with brown sugar and they did not have white sugar sprinkled over their tops.

Then Pa and Ma and Mr. Edwards sat by the fire and talked about Christmas times back in Tennessee and up north in the Big Woods.

But Mary and Laura looked at their beautiful cakes and played with their pennies and drank water out of their new cups. And little by little they licked and sucked their sticks of candy, till each stick was sharp-pointed on one end.

That was a happy Christmas.

Is There a Santa Claus?

(*This famous editorial first appeared in the* New York Sun, *September 21, 1897*)

WE take pleasure in answering at once and thus prominently the communication below, expressing at the same time our great gratification that its faithful author is numbered among the friends of *The Sun:*

> Dear Editor:
>
> I am 8 years old.
> Some of my little friends say there is no Santa Claus.
> Papa says "If you see it in *The Sun* it's so."
> Please tell me the truth, is there a Santa Claus?
>
> > Virginia O'Hanlon
> > 115 West 95th Street

Virginia, your little friends are wrong. They have been affected by the skepticism of a skeptical age. They do not believe except what they see. They think that nothing can be which is not comprehensible by their little minds. All minds, Virginia, whether they be men's or children's, are little. In this great universe of ours man is a mere insect, an ant, in his intellect, as compared with the boundless world about him, as measured by the intelligence capable of grasping the whole of truth and knowledge.

Yes, Virginia, there is a Santa Claus. He exists as certainly as love and generosity and devotion exist, and you know that they abound and give to your life its highest beauty and joy. Alas! how dreary would be the world if there were no Santa Claus! It would be as dreary as if there were no Virginias. There would be no childlike faith then, no poetry, no romance to make tolerable this existence. We should have no enjoyment, except in sense and sight. The eternal light with which childhood fills the world would be extinguished.

Not believe in Santa Claus! You might as well not believe in fairies! You might get your papa to hire men to watch in all the chimneys on Christmas eve to catch Santa Claus, but even if they did not see Santa Claus coming down, what would that prove? Nobody sees Santa Claus, but that is no sign that there is no Santa Claus. The most real things in the world are those that neither children nor men can see. Did you ever see fairies dancing on the lawn? Of course not, but that's no proof that they are not there. Nobody can conceive or imagine all the wonders there are unseen and unseeable in the world.

You tear apart the baby's rattle and see what makes the noise inside, but there is a veil covering the unseen world which not the strongest man, nor even the united strength of all the strongest men that ever lived, could tear apart. Only faith, fancy, poetry, love, romance, can push aside that curtain and view and picture the supernal beauty and glory beyond. Is it all real? Ah, Virginia, in all this world there is nothing else real and abiding.

No Santa Claus! Thank God he lives, and he lives forever. A thousand years from now, Virginia, nay, ten times ten thousand years from now, he will continue to make glad the heart of childhood.

III

POEMS AND CAROLS

LEWIS CARROLL

~⧉~

Christmas Greeting from a Fairy to a Child

Lady, dear, if Fairies may
 For a moment lay aside
Cunning tricks and elfish play,
 'Tis at happy Christmas-tide.

We have heard the children say—
 Gentle children, whom we love—
Long ago on Christmas Day,
 Came a message from above.

Still, as Christmas-tide comes round,
 They remember it again—
Echo still the joyful sound
 "Peace on earth, good-will to men!"

Yet the hearts must childlike be
 Where such heavenly guests abide;
Unto children, in their glee,
 All the year is Christmas-tide!

Thus, forgetting tricks and play
 For a moment, Lady dear,
We would wish you, if we may,
 Merry Christmas, glad New Year!

GILBERT KEITH CHESTERTON

The House of Christmas

There fared a mother driven forth
    Out of an inn to roam;
In the place where she was homeless
    All men are at home;
The crazy stable close at hand,
With shaking timber and shifting sand,
Grew a stronger thing to abide and stand
    Than the square stones of Rome.

For men are homesick in their homes,
    And strangers under the sun,
And they lay their heads in a foreign land
    Whenever the day is done.
Here we have battle and blazing eyes,
And chance and honour and high surprise;
But our homes are under miraculous skies
    Where the Yule tale was begun.

A child in a foul stable,
    Where the beasts feed and foam;
Only where He was homeless
    Are you and I at home;
We have hands that fashion and heads that know
But our hearts we lost—how long ago!—
In a place no chart nor ship can show
    Under the sky's dome.

This world is wild as an old wives' tale,
    And strange the plain things are,
The earth is enough and the air is enough
    For our wonder and our war;
But our rest is as far as the fire-drake swings,
And our peace is put in impossible things
Where clashed and thundered unthinkable wings
    Round an incredible star.

To an open house in the evening
    Home shall men come,
To an older place than Eden
    And a taller town than Rome;
To the end of the way of the wandering star,
To the things that cannot be and that are,
To the place where God was homeless
    And all men are at home.

ELEANOR FARJEON

The Shepherd and the King

The Shepherd and the King,
The Angel and the Ass,
They heard Sweet Mary sing
When her joy was come to pass;
They heard Sweet Mary sing
To the Baby on her knee;
Sing again, Sweet Mary,
And we will sing with thee!
　　Earth, bear a berry!
　　Heaven, bear a light!
　　Man, make you merry
　　On Christmas night.

The Oxen in the stall,
The Sheep upon the hill,
They are waking all
To hear Sweet Mary still.
The Baby is a Child,
And the Child is running free;
Sing again, Sweet Mary,
And we will sing with thee!
　　Earth, bear a berry!
　　Heaven, bear a light!
　　Man, make you merry
　　On Christmas night.

The People in the land,
So many million strong,
All silently do stand
To hear Sweet Mary's song.
The Child He is a Man,
And the Man hangs on a tree.
Sing again, Sweet Mary,
And we will sing with thee.
 Earth, bear a berry!
 Heaven, bear a light!
 Man, make you merry
 On Christmas night.

The Stars that are so old,
The Grass that is so young,
They listen in the cold
To hear Sweet Mary's tongue.
The Man's the Son of God,
And in Heaven walketh He.
Sing again, Sweet Mary,
And we will sing with thee!
 Earth, bear a berry!
 Heaven, bear a light!
 Man, make you merry
 On Christmas night.

ROBERT FROST

❦

Christmas Trees

A CHRISTMAS CIRCULAR LETTER

The city had withdrawn into itself
And left at last the country to the country;
When between whirls of snow not come to lie
And whirls of foliage not yet laid, there drove
A stranger to our yard, who looked the city,
Yet did in country fashion in that there
He sat and waited till he drew us out
A-buttoning coats to ask him who he was.
He proved to be the city come again
To look for something it had left behind
And could not do without and keep its Christmas.
He asked if I would sell my Christmas trees;
My woods—the young fir balsams like a place
Where houses all are churches and have spires.
I hadn't thought of them as Christmas trees.
I doubt if I was tempted for a moment
To sell them off their feet to go in cars
And leave the slope behind the house all bare,
Where the sun shines now no warmer than the moon.
I'd hate to have them know it if I was.
Yet more I'd hate to hold my trees except
As others hold theirs or refuse for them,
Beyond the time of profitable growth,
The trial by market everything must come to.
I dallied so much with the thought of selling.

Then whether from mistaken courtesy
And fear of seeming short of speech, or whether
From hope of hearing good of what was mine,
I said, "There aren't enough to be worth while."

"I could soon tell how many they would cut,
You let me look them over."

                    "You could look.
But don't expect I'm going to let you have them."
Pasture they spring in, some in clumps too close
That lop each other of boughs, but not a few
Quite solitary and having equal boughs
All round and round. The latter he nodded "Yes" to,
Or paused to say beneath some lovelier one,
With a buyer's moderation, "That would do."
I thought so too, but wasn't there to say so.
We climbed the pasture on the south, crossed over,
And came down on the north.

                    He said, "A thousand."

"A thousand Christmas trees!—at what apiece?"

He felt some need of softening that to me:
"A thousand trees would come to thirty dollars."

Then I was certain I had never meant
To let him have them. Never show surprise!
But thirty dollars seemed so small beside
The extent of pasture I should strip, three cents
(For that was all they figured out apiece),
Three cents so small beside the dollar friends
I should be writing to within the hour
Would pay in cities for good trees like those,
Regular vestry-trees whole Sunday Schools
Could hang enough on to pick off enough.

A thousand Christmas trees I didn't know I had!
Worth three cents more to give away than sell
As may be shown by a simple calculation.
Too bad I couldn't lay one in a letter.
I can't help wishing I could send you one,
In wishing you herewith a Merry Christmas.

❧

Carol

Villagers all, this frosty tide,
Let your doors swing open wide,
Though wind may follow, and snow beside,
Yet draw us in by your fire to bide;
    Joy shall be yours in the morning!

Here we stand in the cold and the sleet,
Blowing fingers and stamping feet,
Come from far away you to greet—
You by the fire and we in the street—
    Bidding you joy in the morning!

For ere one half of the night was gone,
Sudden a star has led us on,
Raining bliss and benison—
Bliss tomorrow and more anon,
    Joy for every morning!

Goodman Joseph toiled through the snow—
Saw the star o'er a stable low;
Mary she might not further go—
Welcome thatch and litter below!
    Joy was hers in the morning!

And then they heard the angels tell
"Who were the first to cry Nowell?
Animals all, as it befell,
In the stable where they did dwell!
    Joy shall be theirs in the morning!"

THOMAS HARDY

The Oxen

Christmas Eve, and twelve of the clock.
   "Now they are all on their knees,"
An elder said as we sat in a flock
   By the embers in hearthside ease.

We pictured the meek mild creatures where
   They dwelt in their strawy pen,
Nor did it occur to one of us there
   To doubt they were kneeling then.

So fair a fancy few would weave
   In these years. Yet, I feel,
If some one said on Christmas Eve,
   "Come; see the oxen kneel

"In the lonely barton by yonder coomb
   Our childhood used to know,"
I should go with him in the gloom,
   Hoping it might be so.

ROBERT HERRICK

To a Child

Go, pretty child, and bear this flower
  Unto thy little Saviour,
And tell him, by that bud now blown,
He is the Rose of Sharon known.
When thou has said so, stick it there
Upon his bib or stomacher;
And tell him, for good handsel too,
That thou has brought a whistle new,
Made of a clean straight oaten reed,
To charm his cries at time of need.
Tell him, for coral thou has none,
But, if thou hadst, he should have one;
But poor thou art, and known to be
Even as moneyless as he.
Lastly, if thou canst win a kiss
From those mellifluous lips of his,
Then never take a second on,
To spoil the first impression.

HENRY WADSWORTH LONGFELLOW

❦

Christmas Bells

I heard the bells on Christmas Day
Their old, familiar carols play,
    And wild and sweet
    The words repeat
Of peace on earth, good-will to men!

And thought how, as the day had come,
The belfries of all Christendom
    Had rolled along
    The unbroken song
Of peace on earth, good-will to men!

Till, ringing, swinging on its way,
The world revolved from night to day
    A voice, a chime,
    A chant sublime
Of peace on earth, good-will to men!

Then from each black, accursèd mouth
The cannon thundered in the South
    And with the sound
    The carols drowned
Of peace on earth, good-will to men!

It was as if an earthquake rent
The hearth-stones of a continent,
    And made forlorn

The households born
Of peace on earth, good-will to men!

And in despair I bowed my head;
"There is no peace on earth," I said;
   "For hate is strong
   And mocks the song
Of peace on earth, good-will to men!"

Then pealed the bells more loud and deep,
"God is not dead; nor doth He sleep!
   The Wrong shall fail,
   The Right prevail,
With peace on earth, good-will to men!"

WALTER DE LA MARE

Nowel

Holly dark: pale Mistletoe—
Christmas Eve is come, and lo,
Wild are the bells across the snow,
Waits in the dark streets carolling go;
   "Nowel! Nowel!" they shout—and, oh,
      How live out the day!
Each breath I breathe turns to a sigh;
      My heart is flown away;
The things I see around me seem
Entranced with light—as in a dream;
The candles dazzle in my eyes,
And every leaping fireflame tries
      To sing, what none could say.

JOHN MASEFIELD

❦

Christmas Eve at Sea

A wind is rustling "south and soft,"
   Cooing a quiet country tune,
The calm sea sighs, and far aloft
   The sails are ghostly in the moon.

Unquiet ripples lisp and purr,
   A block there pipes and chirps i' the sheave,
The wheel-ropes jar, the reef-points stir
   Faintly—and it is Christmas Eve.

The hushed sea seems to hold her breath,
   And o'er the giddy, swaying spars,
Silent and excellent as Death,
   The dim blue skies are bright with stars.

Dear God—they shone in Palestine
   Like this, and yon pale moon serene
Looked down among the lowing kine
   On Mary and the Nazarene.

The angels called from deep to deep,
   The burning heavens felt the thrill,
Startling the flocks of silly sheep
   And lonely shepherds on the hill.

To-night beneath the dripping bows,
   Where flashing bubbles burst and throng,

The bow-wash murmurs and sighs and soughs
A message from the angels' song.

The moon goes nodding down the west,
The drowsy helmsman strikes the bell;
Rex Judaeorum natus est,
I charge you, brothers, sing *Nowell,*
Nowell,
Rex Judaeorum natus est.

PHYLLIS MCGINLEY

عف؟ه

The Ballad of Befana

AN EPIPHANY LEGEND

Befana the Housewife, scrubbing her pane,
Saw three old sages ride down the lane,
Saw three gray travelers pass her door—
Gaspar, Balthazar, Melchior.

"Where journey you, sirs?" she asked of them.
Balthazar answered, "To Bethlehem,

For we have news of a marvelous thing.
Born in a stable is Christ the King."

"Give Him my welcome!"
Then Gaspar smiled,
  "Come with us, mistress, to greet the Child."

"Oh, happily, happily would I fare,
Were my dusting through and I'd polished the stair."

Old Melchior leaned on his saddle horn.
  "Then send but a gift to the small Newborn."

"Oh, gladly, gladly I'd send Him one,
Were the hearthstone swept and my weaving done.

"As soon as ever I've baked my bread,
I'll fetch Him a pillow for His head,
And a coverlet too," Befana said.

"When the rooms are aired and the linen dry,
I'll look at the Babe."
But the Three rode by.

She worked for a day and a night and a day,
Then, gifts in her hands, took up her way.
But she never could find where the Christ Child lay.

And still she wanders at Christmastide,
Houseless, whose house was all her pride,

Whose heart was tardy, whose gifts were late;
Wanders, and knocks at every gate,
Crying, "Good people, the bells begin!
Put off your toiling and let love in."

CLEMENT CLARKE MOORE

~§ ह~

A Visit from St. Nicholas

'Twas the night before Christmas, when all through the house
Not a creature was stirring, not even a mouse.
The stockings were hung by the chimney with care,
In hopes that St. Nicholas soon would be there.
The children were nestled all snug in their beds,
While visions of sugar-plums danced in their heads;
And mamma in her kerchief, and I in my cap,
Had just settled our brains for a long winter's nap—
When out on the lawn there arose such a clatter
I sprang from my bed to see what was the matter.
Away to the window I flew like a flash,
Tore open the shutter, and threw up the sash.
The moon on the breast of the new-fallen snow
Gave a lustre of midday to objects below;
When what to my wondering eye should appear
But a miniature sleigh and eight tiny reindeer,
With a little old driver, so lively and quick,
I knew in a moment it must be St. Nick!
More rapid than eagles his coursers they came,
And he whistled and shouted and called them by name.
"Now, Dasher! now, Dancer! now, Prancer and Vixen!
On, Comet! on, Cupid! on, Donder and Blitzen!—
To the top of the porch, to the top of the wall,
Now, dash away, dash away, dash away all!"
As dry leaves that before the wild hurricane fly,
When they meet with an obstacle mount to the sky,
So, up to the housetop the coursers they flew,

With a sleigh full of toys—and St. Nicholas, too.
And then, in a twinkling, I heard on the roof
The prancing and pawing of each little hoof.
As I drew in my head and was turning around,
Down the chimney St. Nicholas came with a bound:
He was dressed all in fur from his head to his foot,
And his clothes were all tarnished with ashes and soot:
A bundle of toys he had flung on his back,
And he looked like a peddler just opening his pack.
His eyes, how they twinkled! his dimples, how merry!
His cheeks were like roses, his nose like a cherry;
His droll little mouth was drawn up like a bow,
And the beard on his chin was as white as the snow.
The stump of a pipe he held tight in his teeth,
And the smoke, it encircled his head like a wreath.
He had a broad face and a little round belly
That shook, when he laughed, like a bowl full of jelly.
He was chubby and plump—a right jolly old elf:
And I laughed when I saw him, in spite of myself;
A wink of his eye, and a twist of his head,
Soon gave me to know I had nothing to dread.
He spoke not a word, but went straight to his work,
And filled all the stockings: then turned with a jerk,
And laying his finger aside of his nose,
And giving a nod, up the chimney he rose.
He sprang to his sleigh, to his team gave a whistle,
And away they all flew like the down of a thistle.
But I heard him exclaim, ere they drove out of sight,
"Happy Christmas to all, and to all a good-night!"

OGDEN NASH

A Carol for Children

God rest you merry, Innocents,
Let nothing you dismay,
Let nothing wound an eager heart
Upon this Christmas day.

Yours be the genial holly wreaths,
The stockings and the tree;
An aged world to you bequeaths
Its own forgotten glee.

Soon, soon enough come crueler gifts,
The anger and the tears;
Between you now there sparsely drifts
A handful yet of years.

Oh, dimly, dimly glows the star
Through the electric throng;
The bidding in temple and bazaar
Drowns out the silver song.

The ancient altars smoke afresh,
The ancient idols stir;
Faint in the reek of burning flesh
Sink frankincense and myrrh.

Gaspar, Balthazar, Melchior!
Where are your offerings now?

What greetings to the Prince of War,
His darkly branded brow?

Two ultimate laws alone we know,
The ledger and the sword—
So far away, so long ago,
We lost the infant Lord.

Only the children clasp His hand;
His voice speaks low to them,
And still for them the shining band
Wings over Bethlehem.

God rest you merry, Innocents,
While Innocence endures.
A sweeter Christmas than we to ours
May you bequeath to yours.

ALFRED NOYES

The Three Ships

As I went up the mountain-side
The sea below me glitter'd wide,
And, Eastward, far away, I spied
    On Christmas Day, on Christmas Day,
The three great ships that take the tide
    On Christmas Day in the morning.

Ye have heard the song, how these must ply
From the harbours of home to the ports o' the sky!
Do ye dream none knoweth the whither and why
    On Christmas Day, on Christmas Day
The three great ships go sailing by
    On Christmas Day in the morning?

Yet, as I live, I never knew
That ever a song could ring so true,
Till I saw them break thro' a haze of blue
    On Christmas Day, on Christmas Day;
And the marvellous ancient flags they flew
    On Christmas Day in the morning!

From the heights above the belfried town
I saw that the sails were patched and brown,
But the flags were a-flame with a great renown
    On Christmas Day, on Christmas Day,
And on every mast was a golden crown
    On Christmas Day in the morning.

Most marvellous ancient ships were these!
Were their prows a-plunge to the Chersonese,
For the pomp of Rome, or the glory of Greece,
    On Christmas Day, on Christmas Day?
Were they out on a quest for the Golden Fleece
    On Christmas Day in the morning?

The sun and the wind they told me there
How goodly a load the three ships bear,
For the first is gold and the second is myrrh
    On Christmas Day, on Christmas Day;
And the third is frankincense most rare,
    On Christmas Day in the morning.

They have mixed their shrouds with the golden sky,
They have faded away where the last dreams die . . .
Ah yet, will ye watch, when the mist lifts high
    On Christmas Day, on Christmas Day?
Will ye see three ships come sailing by
    On Christmas Day in the morning?

SIR WALTER SCOTT

❧ ❧

Christmas in the Olden Time

On Christmas-eve the bells were rung;
The damsel donned her kirtle sheen;
The hall was dressed with holly green;
Forth to the wood did merry men go,
To gather in the mistletoe.
Thus opened wide the baron's hall
To vassal, tenant, serf and all;
Power laid his rod of rule aside
And ceremony doffed his pride.
The heir, with roses in his shoes,
That night might village partner choose;
The lord, underogating, share
The vulgar game of "Post and Pair."
All hailed, with uncontrolled delight,
And general voice, the happy night
That to the cottage, as the crown,
Brought tidings of salvation down.

The fire, with well-dried logs supplied,
Went roaring up the chimney wide;
The huge hall-table's oaken face,
Scrubbed till it shone, the day to grace,
Bore then upon its massive board
No mark to part the squire and lord.
Then was brought in the lusty brawn
By old blue-coated serving man;
Then the grim boar's head frowned on high,

Crested with bays and rosemary.
Well can the green-garbed ranger tell
How, when and where the monster fell;
What dogs before his death he tore,
And all the baitings of the boar.
The wassal round, in good brown bowls,
Garnished with ribbons, blithely trowls.
There the huge sirloin reeked: hard by
Plum-porridge stood, and Chrstimas pye;
Nor failed old Scotland to produce,
At such high-tide, her savory goose.

Then came the merry maskers in,
And carols roared with blithesome din.
If unmelodious was the song,
It was a hearty note, and strong;
Who lists may in their murmuring see
Traces of ancient mystery;
White shirts supplied the masquerade,
And smutted cheeks the visors made;
But O, what maskers richly dight,
Can boast of bosoms half so light!
England was "merry England" when
Old Christmas brought his sports again;
'Twas Christmas broached the mightiest ale,
'Twas Christmas told the merriest tale;
A Christmas gambol oft would cheer
The poor man's heart through half the year.

WILLIAM SHAKESPEARE

≈§§≈

"Some Say..."

FROM HAMLET, ACT 1, SCENE 1

Some say that ever 'gainst that season comes
Wherein our Saviour's birth is celebrated,
The bird of dawning singeth all night long:
And then, they say, no spirit dare stir abroad,
The nights are wholesome, then no planets strike,
No fairy takes nor witch hath power to charm,
So hallow'd and so gracious is the time.

❧ ❦ ❧

Carol

High o'er the lonely hills
　Black turns to grey,
Birdsong the valley fills,
　Mists fold away;
Grey wakes to green again,
Beauty is seen again—
Gold and serene again
　Dawneth the day.

So o'er the hills of life,
　Stormy, forlorn,
Out of the cloud and strife
　Sunrise is born;
Swift grows the light for us;
Ended is night for us;
Soundless and bright for us
　Breaketh God's morn.

Hear we no beat of drums,
　Fanfare nor cry,
When Christ the herald comes
　Quietly nigh;
Splendour he makes on earth;
Colour awakes on earth;
Suddenly breaks on earth
　Light from the sky.

Bid then farewell to sleep:
    Rise up and run!
What though the hill be steep?
    Strength's in the sun.
Now shall you find at last
Night's left behind at last,
And for mankind at last
    Day has begun!

ALFRED TENNYSON

❧

Christmas and New Year Bells

The time draws near the birth of Christ:
   The moon is hid; the night is still;
   The Christmas bells from hill to hill
Answer each other in the mist.

Four voices of four hamlets round,
   From far and near, on mead and moor,
   Swell out and fail, as if a door
Were shut between me and the sound:

Each voice four changes on the wind,
   That now dilate, and now decrease,
   Peace and goodwill, goodwill and peace,
Peace and goodwill, to all mankind.

This year I slept and woke with pain,
   I almost wish'd no more to wake,
   And that my hold on life would break
Before I heard those bells again:

But they the troubled spirit rule,
   For they controll'd me when a boy;
   They bring me sorrow touch'd with joy,
The merry, merry bells of Yule.

Ring out, wild bells, to the wild sky,
   The flying cloud, the frosty light:

The year is dying in the night;
Ring out, wild bells, and let him die.

Ring out the old, ring in the new,
    Ring, happy bells, across the snow:
    The year is going, let him go;
Ring out the false, ring in the true.

Ring out the grief that saps the mind,
    For those that here we see no more;
    Ring out the feud of rich and poor,
Ring in redress to all mankind.

Ring out a slowly dying cause,
    And ancient forms of party strife;
    Ring in the nobler modes of life,
With sweeter manners, purer laws.

Ring out the want, the care, the sin,
    The faithless coldness of the times;
    Ring out, ring out my mournful rhymes,
But ring the fuller minstrel in.

Ring out false pride in place and blood,
    The civic slander and the spite;
    Ring in the love of truth and right,
Ring in the common love of good.

Ring out old shapes of foul disease,
    Ring out the narrowing lust of gold;
    Ring out the thousand wars of old
Ring in the thousand years of peace.

Ring in the valiant man and free,
    The larger heart, the kindlier hand;
    Ring out the darkness of the land,
Ring in the Christ that is to be.

FROM THE REPERTOIRE
OF THE UNITED NATIONS SINGERS

❧

Weihnachtslied/*Silent Night*

Stille Nacht! Heilige Nacht!	Silent night! Holy night!
Alles schläft, einsam wacht	All is calm, all is bright,
Nur das traute, heilige Paar.	Round yon Virgin Mother and Child.
Holder Knabe im lokkigen Haar,	Holy Infant, so tender and mild,
Schlafe in himmlischer Ruh!	Sleep in heavenly peace!
Stille Nacht! Heilige Nacht!	Silent Night! Holy Night!
Gottes Sohn, o wie lacht	Son of God, love's pure light,
Lieb aus deinem göttlichen Mund,	Radiant beams from Thy holy face,
Da uns schlägt die rettende Stund',	With the dawn of redeeming grace,
Jesus, in deiner Geburt.	Jesus, Lord, at Thy birth!

(*Austrian carol. Nineteenth Century.*)

❧ ❦ ❧

What Child Is This?

What Child is this, who, laid to rest
On Mary's lap, is sleeping?
Whom angels greet with anthems sweet,
While shepherds watch are keeping?

Refrain:
This, this is Christ the King,
Whom shepherds guard and angels sing:
Haste, haste to bring Him laud,
The Babe, the Son of Mary.

Why lies He in such mean estate,
Where ox and ass are feeding?
Good Christians fear: for sinners here
The silent Word is pleading.   *Refrain*

So bring Him incense, gold, and myrrh,
Come peasant, King to own Him;
The King of Kings salvation brings;
Let loving hearts enthrone Him!   *Refrain*

(*English. Fifteenth century.*)

331

Il est né, le Divin Enfant/
Born Is Jesus, the Infant King

Il est né, le Divin Enfant,
Jouez haut-bois, résonnez muset-
    tes;
Il est né, le Divin Enfant,
Chantons tous son avènement.

Born is Jesus, the Infant King,
Play merry oboes, sweet pipes re-
    sounding;
Born is Jesus, the Infant King,
Come His Advent on earth to
    sing!

Depuis plus de quatre mille ans
Mous le promettaient les prophè-
    tes.
Depuis plus de quatre mille ans
Nous attendions cet heureux
    temps.

More than four thousand years'
    delay,
Since the prophets of God fore-
    told Him.
More than four thousand years'
    delay
Pass'd before this all joyful day.

Il est né, le Divin Enfant,
Jouez haut-bois, résonnez muset-
    tes;
Il est né, le Divin Enfant,
Chantons tous son avènement.

Born is Jesus, the Infant King,
Play merry oboes, sweet pipes re-
    sounding;
Born is Jesus, the Infant King,
Come His Advent on earth to
    sing!

Qu'il est beau, qu'il est charmant,
Que ses grâces sont parfaites.

Ah, how fair is the Child we sing,
How delightful to behold Him.

Qu'il est beau, Qu'il est charmant,
Qu'il est doux, ce Divin Enfant.

Ah, how fair is the Child we sing,
He is lovely, the Infant King!

Il est né, le Divin Enfant,
Jouez haut-bois, résonnez muset-
tes;
Il est né, le Divin Enfant,
Chantons tous son avènement.

Born is Jesus, the Infant King,
Play merry oboes, sweet pipes re-
sounding;
Born is Jesus, the Infant King,
Come His Advent on earth to
sing!

(*French carol. Traditional.*)

Canzone d'i Zampognari/
Carol of the Bagpipers

Quanno nascette Ninno a Bettelemme,
Era notte e parea mmiezo juorno.
Maje le stelle, lustere e belle,
Se vedettero accussì!
La chiù lucente
Jette a chiammà li Magi, in Oriente.

> When Christ our Lord was born at Bethlehem afar,
> Although 'twas night, there shone as bright as noon a star.
> Never so brightly, never so whitely,
> Shone the stars, as on that night!
> The brightest star went
> Away to call the Wise Men from the Orient.

(*Italian carol. Traditional.*)

334

Gdy Się Chrystus Rodzi/

Jesus Christ Is Born

Gdy się Chrystus rodzi
I na świat przychodzi;
Ciemna noc wjasnościach
Promienistych brodzi.
Aniotowie się radują
Pod niebiosy wyśpiewuja:
Gloria, gloria, gloria in excelsis
Deo!

Jesus Christ is born
Now unto the world.
Ev'ry dark of night
Turned into light.
Hosts of angels, hear them singing
Hymns of joy, and praises ring-
ing:
Gloria, gloria, gloria in excelsis
Deo!

Mowią do pasterzy
Którzy trzód swych strzegli:
Aby do Betlejem
Częmprendzej pobiegli.
Bo się narodzil Zbawiciel
Wszego świata Odkupiciel:
Gloria, gloria, gloria in excelsis
Deo!

In the fields the shepherds
By their flocks abiding,
Harkened to the angel:
Hear ye this great tiding!
Go ye, go to Bethle'm yonder,
There to see salvation's wonder:
Gloria, gloria, gloria in excelsis
Deo!

(Polish carol. Traditional.)

335

A la Nanita Nana

A la nanita nana, nanita ea, nanita ea,
Mi Jesús tiene sueño, bendito sea, bendito sea. } Refrain
Fuentecilla que corres clara y sonora,
ruiseñor q'en la selva cantando lloras,
callad mientras la cuna se balancea.

Refrain { A la nanita nana, nanita ea, nanita ea,
My Jesus, He is sleeping, o come behold Him, o come
behold Him.
Little brook ever-flowing, rushing and ringing,
Nightingale in the forest, sighing and singing,
Quiet now, while the cradle softly enfolds Him.

Refrain

Y tú triste presagio que me torturas,
almacigo de penas y de amarguras,
huye mientras la cuna se balancea. Refrain

Refrain

O thou tragic foreboding of the sad morrow,
Shadow of coming anguish, suff'ring and sorrow,
Fly, shadows, while the cradle softly enfolds Him. Refrain

Refrain

Manojito de rosas y de alelíes,
qué es lo que estás soñando, que te sonríes?
Cuáles son tus ensueños, dilo alma mia;
mas qué es lo que murmuras? "Eucaristía." Refrain

336

Refrain

Fair as violets and roses, Baby beguiling,
Say what visions surround Thee, why art Thou smiling?
Ah, what appears before Thee, Infant so lowly?
Softly Thy sweet lips murmur: "Sacrament Holy." Refrain

Refrain

Yo no sé lo que es eso, Niño del alma,
mas pues esa sonrisa mis penas calma,
sigue, sigue soñando mi dulce Dueño,
sin que nada te ahuyente tan dulce sueño. Refrain

Refrain

I know not to explain it, sorrow has vanished,
O Thy smile, little Jesus, my care has banished.
Dream, dream o gentle Master, dreams without number,
Let no affliction trouble Thy peaceful slumber. Refrain

Refrain

Pajaritos y fuentes, auras y brisas,
respetad ese sueño y esas sonrisas,
callad mientras la cuna se balancea;
que el Niño esta soñando, bendito sea! Refrain

Refrain

Singing birds, flowing fountains, winds gently blowing,
Silence, for He is sleeping, cheeks brightly glowing,
Quiet now, while the cradle softly enfolds Him,
My Holy Child is sleeping, come and behold Him. Refrain

(Spanish carol. Traditional.)

❧❧

Nu är det Jul igen/ Dance Carol

Nu är det Jul igen, och
Nu är det Jul igen, och
Julen vara ska' till Påska.
Så är det Påsk igen, och·
Så är det Påsk igen, och
Påsken vara ska' till Jula.

Yuletide is here again, and
Yuletide is here again, and
Happy days we'll have till Easter.
Then there is Eastertide, and
Then there is Eastertide, and
Happy days we'll have till Christ-
mas.

Nu är det Jul igen, och
Nu är det Jul igen, och
Julen vara ska' till Påska.
Det var inte sant, och
Det var inte sant, för
Där emellan kommer Fastan.

Yuletide is here again, and
Yuletide is here again, and
Happy days we'll have till Easter.
This is not the truth, and
This is not the truth, for
Lent comes in between and fast-
ing.

(Swedish dance carol. Traditional.)